Scott Foresman - Addison Wesley
MATH

Daily Cumulative Review Masters

Grade 6

S F
A W
Scott Foresman - Addison Wesley

Editorial Offices: Glenview, Illinois • New York, New York
Sales Offices: Reading, Massachusetts • Duluth, Georgia • Glenview, Illinois
Carrollton, Texas • Menlo Park, California

http://www.sf.aw.com

Overview

Daily Cumulative Review Masters provide a continuous review of skills and concepts from Scott Foresman - Addison Wesley MATH. A Daily Review master is provided for each lesson in the Student Edition.

The first section of each master reviews a key objective from the previous lesson. The second section of each master reviews material covered two lessons prior to the current lesson. The third section provides a Mixed Review of problems from previous lessons or chapters. Lesson references are provided with each exercise in Mixed Review.

Daily Review Masters for Chapter 1 review key concepts from the previous year as well as from Chapter 1.

The *Daily Cumulative Review* format helps students solidify and retain math skills learned throughout the school year.

ISBN 0-201-36907-9

Printed in the United States of America

2 3 4 5 6 7 8 9 10 – PO – 03 02 01 00

Contents

Chapter 10: Ratio, Proportion, and Percent

Chapter 11: Solids and Measurement

Chapter 12: Probability

Name ______________________________

Daily Review
1-1

Daily Cumulative Review

Mixed Review *(From Last Year)*

Write each number in word form.

1. 2,083,706 ______________________________

____

2. 417,209,512 ______________________________

____

Find each product. Estimate to check.

3. 216×5

4. 37×46

5. 72×39

6. 548×17

Classify each triangle as equilateral, isosceles, or scalene.

7. ______________________________

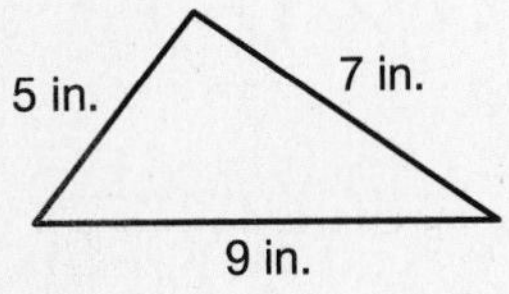

8. ______________________________

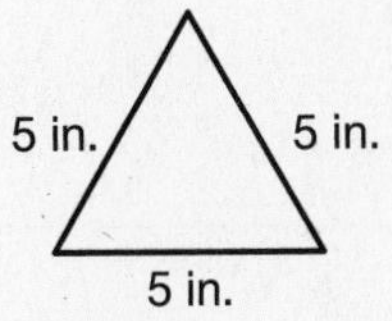

9. ______________________________

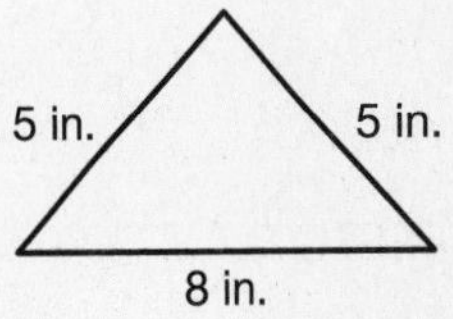

10. Four classes worked together and earned $219 on a newspaper drive. They agreed to split the money equally. How much should each class get? ______________

11. One class collected 843 pounds of newspaper. Another class collected 971 pounds. How much more did the second class collect than the first one? ______________

12. If each of 24 students in one class worked 6 hours on the newspaper drive, how many hours did the class work altogether? ______________

Name ______________________

Daily Review 1-2

Daily Cumulative Review

Use the Expenses graph for 1–5 *(Lesson 1-1)*

1. What is the most costly expense for Mathco? ________
2. For each $100 spent, how much did Mathco spend on computers? ________
3. Which expense is about 5 times as much as the telephone expense? ________
4. For each $100 spent, how much more is spent on utilities and salaries than on rent? ________
5. For each $500 spent, how much would be spent on telephones? ________

Mathco Expenses

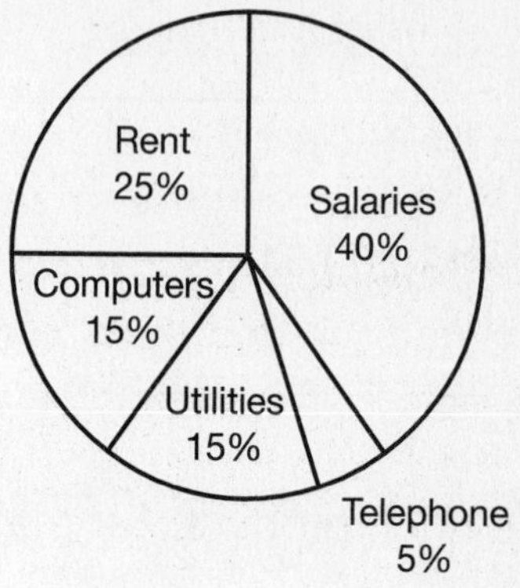

Mixed Review *(From Last Year)*

Find each sum or difference. Then estimate to check.

6. $465 + 279$
7. $803 - 214$
8. $928 - 327$
9. $507 + 236$

Find each sum or difference. Simplify.

10. $\frac{11}{12} - \frac{5}{12}$ ________
11. $\frac{3}{5} + \frac{4}{5}$ ________
12. $\frac{9}{10} - \frac{3}{10}$ ________

Find the perimeter and area of each room.

13.

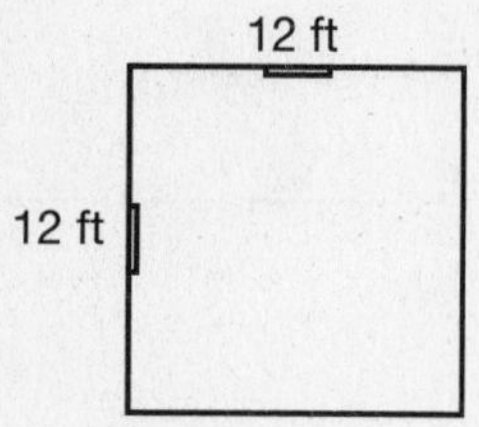

$P =$ ________

$A =$ ________

14.

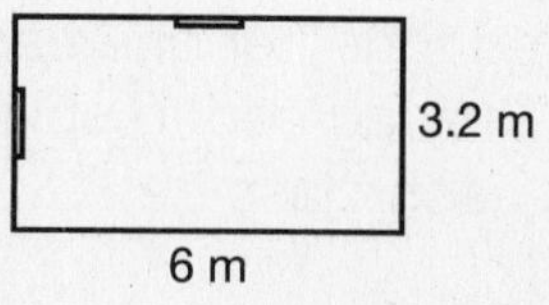

$P =$ ________

$A =$ ________

15. If a square yard of carpet costs $5.75, how much would it cost to carpet a room that has an area of 35 square yards? ________

Name ____________________

Daily Review
1-3

Daily Cumulative Review

Use the Miles Driven bar graph for Exercises 1–4. *(Lesson 1-2)*

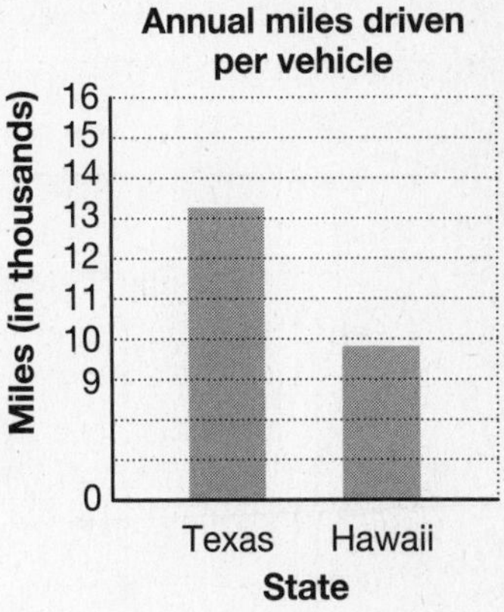

1. The number of miles driven by a vehicle in Texas appears to be how many times greater than the number of miles driven in Hawaii? ________

2. Texas cars are driven about how many miles per year? ________

3. Hawaiian cars are driven about how many miles per year? ________

4. Could the bar graph be misleading? If so, how would you correct the graph?

____

Use the Bushels of Corn pictograph for 5–9. *(Lesson 1-1)*

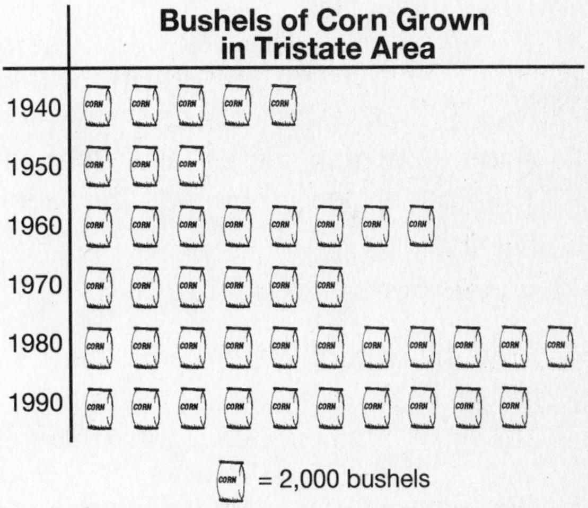

5. In what year was the most corn grown? ________

6. How much more corn was grown in 1990 than in 1960? ________

7. Did 1940 and 1950 together produce more corn than in 1990? ________

8. How many bushels were grown in 1970? ________

9. How many bushels were grown from 1960 to 1990? ________

Mixed Review *(From Last Year)*

Divide.

10. $5\overline{)3\ 4\ 7}$ **11.** $8\overline{)9\ 4}$ **12.** $3\overline{)1\ 8\ 2}$ **13.** $6\overline{)2\ 8\ 9}$

14. An insect is 16 millimeters long. How many centimeters is this? ________

15. Another insect is 2.1 centimeters long. How many millimeters is this? ________

Name ____________________

Daily Review 1-4

Daily Cumulative Review

For each scatterplot, determine if there is a trend. If there is, describe the pattern of the data. *(Lesson 1-3)*

1. ____________________ **2.** ____________________

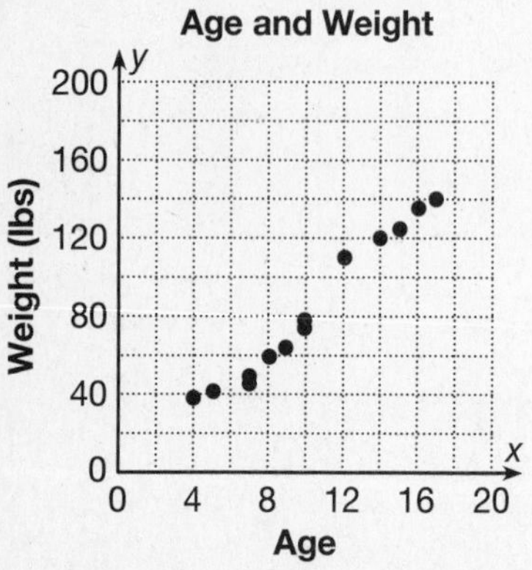

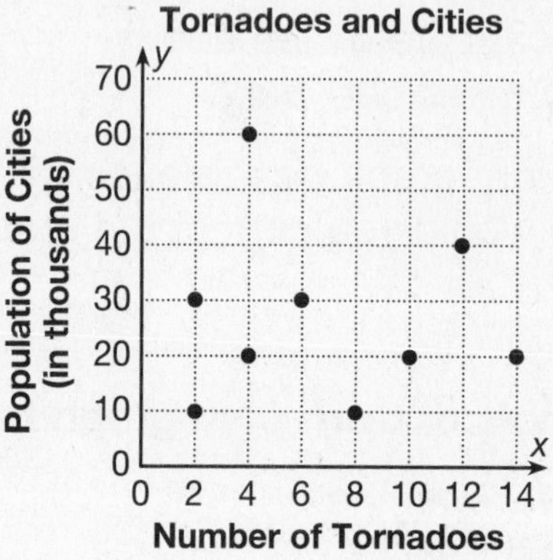

Use the Employment bar graph for 3–5. *(Lesson 1-2)*

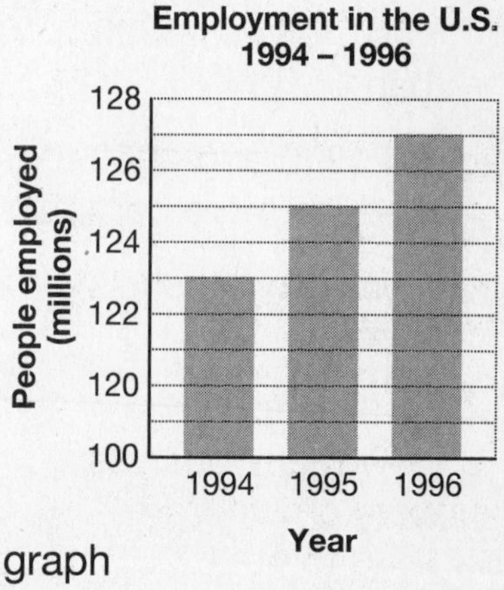

3. About how many times taller does the 1996 bar appear to be than the 1994 bar?

____

4. How many people were employed

in 1994? ____________ in 1996? ____________

5. Compare your answers to Exercises 3–4. Could the bar graph be misleading? If so, how would you correct the graph?

____

Mixed Review

Find equivalent fractions with a denominator of 10.

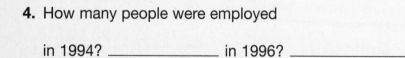

6. *(Gr. 5)* $\frac{3}{5}$ ____________ **7.** *(Gr. 5)* $\frac{16}{20}$ ____________ **8.** *(Gr. 5)* $\frac{1}{2}$ ____________

9. *(Gr. 5)* A movie is $1\frac{1}{4}$ hours long. Its sequel is $1\frac{1}{3}$ hours, and the third movie in the set is $1\frac{5}{6}$ hours. How long are the 3 movies together? ____________

Name ______________________________

Daily Review 1-5

Daily Cumulative Review

Make a frequency chart and line plot for the following data. *(Lesson 1-4)*

Hours of Television Students Watched Last Week:

10, 9, 14, 7, 12, 11, 8, 9, 12, 7

1. Frequency Chart

2. Line Plot

Give the approximate weight and price represented by each point in the scatterplot. *(Lesson 1-3)*

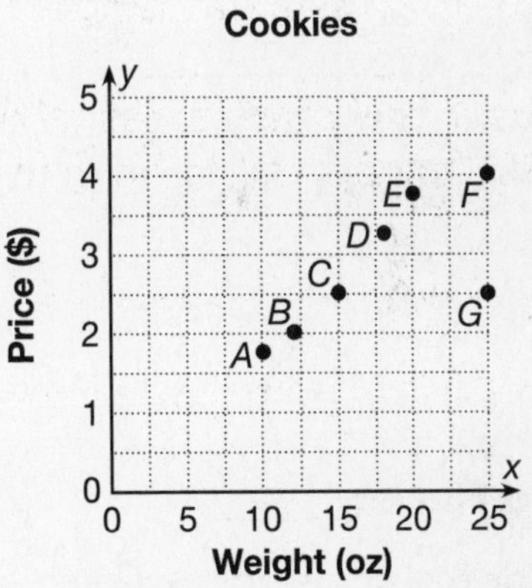

3. *A*: weight ____________ price ____________

4. *B*: weight ____________ price ____________

5. *E*: weight ____________ price ____________

6. *G*: weight ____________ price ____________

Mixed Review

Find each quotient.

7. $91 \div 7$ *(Gr. 5)* ____________

8. $75 \div 5$ *(Gr. 5)* ____________

9. $67 \div 2$ *(Gr. 5)* ____________

10. $124 \div 3$ *(Gr. 5)* ____________

11. *(Gr. 5)* A factory packs 15 pens in a box. How many boxes will be needed for 1680 pens? ____________

Name ______________________________

Daily Review
1-6

Daily Cumulative Review

Use the data for Exercises 1 and 2. *(Lesson 1-5)*

1. Make a bar graph from the data showing the revenues of the leading U.S. telecommunication businesses in 1996.

Company	Billions of Revenue
A	$74.5
B	21.3
C	19.0
D	18.5

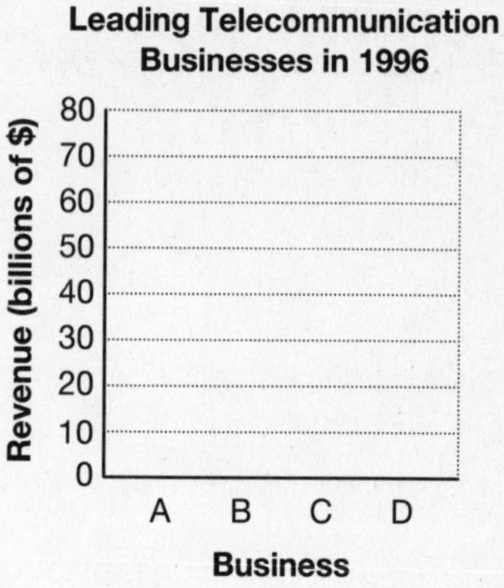

2. What is the range of the data for the revenues in Exercise 1? ____________

Record each set of data in a tally chart. *(Lesson 1-4)*

3. 15, 16, 16, 14, 13, 15, 16, 13
14, 15, 16, 14, 13, 15, 16

Number	Tally

4. 3, 5, 3, 6, 5, 3, 6, 7, 6, 3, 6,
7, 5, 3, 4

Number	Tally

Mixed Review

5. *(1-3)* For the scatterplot shown, determine if there is a trend. If there is, describe the pattern of the data.

____

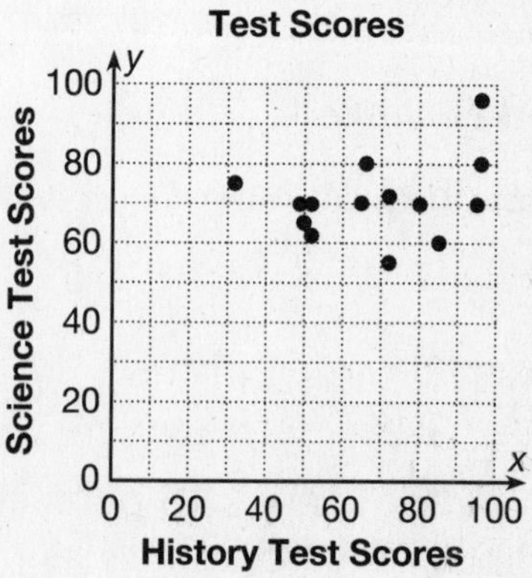

6. *(Gr. 5)* Write the fractions in order from least to greatest.

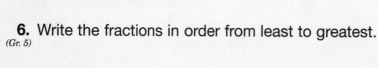

$\frac{3}{9}, \frac{3}{4}, \frac{3}{5}$ ______________________

Name ______________________

Daily Review 1-7

Daily Cumulative Review

Use the stem-and-leaf diagram for Exercises 1–4. *(Lesson 1-6)*

Stem	Leaf
5	6 7 7
6	0 1 3 4 8 8
7	1 4 4 4 7 9
8	0 2 6

1. What is the range of the values? ______

2. What value appears most often? ______

3. How many times does the value 68 appear? ______

4. What is the largest number in the data that is less than 80? ______

Make a bar graph of the data. *(Lesson 1-5)*

5. The data shows the average shoe size for middle school age girls.

Age	Average Shoe Size
11	4
12	5.5
13	6.5
14	8

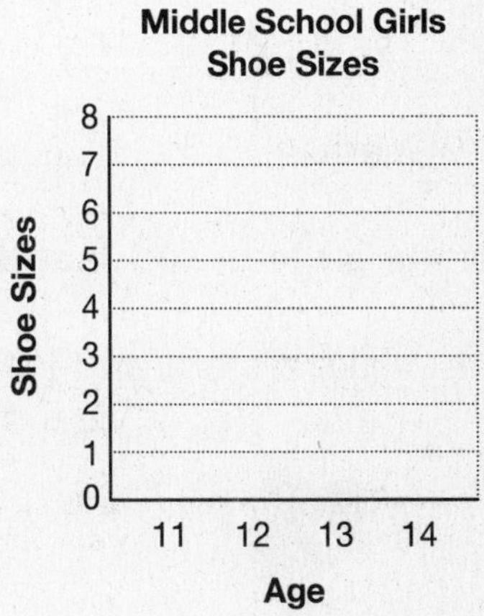

Mixed Review

6. *(1-4)* Make a line plot of the number of movies watched last week by a group of students.

Movies	Frequency
0	4
1	8
2	4
3	1

7. *(1-2)* About how many times taller does the bar showing Mr. Ortiz's sales appear to be than the bar showing Mr. Jones' sales? ______

Is the bar graph misleading? If so, how would you correct the graph?

____

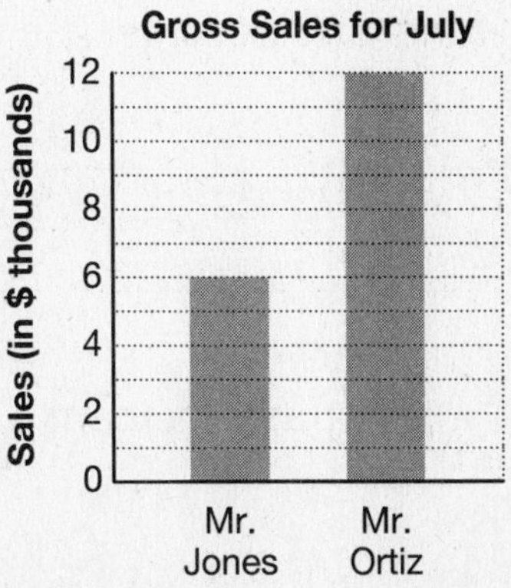

Name ______________________________

Daily Review 1-8

Daily Cumulative Review

Find the median and mode(s). *(Lesson 1-7)*

1. median ______________

mode(s) ______________

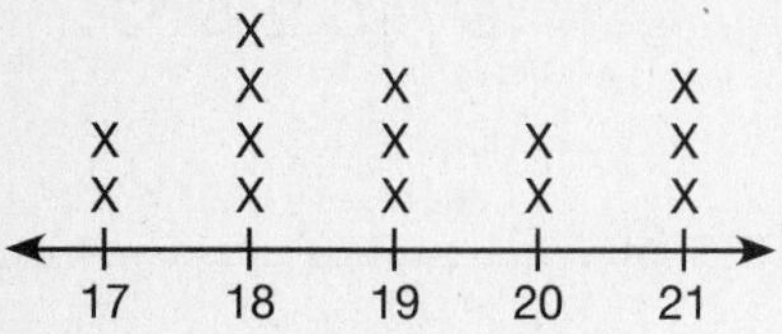

2. median ______________

mode(s) ______________

Stem	Leaf
2	7 7 9
3	0 3 5 5 7
4	2 5 8
5	3 5 6

3. 14, 20, 21, 23, 25, 20, 15, 19, 21, 20, 33, 18, 41, 28, 26, 36, 29

median ______________ mode(s) ______________

Make a stem-and-leaf diagram. *(Lesson 1-6)*

4. Make a stem-and-leaf diagram of the data showing the number of videos owned by some students.

6, 12, 9, 3, 17, 24, 0, 4, 10, 20, 13, 4, 9, 15

Stem	Leaf

Mixed Review

5. What is the range of the data for Exercise 3? ______
(1-5)

Use the scatterplot for Exercises 6 and 7.

6. How many people exercised 7 hours per week? ______
(1-3)

7. For the scatterplot shown, determine if there is a trend. If there is, describe the pattern.
(1-3)

____

____

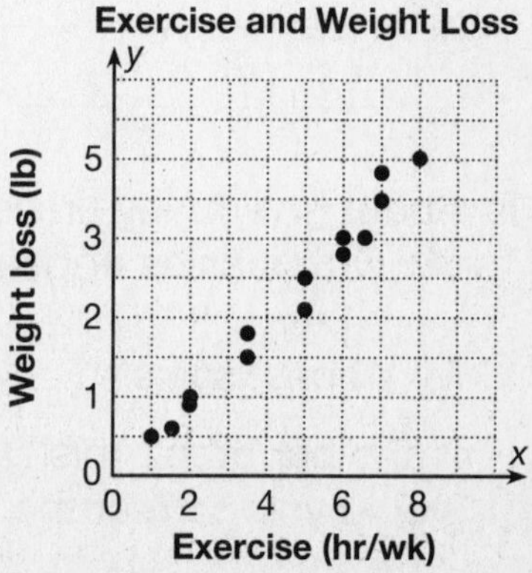

8. Write $\frac{3}{10}$ as a percent. ______________
(Gr. 5)

Name ______________________________

Daily Review
1-9

Daily Cumulative Review

Find the mean of each set of data. *(Lesson 1-8)*

1. mean __________

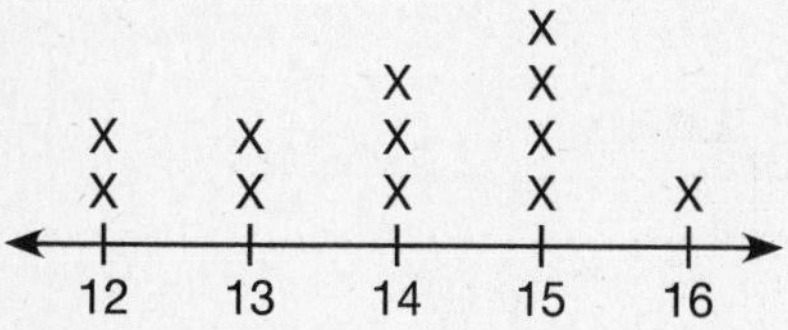

2. mean __________

Stem	Leaf
0	6 6 7
1	0 1 4 7 8 8
2	0 0 1 4 4 6 7 9
3	0 3

3. mean __________

23, 28, 36, 36, 42, 42, 49, 64, 94

Find the median and mode(s) of each data set. *(Lesson 1-7)*

4. median __________

mode(s) __________

7, 4, 9, 8, 6, 8, 7, 3, 10, 10, 5, 4, 10

5. median __________

mode(s) __________

Stem	Leaf
3	4 7 8
4	0 1 3 3 7 9
5	1 1 4 6
6	0 1

Mixed Review

6. *(1-6)* Make a stem-and-leaf diagram of the data showing the number of members of local scout troops.

40, 74, 31, 70, 66, 53,
49, 70, 35, 57, 62, 39

Stem	Leaf

Use the Children in U.S. Families graph to answer Exercises 7 and 8.

7. *(1-1)* What category represents about $\frac{1}{2}$ of U.S. families? __________

8. *(1-1)* What percent of familes have 2 or more children? __________

Children in U.S. Families

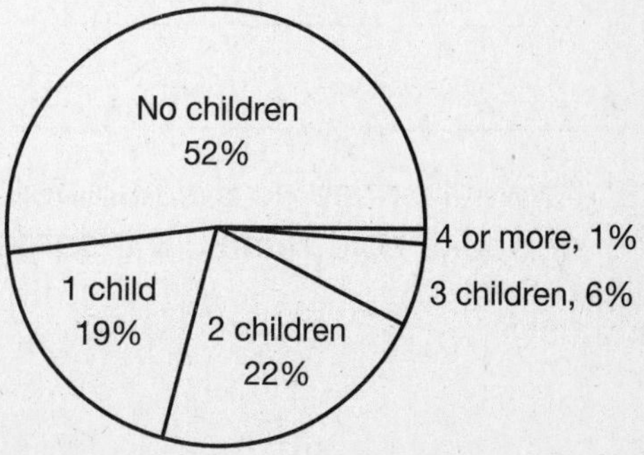

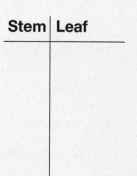

Name ______________________

Daily Review 2-1

Daily Cumulative Review

Identify the outlier in each data set. *(Lesson 1-9)*

1. ______________

22, 35, 21, 32, 85, 28, 30, 29

2. ______________

Stem	Leaf
3	1
4	7 9 9 8 9
5	0 1 1 2 5 8 9
6	0 1

3. ______________

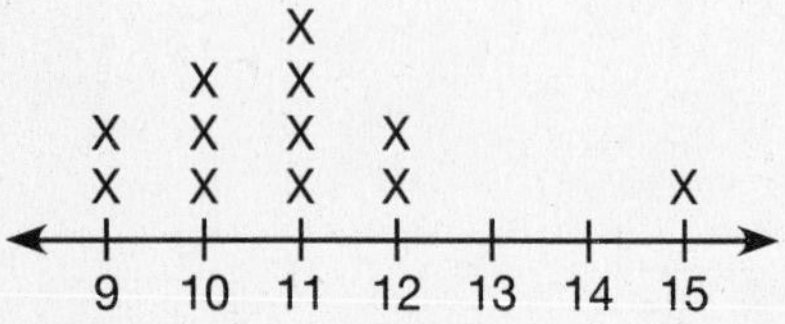

Find the mean of each set of data. *(Lesson 1-8)*

4. 41, 18, 62, 24, 38, 72, 81, ______________

5. 87, 102, 98, 92, 79, 80, 88, 82, 90, 93 ______________

Mixed Review

6. *(1-4)* Make a line plot for 12, 21, 17, 14, 19, 12, 17, 14, 21, 17, 14, 13

7. *(1-7)* Find the median and mode(s) for the data in Exercise 6.

median ______________ mode ______________

Use the scatterplot for Exercices 8 and 9.

8. *(1-3)* Is there a trend? If so, describe the pattern of data.

____

____

9. *(1-3)* At what prices do the number of books sold remain the same? ______________

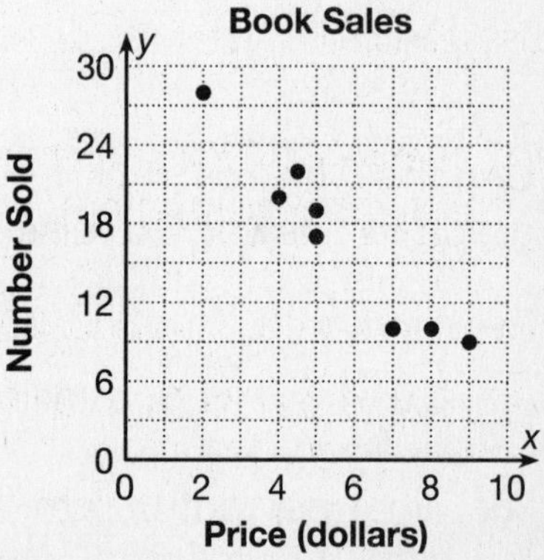

Name ______________________________

Daily Review
2-2

Daily Cumulative Review

Write the number in words. *(Lesson 2-1)*

1. 6,895 ______________________________

2. 943,201 ______________________________

3. 51,207,050 ______________________________

Identify the outlier in each data set. *(Lesson 1-9)*

4. 100, 125, 200, 400, 225, 210 ______________

5. ______________

Stem	Leaf
2	0 0 2 2 5
3	0 2 6 7
4	0 5 6 7
8	0

Mixed Review

6. Using the table, find the mean ACT score.
(1-8)

____

7. Using the table, find the median and mode(s).
(1-7)

median ____________ mode(s) ____________

Midville High School ACT Scores			
14	17	21	30
22	20	21	22
25	15	24	21

Use the pictograph for Exercises 8 and 9.

8. Which grade filled the most recycling bins?
(1-1)

____

9. How many recycling bins did Grade 8 fill?
(1-1)

____

Recycling Collection

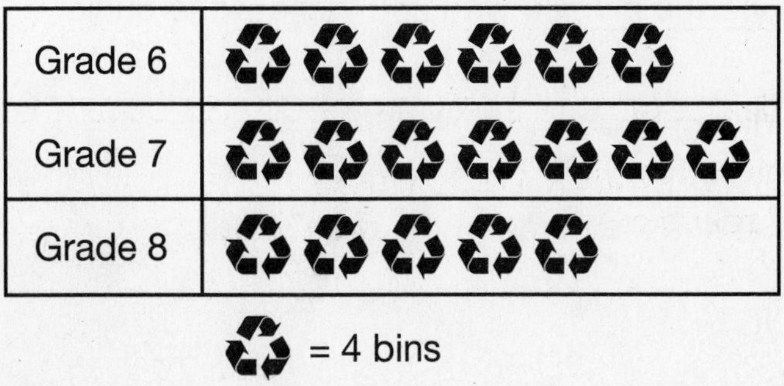

Name ______________________________

Daily Review
2-3

Daily Cumulative Review

Round to the given place. *(Lesson 2-2)*

1. 47,621,920; ten millions ____________

2. 342,392; ten thousands ____________

3. 1,591,327; tens ____________

4. 73,273,736,903; hundred millions ____________

Write each number in standard form. *(Lesson 2-1)*

5. 3 million ____________

6. 27 thousand ____________

7. six billion, seven hundred twenty-three million, nine hundred sixteen thousand

____

8. four million, nineteen thousand, two hundred fifty-seven

____

Mixed Review

Use the table at the right to answer Exercises 9–12.

1996 Population of Selected States (thousands)	
WA	5,533
AR	2,510
SC	3,699
MN	4,658
WY	481
KY	3,884

9. *(1-9)* Identify the outlier. ____________

10. *(1-8)* Find the mean with and without the outlier. Round to the nearest one.

with ________ without ________

11. *(1-7)* Find the median with and without the outlier.

with ________ without ________

12. *(1-5)* What is the range of the data? ____________

Name ______________________________

Daily Review
2-4

Daily Cumulative Review

Order each group of numbers from least to greatest. *(Lesson 2-3)*

1. 2,000; 70,000; 300; 80 ______________________________

2. 2,123; 2,213; 2,312; 2,231 ______________________________

3. 72,270; 73,100; 72,200; 72,160 ______________________________

4. 10 billion, 100 million, 10 thousand ______________________________

In 1996 the United States population was 265,283,783. Round the population to the given place. *(Lesson 2-2)*

5. thousands ______________ **6.** millions ______________

7. hundred thousands ______________ **8.** hundred millions ______________

Mixed Review

9. Write the 1996 United States population (given above) in word form.
(2-1)

____

____

10. Write 6 trillion in standard form.
(2-1)

____

Use the Rainfall graph for Exercises 11 and 12.

11. How many inches of rain did Maysville receive in
(1-1)

May 1995? ______________ May 1996? ______________

12. Could the bar graph be misleading? If so, how would you correct the graph?
(1-2)

____

____

____

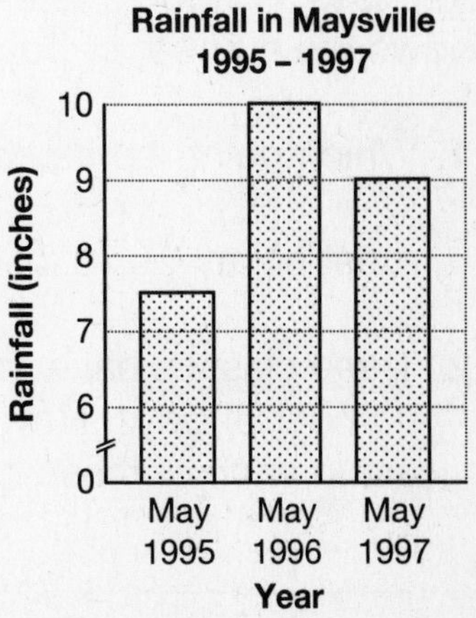

Name ______________________________

Daily Review
2-5

Daily Cumulative Review

In Exercises 1–4, answer the questions about exponents. *(Lesson 2-4)*

1. What is the base of 11^4? ______________

2. What is the power of 11^4? ______________

3. What is the exponent of 11^4? ______________

4. Use a calculator to write 11^4 in standard form. ______________

Order each group of numbers from greatest to least. *(Lesson 2-3)*

5. 57,000; 56,940; 57,010 ______________

6. 2,222; 22,222; 22; 222 ______________

7. 66,606; 66,000; 66,600; 60,000 ______________

8. 12 thousand; 12 million; 120,000 ______________

Mixed Review

9. *(2-1)* In 1996 Chicago O'Hare Airport had 69,133,189 arrivals and departures. Write this number in words.

____

____

10. *(1-1)* Round the number given in Exercise 9 to the nearest million. ______________

Exercises 11 and 12 refer to the scatterplot on the right which shows the number of boys and girls in several classes.

11. *(1-3)* Which point represents the class with the

most boys? ________ most girls? ________

12. *(1-3)* Three classes have the same number of boys. How many boys are in each of these classes?

____

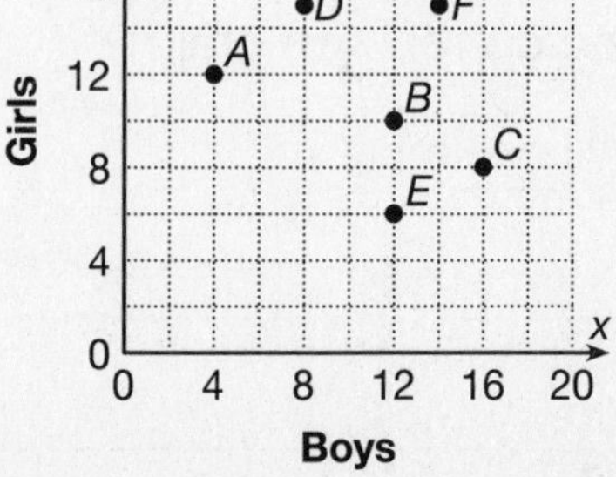

Name ______________________________

Daily Review
2-6

Daily Cumulative Review

Simplify using mental math. *(Lesson 2-5)*

1. 30×80 ________ **2.** $20 \times 53 \times 50$ ________ **3.** $3{,}600 \div 9$ ________

4. $152 + 47$ ________ **5.** $725 + 523 + 275$ ________ **6.** $152 - 98$ ________

7. $2{,}600 \div 13$ ________ **8.** $287 - 195$ ________ **9.** 69×4 ________

Compare using $<$, $>$, or $=$. *(Lesson 2-4)*

10. 3^4 ◯ 4^3 **11.** 4^7 ◯ 4^8 **12.** 4^3 ◯ $4 \times 4 \times 4$

13. 10^5 ◯ 5×10 **14.** 10^5 ◯ $10 + 10 + 10 + 10 + 10$

15. 6^3 ◯ $3 \times 3 \times 3 \times 3$

Mixed Review

16. *(2-3)* One major company made 22,641,502 bolts one year. Another company made 21,963,212 bolts during the same year. Compare these numbers using $<$ or $>$.

____

17. *(2-1)* Write $12,000,000,000 in

word form ________________ number-word form ________________

18. *(1-5)* Make a bar graph showing the number of dogs registered in the American Kennel Club.

Dog	Thousands Registered in 1996
Golden Retriever	69
Beagle	57
Dalmation	33
Collie	13
Dachshund	48

American Kennel Club
1996 Registration

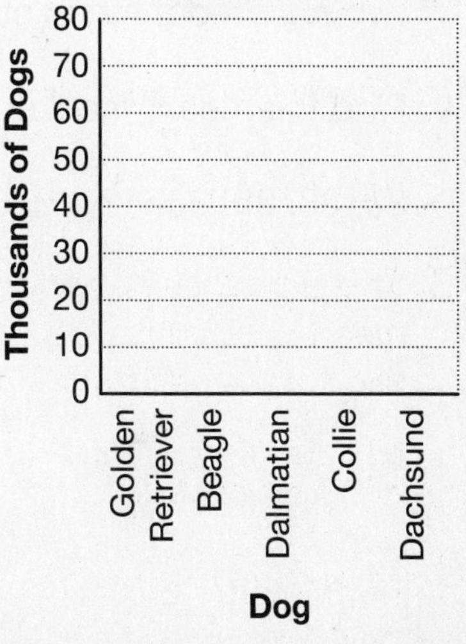

Name ______________________

Daily Review
2-7

Daily Cumulative Review

Estimate the following sums and differences. *(Lesson 2-6)*

1. 28,724 + 93,201 ______

2. 37,723 − 11,389 ______

3. 47 + 51 + 53 ______

4. 285 + 315 + 306 ______

5. 723,468 + 316,728 ______

6. 827,157 − 362,206 ______

Simplify using mental math. *(Lesson 2-5)*

7. 70×80 ______

8. 272 + 27 ______

9. $2 \times 23 \times 5$ ______

10. $3,200 \div 40$ ______

11. 53,625 − 200 ______

12. 37×9 ______

13. 491 + 209 ______

14. $48,000 \div 120$ ______

15. 21×7 ______

Mixed Review

16. *(2-4)* Compare using <, >, or =. 4^3 ◯ 3^4

17. *(2-3)* Compare using <, >, or =. 5,000,000,000 ◯ 5 trillion

18. *(2-2)* Round 36,852,706,079,821 to the nearest ten thousand.

______

19. *(2-1)* Write six million, seven hundred twenty thousand, two hundred three in standard form. ______

20. *(1-8)* Find the mean, median, and mode(s) of the following set of data:

33, 38, 36, 36, 42, 49, 64, 73, 84

mean ______ median ______ mode(s) ______

Name ______________________

Daily Review
2-8

Daily Cumulative Review

Estimate the following products and quotients. *(Lesson 2-7)*

1. 48×37 ________ **2.** 78×51 ________ **3.** 657×11 ________

4. $152 \div 29$ ________ **5.** $796 \div 192$ ________ **6.** $6{,}315 \div 69$ ________

7. $120{,}985 \div 108$ ________ **8.** $31 \times 68 \times 99$ ________

Estimate the following sums and differences. *(Lesson 2-6)*

9. $57{,}823 + 64{,}184$ ________ **10.** $28 + 51 + 32$ ________

11. $725{,}167 - 263{,}198$ ________ **12.** $5425 - 2880$ ________

Mixed Review

13. Write $3 \times 3 \times 3 \times 3 \times 3 \times 3$ using exponents. ________
(2-4)

14. Compare using $<$, $>$, or $=$. three thousand, twenty-five ◯ 32,500
(2-3)

15. The following data set shows the quiz scores for Mrs. Hanson's 10 point math quiz: 8, 7, 8, 6, 8, 7, 9, 7, 9, 10, 6, 8, 10, 9, 7.
(1-4)

a. Make a frequency chart **b.** Make a line plot

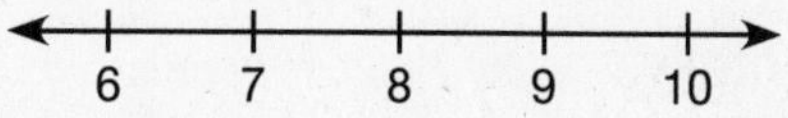

16. Find the median, mode, and range of 22, 12, 16, 20, 12, 20, 21.
(1-7)

median ________ mode ________ range ________

Name ______________________________

Daily Review
2-9

Daily Cumulative Review

Evaluate the expression. *(Lesson 2-8)*

1. $7 \times 6 \div 3$ ________

2. $3 + 4 \times 6$ ________

3. $16 \div 4 + 3$ ________

4. $35 - (22 - 10)$ ________

5. 5×2^3 ________

6. $(24 \div 12)^4$ ________

7. $8^2 - 2^4$ ________

8. $64 \div (16 \div 4)$ ________

9. $128 \div 8 - 8 \times 2$ ________

10. $(9 \div 3)^4$ ________

Estimate the following products and quotients. *(Lesson 2-7)*

11. $182 \div 31$ ________

12. 389×31 ________

13. $888 \div 91$ ________

14. $9 \times 12 \times 19$ ________

15. $3258 \times 5 \times 9$ ________

16. $4825 \div 69$ ________

Mixed Review

17. *(2-6)* In 1996 the population for Cook County in Illinois was 5,096,540. The population in Los Angeles County, California was 9,127,751. Estimate the combined population of these two cities.

____

Simplify mentally.

18. *(2-5)* $74 + 101$ ________

19. *(2-5)* $1653 - 101$ ________

20. *(2-5)* 31×5 ________

Write using exponents.

21. *(2-4)* $4 \times 4 \times 4 =$ ________

22. *(2-4)* $6 \times 2 \times 2 \times 2 =$ ________

23. *(2-4)* $82 \times 82 =$ ________

24. *(2-1)* The Dallas-Ft. Worth Airport handled over 58,000,000 arrivals and departures in 1996. Write this number in word-number form.

____

Name ______________________

Daily Review 2-10

Daily Cumulative Review

Find the next three numbers in the pattern. *(Lesson 2-9)*

1. 4, 7, 10, 13, 16, ______, ______, ______

2. 124, 112, 100, 88, 76, ______, ______, ______

3. 98, 99, 101, 104, 108, ______, ______, ______

4. 110, 100, 91, 83, 76, ______, ______, ______

5. 16, 26, 24, 34, 32, ______, ______, ______

Evaluate each expression. *(Lesson 2-8)*

6. $8 - 3 - 2$ ______

7. $8 - (3 - 2)$ ______

8. $8^2 - 3^2$ ______

9. $4 \times (5 - 3)$ ______

10. $(4 \times 5) - 3$ ______

11. $(4 + 5)^2 \div 3$ ______

Mixed Review

Estimate.

12. $2895 \div 511$ ______ *(2-7)*

13. 206×9 ______ *(2-7)*

Simplify mentally.

14. $54 + 105$ ______ *(2-5)*

15. $250 - 151$ ______ *(2-5)*

16. $56{,}000 \div 800$ ______ *(2-5)*

Use the circle graph for Exercices 17 and 18.

17. How much of the family budget is spent on clothing and food for each $100 of the budget. *(1-1)*

______

18. For each $100, how much money is left over after food, housing, and clothes? *(1-1)*

______

Family Budget (for each $100)

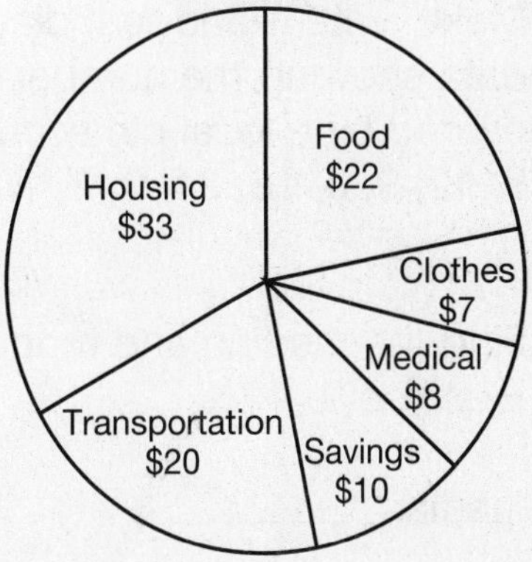

Name ____

Daily Review
2-11

Daily Cumulative Review

Complete the table by evaluating each expression for x = 2, 3, 4, and 5. *(Lesson 2-10)*

1.

x	$x + 7$	$20 - x$	$8x$	$\frac{120}{x}$	$x \times x$	$x \div x$	x^3
2							
3							
4							
5							

Find the next three numbers in the pattern. *(Lesson 2-9)*

2. 5, 7, 11, 17, 25, ________, ________, ________

3. 3, 6, 12, 24, 48, ________, ________, ________

4. 1, 3, 9, 27, 81, ________, ________, ________

5. 31, 36, 33, 38, 35, ________, ________, ________

Mixed Review

6. Estimate. 891 + 921 + 889 + 906 + 875 + 902 ________
(2-6)

Compare using <, >, or =.

7. 3^5 ◯ $3 \times 3 \times 3 \times 3 \times 3$
(2-4)

8. 5×10 ◯ 10^5
(2-4)

9. Make a stem-and-leaf diagram of the data showing the number of badges earned by a local girl scout troop.
(1-6)
8, 12, 9, 3, 18, 24, 0, 3, 10, 20, 12, 3, 6, 5, 15

Stem	Leaf

10. Find the median and mode(s) for the data in Exercise 9.
(1-7)

median ________ mode(s) ________

Name ______________________________

Daily Review
2-12

Daily Cumulative Review

Write the phrase as an expression. *(Lesson 2-11)*

1. 8 more than x __________ **2.** x less than 23 __________

3. one-fourth of b __________ **4.** a multiplied by 5 __________

5. c squared __________ **6.** d increased by 10 __________

7. e doubled __________ **8.** f divided by 12 __________

Complete the table by evaluating each expression for x = 2, 5, and 8. *(Lesson 2-10)*

9.

x	$12 + x$	$x - 2$	$15 \times x$	$120 \div x$	$7x$	x^2
2						
5						
8						

Mixed Review

10. Find the next three numbers in the pattern.
(2-9)

13, 18, 23, 28, 33, ________, ________, ________

Simplify.

11. $(4 + 4^2) \div 5$ __________
(2-8)

12. $(2^3 + 6) \div 7$ __________
(2-8)

13. 3^4 __________
(2-4)

14. 4^3 __________
(2-4)

15. 12^4 __________
(2-4)

16. How are the two graphs alike?
(1-2) How are they different?

____

____

____

NASA Payloads, 1950 – 1996

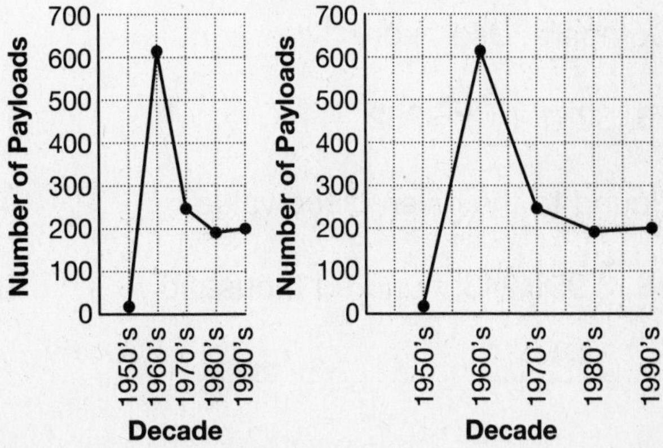

Name ______________________________

Daily Review
2-13

Daily Cumulative Review

Is the equation true for the given value of the variable? *(Lesson 2-12)*

1. $x + 6 = 24, x = 30$ ________

2. $13 - x = 7, x = 6$ ________

3. $6x = 42, x = 7$ ________

4. $y - 8 = 15, y = 7$ ________

5. $y \div 8 = 3, y = 24$ ________

6. $24 + y = 36, y = 10$ ________

7. $12 \times t = 144, t = 11$ ________

8. $t \div 5 = 15, t = 75$ ________

Write an expression to answer each question. *(Lesson 2-11)*

9. What is the product of 24 and *x*? ______________________

10. What is the sum of *x* and 12? ______________________

11. What is the quotient of 32 and *y*? ______________________

12. What is the difference between *y* and 16? ______________________

Mixed Review

13. Evaluate $15 - x$ for $x = 2$, 3, and 4. ________, ________, ________
(2-10)

14. Insert parentheses to make this statement true.
(2-8)

$6 + 4 \div 2 = 5$

15. New Jersey has 1,792 miles of shoreline. Virginia has 3,315 miles of shoreline.
(2-6)

Estimate the difference in miles of shoreline. ____________

Compare. Use > or <.

16. 3251 ◯ 3252
(2-3)

17. 234,625,129 ◯ 234,626,874
(2-3)

Round to the given place value.

18. 3,957,243; hundred thousand
(2-2)

____

19. 3,697,205; hundred
(2-2)

____

Name ______________________________

Daily Review
3-1

Daily Cumulative Review

Solve the following equations. *(Lesson 2-13)*

1. $x + 8 = 32$ ________ **2.** $m - 7 = 15$ ________ **3.** $\frac{x}{5} = 12$ ________

4. $9t = 63$ ________ **5.** $15 + x = 38$ ________ **6.** $m - 23 = 71$ ________

Write an equation for each situation. *(Lesson 2-12)*

7. Todd had 6 shirts. He bought x more. Then he had 13 shirts.

____

8. Terri had c pieces of candy. She gave Mike 7 pieces. She had 23 pieces left.

____

9. A package of 42 cookies was equally divided among x children. Each child had 7 cookies.

____

10. Each of the 32 school buses had t tires. If all the buses got new tires, there would be 192 new tires.

____

Mixed Review

11. Evaluate $3k$ when $k = 4, 6, 10$. ______________________
(2-10)

Estimate.

12. $61{,}305 \div 4{,}988$ ________ *(2-7)* **13.** 102×72 ________ *(2-7)*

14. Compare, using $<$, $>$, or $=$. 1^{10} ◯ 10^{1}
(2-4)

15. Order from least to greatest. 333; 3,333; 33; 3; 33,333
(2-3)

____

Name ______________________________

Daily Review 3-2

Daily Cumulative Review

Write the following numbers as decimals. *(Lesson 3-1)*

1. five tenths ________

2. twenty-two thousandths ________

3. two and five hundredths ________

Solve the following equations. *(Lesson 2-13)*

4. $x - 15 = 27$ ______

5. $m + 8 = 37$ ______

6. $\frac{s}{7} = 12$ ______

7. $11y = 55$ ______

8. $b - 27 = 101$ ______

9. $7u = 84$ ______

Mixed Review

10. Use the data set to make a bar graph.
(1-5)

Number of Televisions in House	
0	1
1	4
2	10
3 or more	3

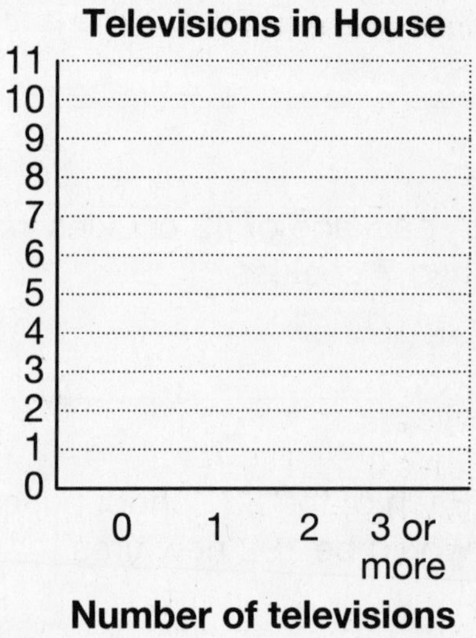

11. Find the mean, median, and mode(s) without the outlier.
(1-9)

mean ______ median ______

mode(s) ______________

Stem	Leaf
2	0 0 2 2 4
3	0 2 6 7
4	0 3 4 6
8	0

12. Mars is 128,400,000 miles from the sun. Write this distance in word form and in number-word form.
(2-1)

____

____

Name ________________________________

Daily Review 3-3

Daily Cumulative Review

Round to the underlined place value. *(Lesson 3-2)*

1. 3<u>1</u>.4 ________

2. 8.<u>8</u>931 ________

3. 85.<u>0</u>7 ________

4. 13.10<u>6</u>3 ________

5. 2.<u>7</u>7 ________

6. 3<u>5</u>.16 ________

7. 29<u>3</u>.7 ________

8. 6.0<u>9</u>2 ________

Write the decimal in word form. *(Lesson 3-1)*

9. 0.57 ____________________

10. 6.5 ____________________

11. 0.013 ____________________

12. 0.06 ____________________

Mixed Review

13. *(2-13)* Find the values for the variable that will provide the given values for the expression.

x	$x + 14$
	18
	60
	88

14. *(2-10)* Complete the table. One large pizza feeds 3 hungry boys.

Number of boys	Number of pizzas
3	
9	
15	
b	

15. *(2-4)* Write 9 cubed in standard form. ____________________

16. *(1-7)* Find the median, mode(s), and range of the following test scores:

98, 86, 98, 98, 87, 92, 92

median ________ mode(s) ________ range ________

Name ___________________________________

Daily Review
3-4

Daily Cumulative Review

Compare using >, <, or =. *(Lesson 3-3)*

1. 0.487 ◯ 0.478 **2.** 5.2 ◯ 5.21 **3.** 6.45 ◯ 6.449

4. 7.15 ◯ 7.51 **5.** 91.06 ◯ 91.6 **6.** 18.97 ◯ 18.970

Estimate each object's length to the nearest centimeter and tenth of a centimeter. *(Lesson 3-2)*

7. nearest cm: ________ nearest tenth: ________ **8.** nearest cm: ________ nearest tenth: ________

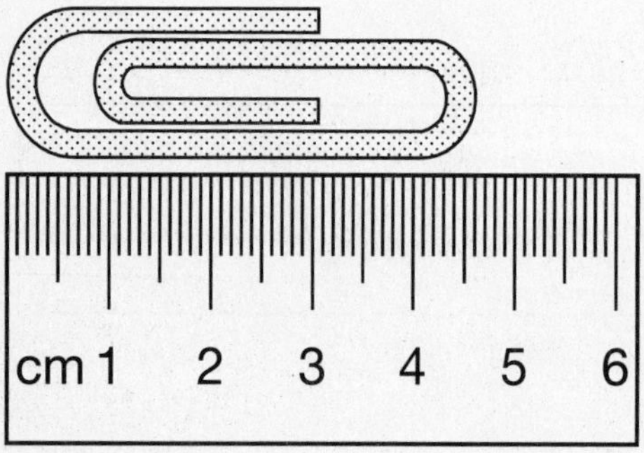

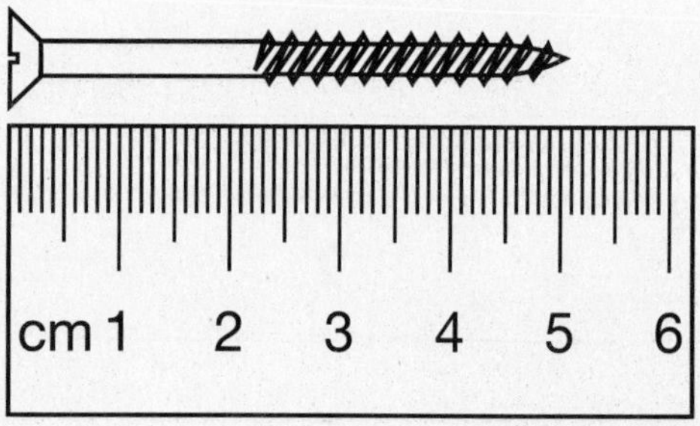

Mixed Review

9. Is 64 ÷ n = 16 true when n = 8? ________
(2-12)

10. Write "x less than 25" as an expression. ________
(2-11)

11. Find the next three numbers in the pattern.
(2-9)

1, 3, 9, 27, 81, ______, ______, ______

12. Round 851,309,069,823 to the nearest million. ________________
(2-2)

13. For the given data, make a stem-and-leaf diagram.
(1-6)
17, 19, 20, 23, 22, 21, 16, 14, 17, 13, 16, 20, 23, 26, 23, 21

Stem	Leaf

14. In the data for Exercise 13, what are the median and mode(s)?
(1-7)

median ________ mode(s) ________

Name ______________________________

Daily Review
3-5

Daily Cumulative Review

In Exercises 1–8, write the number in standard form. *(Lesson 3-4)*

1. 3.15×10^2 ______ **2.** 3.891×10^5 ______ **3.** 5.723×10^4 ______ **4.** 9.36×10^3 ______

5. 5.36×10^6 ______ **6.** 3.693×10^3 ______ **7.** 6.154×10^4 ______ **8.** 1.365×10^5 ______

Order from least to greatest. *(Lesson 3-3)*

9. 31.700, 31.007, 31.070 ______

10. 24.44, 24.444, 24.4 ______

11. 6.54, 6.145, 6.154, 6.514 ______

12. 7.568, 6.758, 6.578, 6.875 ______

Mixed Review

13. *(3-2)* One centimeter is equal to 0.3937 inch. Round this value to the nearest hundredth of an inch. ______

14. *(3-1)* One inch is equal to 2.54 centimeters. Write 2.54 in word form.

______

15. *(2-8)* Insert parentheses to make the following statement true.

$6 \times 2^2 + 1 = 30$

Use mental math to simplify.

16. *(2-5)* 30×71 ______

17. *(2-5)* $232 + 421$ ______

18. *(2-5)* $54{,}000 \div 90$ ______

19. *(1-8)* Find the mean of the following data showing the numbers of points scored by the local basketball team last season.
65, 88, 92, 67, 72, 91, 59, 92, 68, 78, 86 ______

Name ______________________________

Daily Review
3-6

Daily Cumulative Review

Estimate each sum, difference, product, or quotient. *(Lesson 3-5)*

1. 4.68 + 2.75 ________

2. 28.89 × 6.8 ________

3. 21.837 − 1.12 ________

4. 80.89 ÷ 8.9 ________

5. 14.675 + 4.91 ________

6. 27.264 − 7.35 ________

7. 41.16 × 4.91 ________

8. 84.12 ÷ 6.22 ________

Write in scientific notation. *(Lesson 3-4)*

9. 26,500 ________

10. 12 million ________

11. 40,000 ________

12. 23,590 ________

13. 82 billion ________

14. 6,813,000,000,000 ________

Mixed Review

Use the bar graph to answer the following questions.

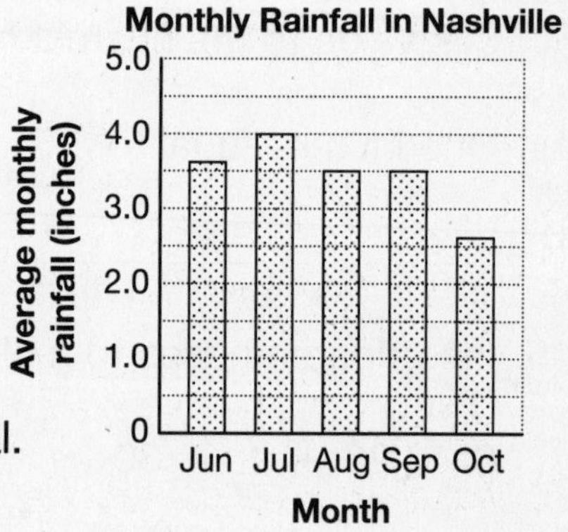

15. Which month had the most rainfall? ________
(3-3)

16. Which months had the same amount of rainfall? ________________
(3-3)

17. Write two hundred sixty-one thousandths as a decimal.
(3-1)

____

Round to the given place.

18. 6,703; hundreds
(2-2)

____

19. 6,875,000; hundred-thousands
(2-2)

____

20. Draw a line plot of the hours spent doing homework each week.
(1-4)

10, 6, 7, 10, 7, 8, 9, 10, 7, 7, 6, 7, 8, 10, 8, 6, 9

Name ______________________

Daily Review 3-7

Daily Cumulative Review

Simplify. *(Lesson 3-6)*

1. 2.72 + 2.8 ________

2. 4.934 − 1.85 ________

3. 8.976 + 1.328 ________

4. 7.58 − 1.32 ________

5. \$2.85 + \$13.91 ________

6. 32.874 − 4.69 ________

7. 6.2 + 7.31 ________

8. 85.7 − 6.913 ________

Estimate each sum, difference, product, or quotient. *(Lesson 3-5)*

9. 2.08 + 3.01 ________

10. \$62.91 − \$15.25 ________

11. 16.95 × 1.82 ________

12. 56.23 ÷ 13.9 ________

13. 56.13 + 9.2 ________

14. 213.45 − 23.2 ________

15. 4.6 × 5.12 ________

16. 12.13 ÷ 3.57 ________

Mixed Review

17. *(3-4)* Venus is 66,800,000,000 miles from the sun. Write the number in scientific notation. ________

18. *(3-3)* In 1996, a German deutsche mark was worth \$0.66454, a Canadian dollar was worth \$0.73341, and a United Kingdom pound was worth \$0.64033. Order these currencies from the least value to the greatest.

____

19. *(1-6)* Make a stem-and-leaf diagram of the data showing the number of books read by a sixth-grade class during the school year.

5, 8, 12, 18, 22, 6, 9, 8, 12, 13, 21, 20, 26, 9, 3, 15, 17, 19, 23, 21, 9, 4, 24, 16, 10

Stem	Leaf

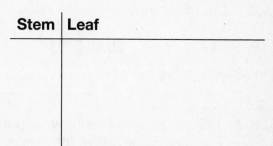

Solve the following equations.

20. *(2-13)* $x - 5 = 23$ ________

21. *(2-13)* $m + 15 = 47$ ________

Name ______________________________

Daily Review
3-8

Daily Cumulative Review

Solve each equation. *(Lesson 3-7)*

1. $h + 3.8 = 8.8$ **2.** $b - 6 = 15.1$ **3.** $8 + t = 14.6$ **4.** $9 - a = 2.4$

$h =$ ________ $b =$ ________ $t =$ ________ $a =$ ________

5. $m + 6.2 = 8.1$ **6.** $d - 8.3 = 1.8$ **7.** $6.38 + f = 12.5$ **8.** $3.8 - c = 3.2$

$m =$ ________ $d =$ ________ $f =$ ________ $c =$ ________

Simplify. *(Lesson 3-6)*

9. 6.97 + 3.421 **10.** 6.723 − 1.38 **11.** \$46.23 − \$26.52 **12.** 22 + 2.315

________ ________ ________ ________

13. 3.275 + 6.941 + 9.2894 **14.** 7.23 + 12.6 + 5.73

________ ________

Mixed Review

Estimate.

15. 5.12 + 1.87 *(3-5)* **16.** 68.73 × 9.8 *(3-5)* **17.** 25.967 − 11.98 *(3-5)* **18.** 62.9 ÷ 7.12 *(3-5)*

________ ________ ________ ________

Round to the underlined place value.

19. 5<u>3</u>.4 *(3-2)* **20.** 6.<u>6</u>961 *(3-2)* **21.** 12.10<u>9</u>2 *(3-2)* **22.** 69.3<u>0</u>5 *(3-2)*

________ ________ ________ ________

23. *(2-6)* In 1996, London's Heathrow airport handled 56,037,813 arrivals and departures. In the same year, Tokyo International Airport handled 46,631,475. Estimate the combined arrivals and departures of these two busy airports.

____

Name ______________________

Daily Review
3-9

Daily Cumulative Review

Insert a decimal point in the answer to make the equation true. *(Lesson 3-8)*

1. $14 \times 8.56 = 1\ 1\ 9\ 8\ 4$ **2.** $3.27 \times 6 = 1\ 9\ 6\ 2$ **3.** $2.375 \times 8 = 1\ 9\ 0\ 0\ 0$

4. $6 \times 3.891 = 2\ 3\ 3\ 4\ 6$ **5.** $9.17 \times 14 = 1\ 2\ 8\ 3\ 8$ **6.** $3.27 \times 22 = 7\ 1\ 9\ 4$

Solve. *(Lesson 3-7)*

7. $x + 2.5 = 8.5$ **8.** $a - 7 = 14.7$ **9.** $11 - b = 6.2$ **10.** $14.2 + f = 21.6$

$x =$ ______ $a =$ ______ $b =$ ______ $f =$ ______

Mixed Review

11. Pluto is 8.374×10^8 miles from the sun. Write this number in standard form.
(3-4)

____

12. Write 8.374 in word form.
(3-1)

____

13. Evaluate $40 - x$ when $x = 3, 15, 22$. ______________
(2-10)

14. Write 2^8 in standard form. ______________
(2-4)

15. Is $\frac{x}{4} = 22$ true when $x = 84$? Explain.
(2-12)

____

16. Determine if there is a trend on the scatterplot.
(1-3) If there is, describe the pattern of the data.

____

____

____

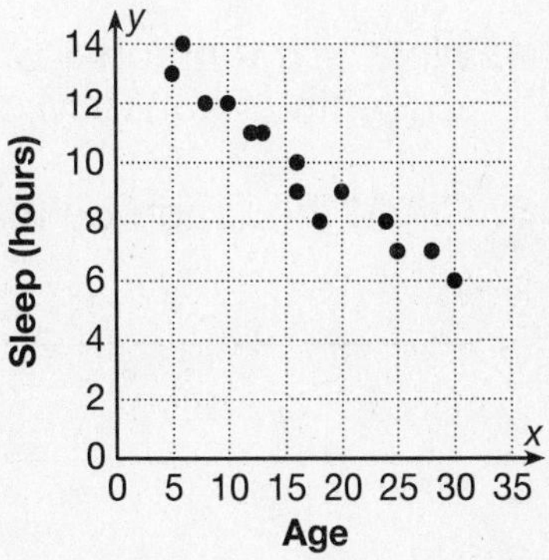

Name ______________________________

Daily Cumulative Review

Insert a decimal point in the answer to make the equation true. *(Lesson 3-9)*

1. $4.7 \times 21.6 = 1\ 0\ 1\ 5\ 2$ **2.** $6.3 \times 18.7 = 1\ 1\ 7\ 8\ 1$

3. $3.8 \times 12.56 = 4\ 7\ 7\ 2\ 8$ **4.** $10.8 \times 10.312 = 1\ 1\ 1\ 3\ 6\ 9\ 6$

Multiply. *(Lesson 3-8)*

5. 3.75×10 ________ **6.** 3.75×100 ________ **7.** 3.75×1000 ________ **8.** 6.125×20 ________

Mixed Review

9. Solve. $x + 2.6 = 11$ $x =$ ________
(3-7)

10. Add. $8.45 + 6.38 + 6.42 + 31.62$ ________
(3-6)

11. Measure the crayon to the nearest centimeter. ________
(3-2)

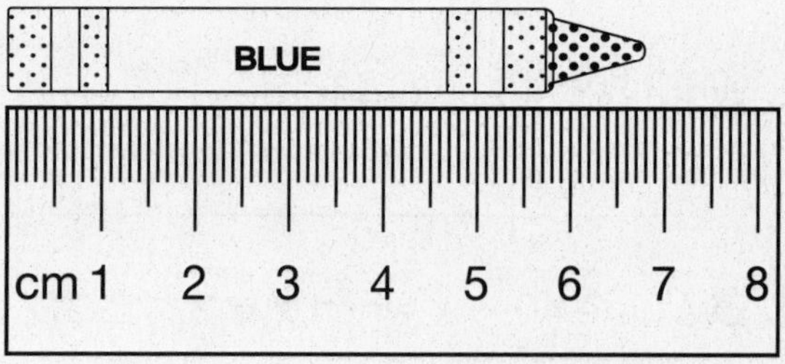

12. Find the next three numbers in the pattern.
(2-9)

5, 8, 14, 26, 50, ______, ______, ______

13. Evaluate $(21 - 17)^2 + 5$. ________
(2-8)

Use the bar graph for Exercises 14 and 15.

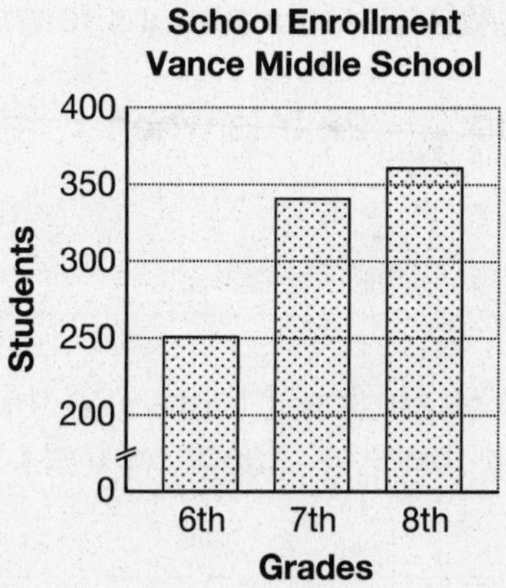

14. What is the number of eighth-grade students at Vance Middle School? ________
(1-2)

15. Could the graph be misleading? If so, how would you correct the graph?
(1-2)

____

____

____

Name ______________________________

Daily Review
3-11

Daily Cumulative Review

Insert a decimal point in the answer to make the equation true. *(Lesson 3-10)*

1. 44.764 ÷ 76 = 0 5 8 9 **2.** 98.784 ÷ 28 = 3 5 2 8 **3.** 35.34 ÷ 6 = 5 8 9

4. 5.6 ÷ 7 = 0 8 **5.** 14.505 ÷ 3 = 4 8 3 5 **6.** 7.896 ÷ 3 = 2 6 3 2

Multiply. *(Lesson 3-9)*

7. 8.032×0.5 **8.** 0.02×8.3 **9.** 51.8×0.8 **10.** 0.03×0.6

________ ________ ________ ________

Mixed Review

11. Multiply. 4×16.83
(3-8)

____

12. Solve. $c + 4.7 = 8.9$
(3-7)

$c =$ ________

Estimate.

13. $1.08 + 5.03$
(3-5)

____

14. $28.89 - 12.72$
(3-5)

____

15. $95.87 \div 11.9$
(3-5)

____

16. Jason earns $75 per day on his job. If he worked 200 days last year, how much did he earn? ________
(2-5)

17. The line plot shows the highest temperature recorded by several states during a drought year.
(1-9)

a. Find the mean, median, and mode(s) of the data.

mean ________ median ________

mode(s) ________

b. Did the outlier affect the mean? Explain.

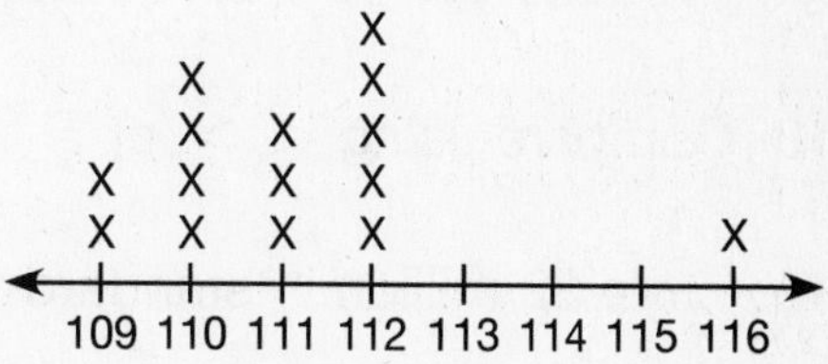

____

18. What is the range of the data for the temperatures in Exercise 17? ________
(1-5)

Name ______________________

Daily Review
3-12

Daily Cumulative Review

Insert a decimal point in the answer to make the equation true. *(Lesson 3-11)*

1. $11.2602 \div 2.1 = 5\ 3\ 6\ 2$

2. $15.2358 \div 3.79 = 4\ 0\ 2$

3. $5.018 \div 2.6 = 1\ 9\ 3\ 0$

4. $8.892 \div 1.3 = 6\ 8\ 4$

Divide. *(Lesson 3-10)*

5. $37.848 \div 12$ ______

6. $210.56 \div 28$ ______

7. $174.4 \div 8$ ______

8. $9.87 \div 42$ ______

Mixed Review

9. Multiply. 53.7×0.06 ______
(3-9)

10. Multiply. $\$11.73 \times 9$ ______
(3-8)

11. Simplify. $183.6 - 21.92$ ______
(3-6)

12. Write 63 trillion in scientific notation. ______
(3-4)

13. Order from least to greatest. 7.34, 7.243, 7.234, 7.324
(3-3)

______

14. Write sixteen thousandths as a decimal. ______
(3-1)

15. Solve. $x - 8 = 32$ $x =$ ______
(2-13)

16. Write an expression for the phrase "5 less than *k*" ______
(2-11)

17. Evaluate $4 + (2 + 3)^3$ ______
(2-8)

18. Compare using <, >, or =. 4^3 ◯ 4×3
(2-4)

19. Write 32 million in standard form. ______
(2-1)

20. Find the median and mode(s).
(1-7)
3, 9, 10, 12, 14, 9, 4, 8, 10, 9, 22, 7, 30, 17, 15, 25, 18

median ______ mode(s) ______

Name ______________________________

Daily Review 4-1

Daily Cumulative Review

Solve. *(Lesson 3-12)*

1. $4x = 10.08$ $x =$ ________

2. $\frac{a}{3.1} = 2.36$ $a =$ ________

3. $0.8k = 5.04$ $k =$ ________

4. $\frac{s}{0.62} = 3.2$ $s =$ ________

Divide. *(Lesson 3-11)*

5. $4.392 \div 0.6$ ________

6. $0.325 \div 0.13$ ________

7. $13.26 \div 4.25$ ________

8. $0.1456 \div 2.6$ ________

Mixed Review

9. *(3-10)* Divide. $20.605 \div 5$ ________

10. *(3-9)* Multiply. 53.2×0.06 ________

11. *(3-8)* Multiply. $\$2.63 \times 5$ ________

12. *(3-7)* Solve. $4.17 + x = 6.3$ $x =$ ________

13. *(2-7)* Estimate. $64{,}895 \div 131$ ________

14. *(2-5)* Simplify. $25 \times 40 \times 18$ ________

15. *(1-8)* Find the mean of the data in the stem-and-leaf plot. ________

Stem	Leaf
2	4 7 8
3	0 1 3 3 7 9
4	1 1 4 6
5	0 1

16. *(1-4)* Make a line plot with the hours of sleep reported by college students:
6, 5, 7, 4, 8, 6, 6, 5, 7, 7, 5, 4, 8, 7, 6, 5

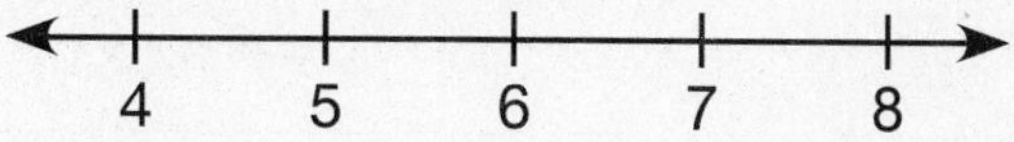

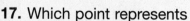

Use the scatterplot to answer the questions.

17. *(1-3)* Which point represents the tallest person? ________

18. *(1-3)* Name two points that represent people who are the same height. ________

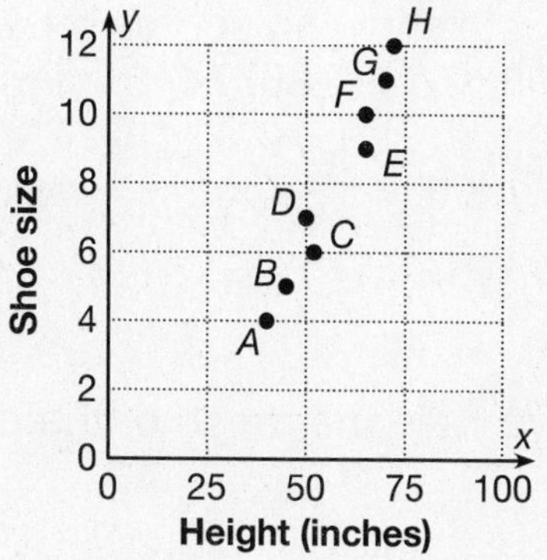

Name ______________________________

Daily Review
4-2

Daily Cumulative Review

Find the perimeter. *(Lesson 4-1)*

1. ____________ **2.** ____________ **3.** ____________

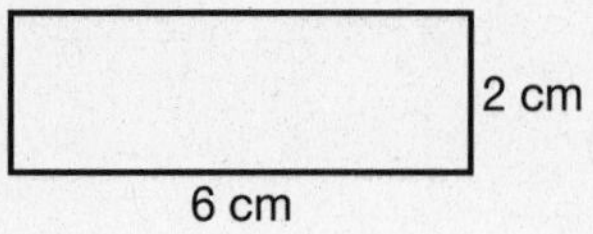

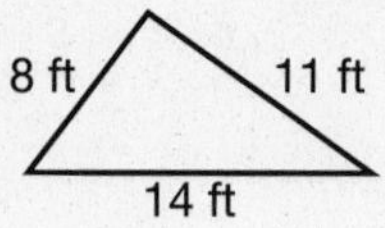

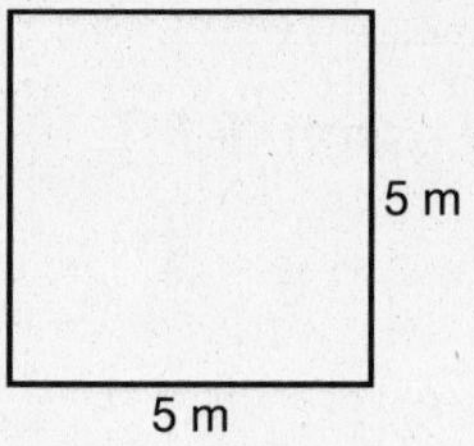

Solve. *(Lesson 3-12)*

4. $6n = 7.95$ **5.** $\frac{d}{3.6} = 1.325$ **6.** $0.1x = 2.3$ **7.** $\frac{m}{2.309} = 5$

$n =$ ________ $d =$ ________ $x =$ ________ $m =$ ________

Mixed Review

8. Divide. $1.836 \div 0.2$
(3-11)

____

9. Add. $5.2 + 7.38$
(3-6)

____

10. Compare with $>$ or $<$
(3-3)

75.6 ◯ 75.06

11. Solve. $x + 23 = 35$
(2-13)

$x =$ ____________

12. Evaluate. $8 + 6 \div 2$
(2-8)

____

13. Simplify. $360 - 142$
(2-5)

____

14. Write 730,153 in words.
(2-1)

____

15. Make a stem-and-leaf diagram of the data showing scores on a test:
(1-6)
83, 92, 71, 86, 74, 85, 96, 67, 73, 85, 90, 63, 82, 78, 79, 71, 82, 75, 89, 76

Stem	Leaf

16. What is the range of the data for the test scores in Exercise 15? ____________
(1-5)

Name ______________________________

Daily Review
4-3

Daily Cumulative Review

Name an appropriate metric unit of measure. *(Lesson 4-2)*

1. Weight of a pencil ____________

2. Height of a basketball player ____________

3. Amount of milk in a carton ____________

4. Distance from Dallas to New York City ____________

Find the length of each unknown side. *(Lesson 4-1)*

5. $a =$ ______, $b =$ ______ **6.** $c =$ ______, $d =$ ______ **7.** $x =$ ______, $y =$ ______

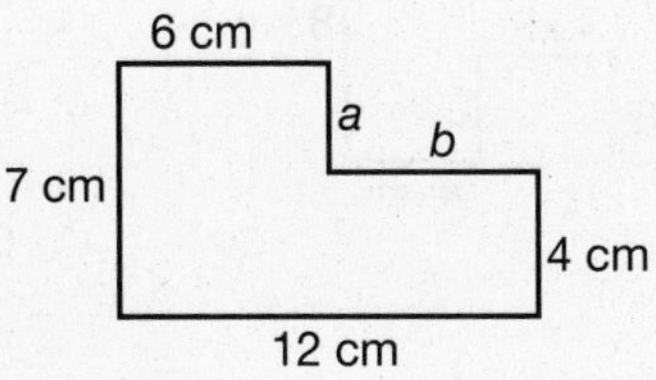

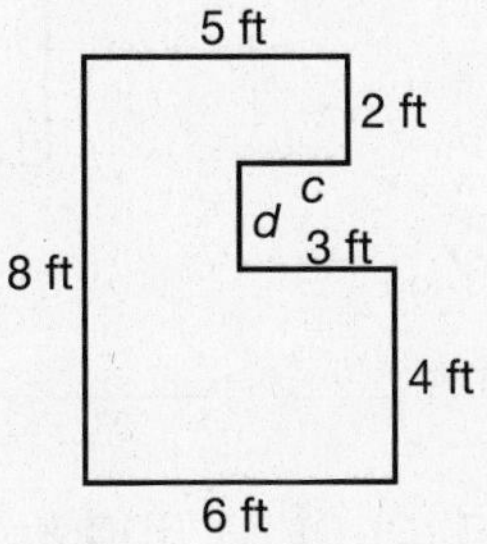

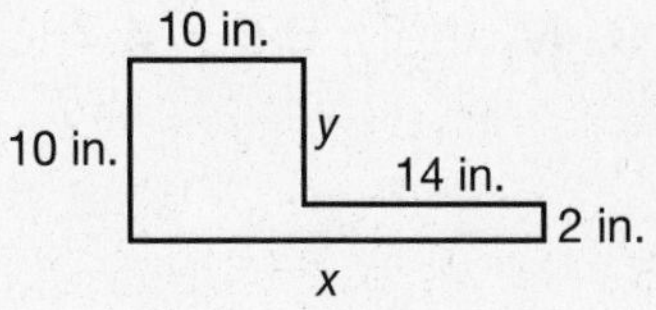

Mixed Review

8. Solve using inverse operations.
(3-12)

a. $0.7p = 3.01$

$p =$ ____________

b. $\frac{m}{3.9} = 0.51$

$m =$ ____________

9. Divide. $0.7296 \div 0.16$
(3-11)

____

10. Multiply. 9×4.183
(3-8)

____

11. Simplify. $184.8 - 21.73$
(3-6)

____

12. Write $\frac{27}{1000}$ as a decimal. ____________
(3-1)

13. Find the next three numbers in the pattern.
(2-9)

6, 13, 20, 27, 34, ________, ________, ________

14. Write $3 \times 3 \times 3 \times 3 \times 3$ using exponents. ________
(2-4)

15. Identify the outlier in the data set. 91, 88, 112, 96, 10, 106, 95, 86 ________
(1-9)

Name ______________________________

Daily Review
4-4

Daily Cumulative Review

Convert. *(Lesson 4-3)*

1. 23 feet = ________ inches **2.** 26 quarts = ________ gallons

3. 12 pounds = ________ ounces **4.** 13,200 feet = ________ miles

Convert within the metric system. *(Lesson 4-2)*

5. 68 g = ________ kg **6.** 3.2 L = ________ mL **7.** 82 cm = ________ m

Mixed Review

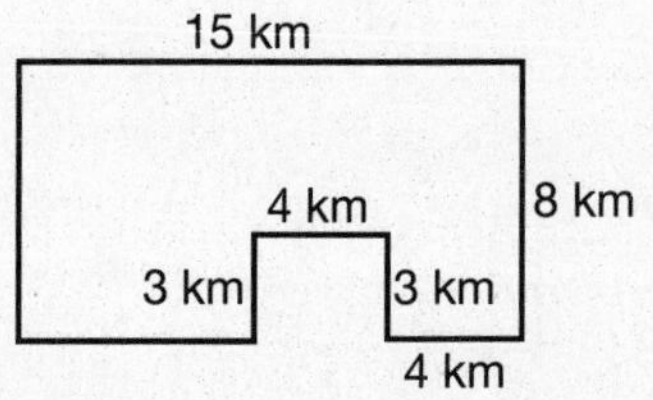

8. Find the perimeter of the figure. ________
(4-1)

9. Multiply. 6.5×4.7 ____________
(3-9)

10. Write 6.31×10^7 in standard form. ______________________
(3-4)

11. Write an expression for "the product of 31 and *x*." ________
(2-11)

12. Round 26,321 to the thousands place. ____________
(2-2)

13. Write 12,000,000,000 in number-word form. ____________
(2-1)

Use the 1996 Election Results graph to answer the following.

14. Who had the most votes? ____________
(1-1)

15. Estimate the total number of votes shown in the data.
(1-1)

____

16. About how many more votes did Bob Dole get than Ross Perot?
(1-1)

____

17. Estimate how many people didn't vote for Bob Dole.
(1-1)

____

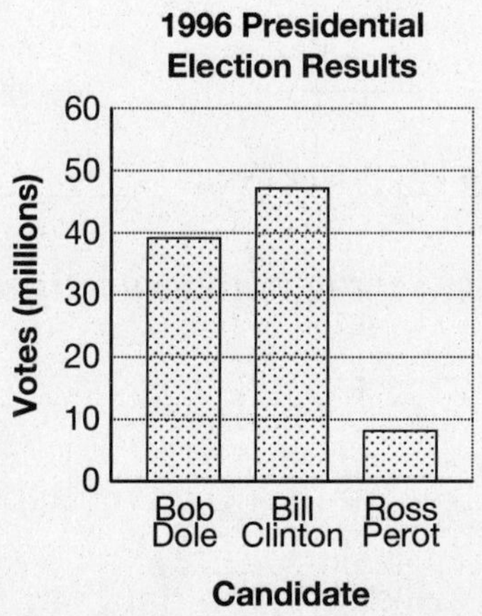

Name ____

Daily Review 4-5

Daily Cumulative Review

Find the missing measurement for each rectangle. *(Lesson 4-4)*

1. Area = ________
Base = 6 ft
Height = 12 ft

2. Area = 56 cm^2
Base = ________
Height = 8 cm

3. Area = 108 in^2
Base = 9 in.
Height = ________

Convert. *(Lesson 4-3)*

4. 36 ft = ______ yd

5. 80 oz = ______ lb

6. 9 gal = ______ qt

Mixed Review

7. Convert. 24,800 m = ________ km *(4-2)*

8. Solve. $6.3x = 20.223$; x = ________ *(3-12)*

9. Estimate. \$52.81 − \$14.21 ________ *(3-5)*

10. One kilometer is about 0.621 mile. Round this value to the nearest tenth of a mile. ________ *(3-2)*

11. Estimate. 28,124 + 91,052 + 67,213 + 52,620 ________________ *(2-6)*

12. Order the following from least to greatest. 82,370; 83,207; 82,200; 83,170 *(2-3)*

____

13. Find the median and mode(s) of the data in the stem-and-leaf diagram. *(1-7)*

median ________

mode(s) ________

Stem	Leaf
4	5 7 9
5	0 2 3 7 8
6	2 4 6 7
7	2 3

14. What is the range of the values in the stem-and-leaf diagram? *(1-6)*

____

15. Find the perimeter of the figure at the right. *(4-1)*

____

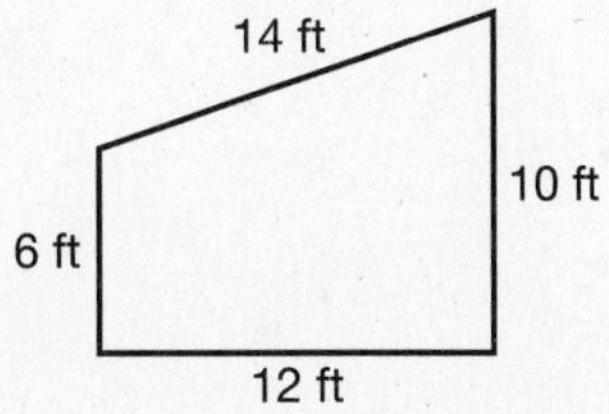

Name ______________________________

Daily Review 4-6

Daily Cumulative Review

Find the area of each parallelogram. The dashed line is a height. *(Lesson 4-5)*

1.

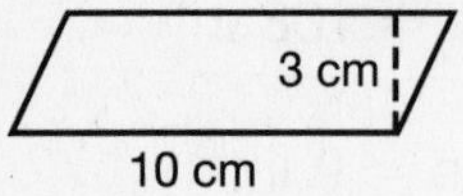

____

2.

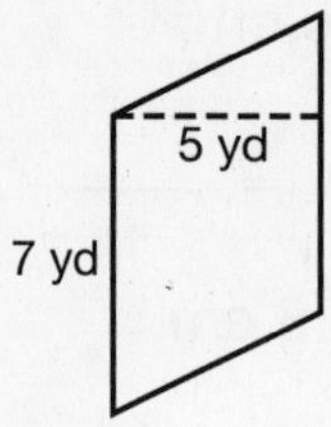

____

3.

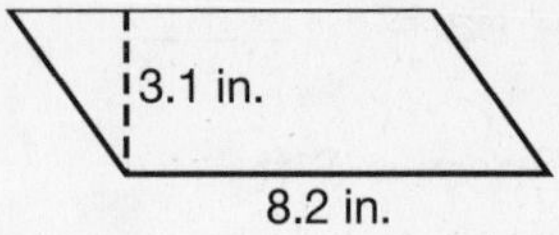

____

Find the area of each figure. *(Lesson 4-4)*

4. Square with sides of length 9 ft ______________

5. Rectangle with sides 3.7 m and 7.2 m ______________

6. Rectangle with sides 12 in. and 7 in. ______________

Mixed Review

7. Convert. 64 qt = ________ gal
(4-3)

8. Convert. 6.21 kg = ________ g
(4-2)

9. Find the perimeter.
(4-1)

____

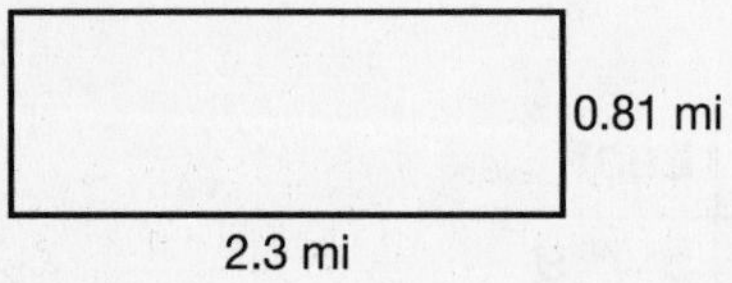

10. Estimate the length of the clothespin to the nearest tenth of a centimeter. ______________
(3-2)

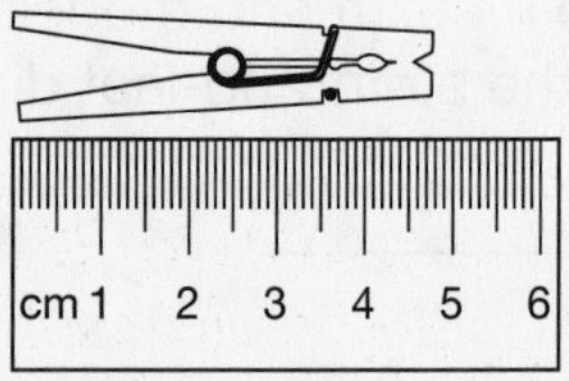

11. Write an equation. James had 85 trading cards. He bought *x* more. Then he had 92 cards. ______________
(2-12)

12. Compare using <, >, or =.
(2-4)

a. $2^5 \bigcirc 5^3$

b. $2 \times 2 \times 2 \bigcirc 2^3$

13. Make a line plot for the numbers of books read:
(1-4)
4, 2, 3, 1, 0, 1, 2, 1, 0, 3, 1, 0, 1, 2, 0, 1

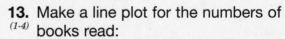

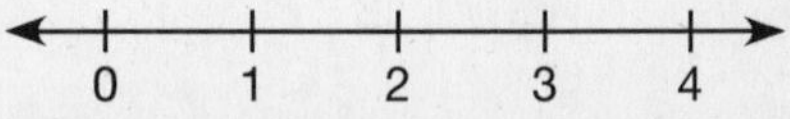

Name ______________________

Daily Review
4-7

Daily Cumulative Review

Find the area of each triangle. The dashed line is a height. *(Lesson 4-6)*

1.

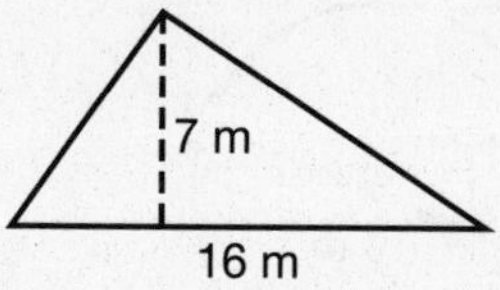

____

2.

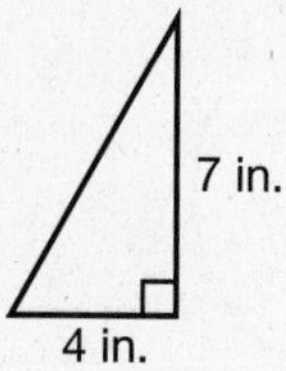

____

3.

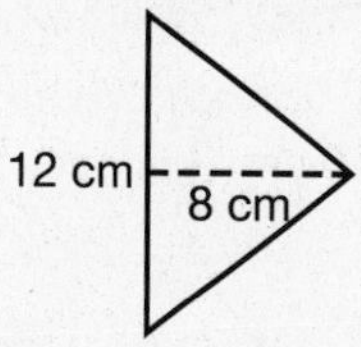

____

Find the area if *b* is the base and *h* is the height of a parallelogram *(Lesson 4-5)*

4. $b = 6$ cm, $h = 11$ cm ______________

5. $b = 6.8$ m, $h = 11.1$ m ______________

6. $b = 24$ in., $h = 88$ in. ______________

Mixed Review

7. *(4-4)* Find the area of a square with sides of length 18 cm.

____

8. *(4-2)* Name an appropriate metric unit of measure for the amount of medicine in an eyedropper.

____

9. *(3-11)* Divide. 8.449 ÷ 3.55

____

10. *(3-9)* Multiply 6.01 x 3.9

____

11. *(3-7)* Solve. $8 - x = 2.3$

$x =$ ______________

12. *(2-10)* Complete the table.
The children at Kennedy School eat 600 slices of bread each day.

Number of days	Number of bread slices
2	
4	
s	

13. *(1-6)* Make a stem-and-leaf diagram:
6, 11, 8, 1, 16, 23, 0, 2, 9, 19, 11, 2, 5
3, 9, 14

Stem	Leaf

Name ____________________

Daily Review
4-8

Daily Cumulative Review

Find each circumference. Use 3.14 for π. *(Lesson 4-7)*

1.

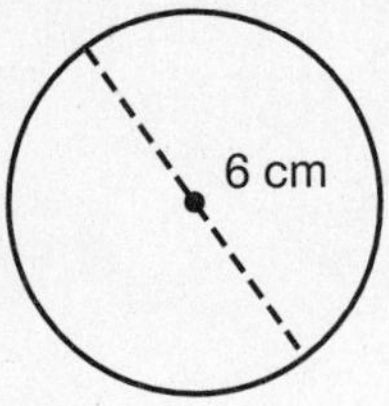

2.

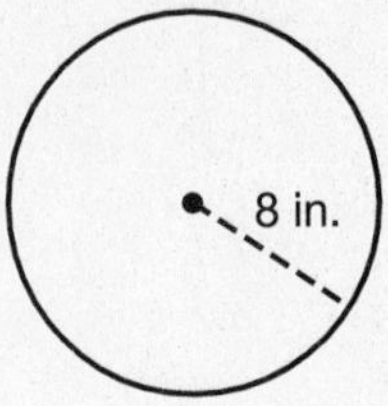

3.

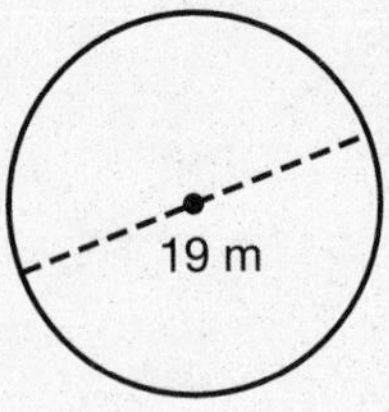

________ ________ ________

Find the area if *b* is the base and *h* is the height of a triangle. *(Lesson 4-6)*

4. $b = 14$ ft, $h = 7$ ft

5. $h = 5$ cm, $b = 9$ cm

6. $b = 6.1$ mi, $h = 8$ mi.

________ ________ ________

Mixed Review

7. *(4-7)* Find the area of a parallelogram with base 7 in. and height 8.6 in.

8. *(4-1)* Find the perimeter of a square with sides of length 12 cm.

________ ________

Estimate each sum, difference, product or quotient.

9. *(3-5)* 13.72 + 5.06

10. *(3-5)* 5.96 − 1.24

11. *(3-5)* \$8.12 x 6.1

12. *(3-5)* 36.14 ÷ 8.91

________ ________ ________ ________

Simplify.

13. *(2-5)* 80 x 30 ________

14. *(2-5)* 272 + 27 ________

15. *(2-5)* 3,600 ÷ 40 ________

16. *(1-2)* Use the Longest Rivers graph.

a About how many times longer does the Nile River appear to be than the Yangtze? ________

b. If the graph is misleading, how would you correct it?

____

____

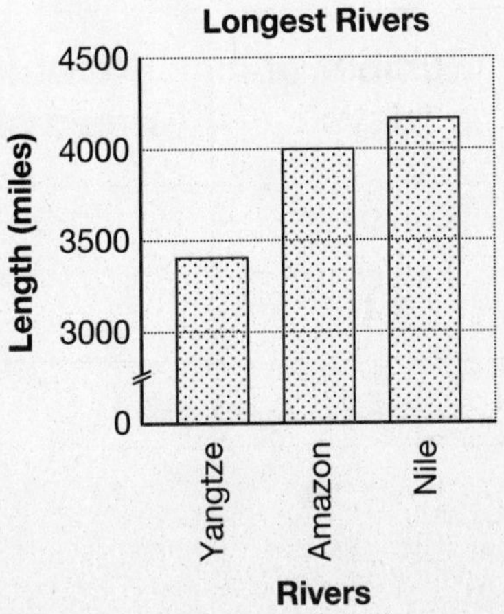

Name ____________________

Daily Review
4-9

Daily Cumulative Review

Find the area of each circle. Use 3.14 for π. *(Lesson 4-8)*

1.

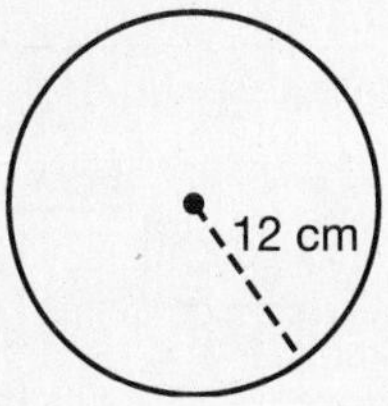

2.

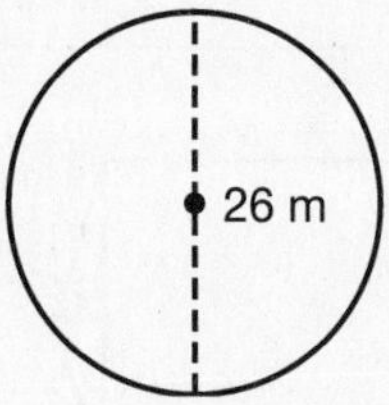

3.

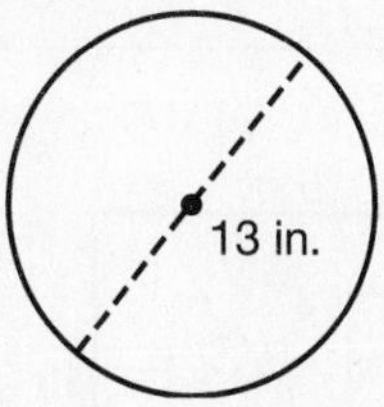

____________________ ____________________ ____________________

Find the missing measurements for each circle where r = radius, d = diameter, and c = circumference. Use 3.14 for π. *(Lesson 4-7)*

4. $r = 6$ cm, $d = 12$ cm, $c =$ ____________

5. $r =$ ____________, $d = 32$ in., $c = 100.48$ in.

6. $r = 3.5$ mm, $d =$ ____________, $c =$ ____________

Mixed Review

7. Convert. 12 mi = ____________ ft
(4-3)

8. Solve. $\frac{m}{12} = 0.13$
(3-12)

$m =$ ____________

9. Write 6 million in scientific notation.
(3-4)

____

10. Write "15 more than x" as an expression
(2-11)

____

Use the City Budget graph.

11. How much more of the budget is spent on schools than on the central office?
(1-1)

____

12. For every $100 spent on the budget, how much is spent on police, fire, and new buildings?
(1-1)

____

City Budget

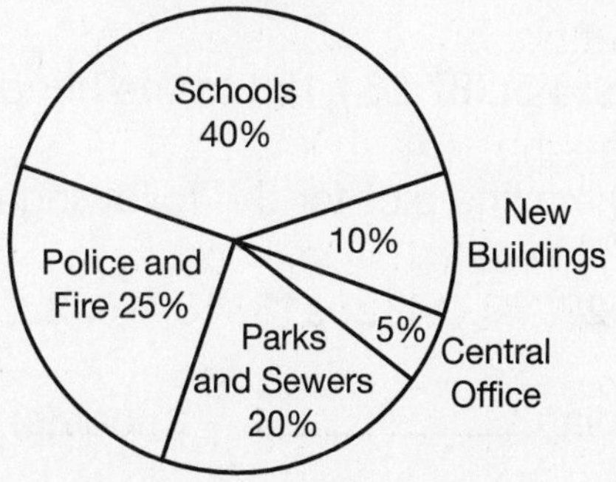

Name ____________________

Daily Review
5-1

Daily Cumulative Review

Find the area of each irregular figure. *(Lesson 4-9)*

1. ____________ **2.** ____________ **3.** ____________

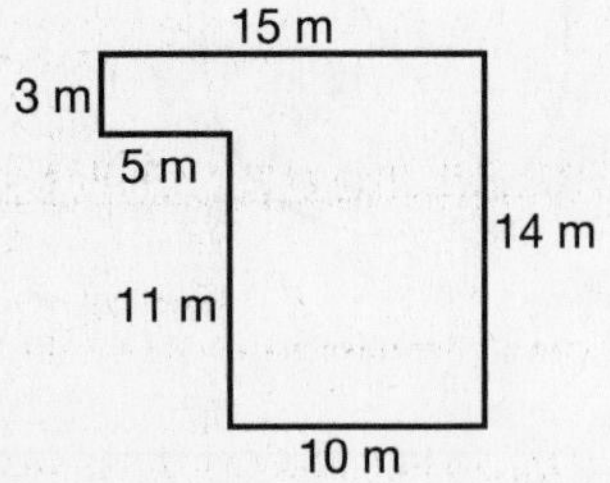

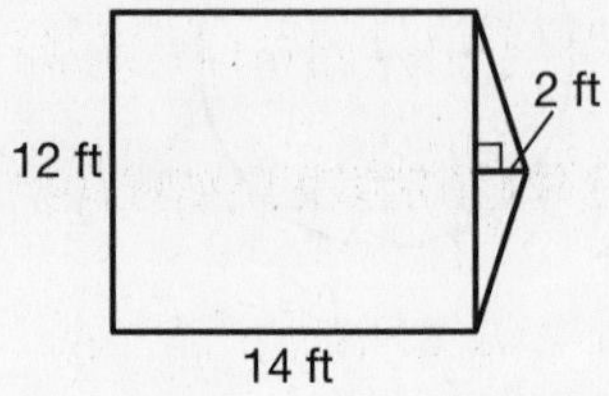

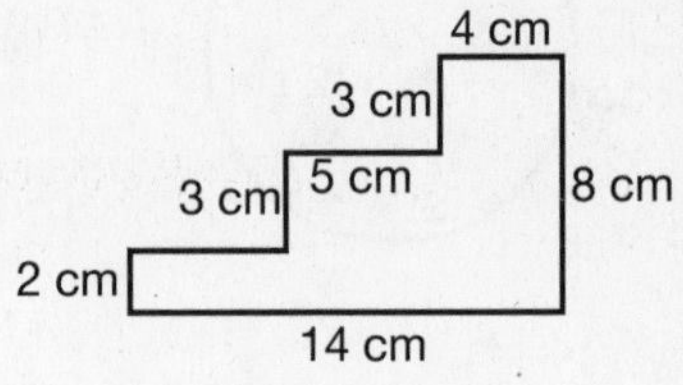

Find the area of each circle where r = radius and d = diameter. Use 3.14 for π. *(Lesson 4-8)*

4. $r = 9$ in. **5.** $d = 24$ cm **6.** $r = 4$ mi **7.** $d = 42$ m

____________ ____________ ____________ ____________

Mixed Review

8. Find the circumference of a circle whose radius is 3.5 mm. Use 3.14 for π.
(4-7)

____

9. Find the area of a parallelogram whose base is 27 cm and whose height is 7.8 cm.
(4-5)

____

10. Divide. $0.594 \div 1.8$ *(3-11)* ____________

11. Multiply. 7.25×20 *(3-8)* ____________

12. Compare using $<$ or $>$. *(3-3)*

12.53 ◯ 12.503

13. Find the next three numbers in the pattern.
(2-9)

140, 134, 128, 122, 116, ________, ________, ________

14. Round 5,387,264,183 to the hundred-millions place. ____________
(2-2)

15. Make a line plot for the following data. Then find the median and mode(s).
(1-7)

13, 22, 18, 14, 20, 13, 18, 16, 22, 18, 15, 14

median ________ mode(s) ________

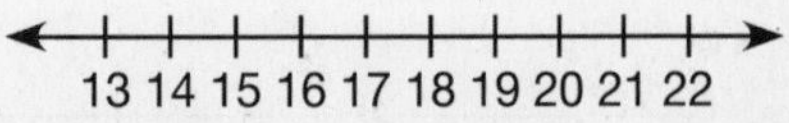

Name ________________________________

Daily Review
5-2

Daily Cumulative Review

Tell whether the number is divisible by 2, 3, 5, 6, 7, 9, or 10. *(Lesson 5-1)*

1. 70 ____________

2. 120 ____________

3. 63 ____________

4. 210 ____________

Find the area of each irregular figure. Use 3.14 for π. *(Lesson 4-9)*

5. ____________

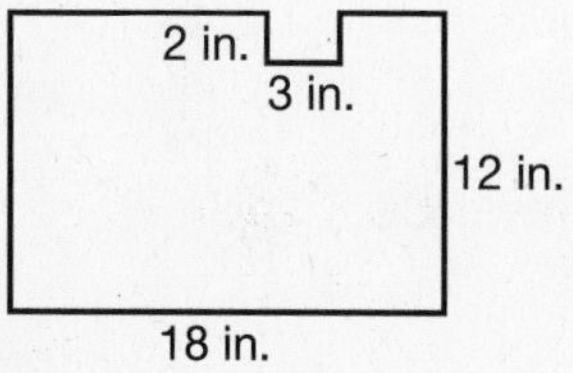

6. ____________

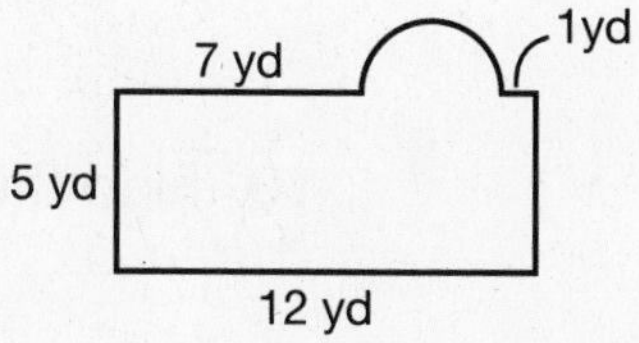

7. ____________

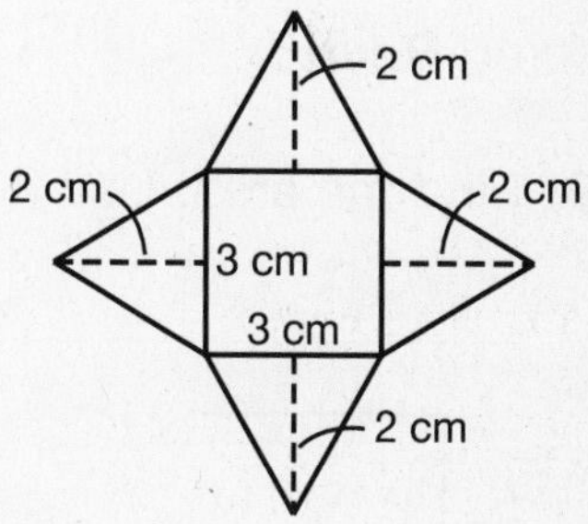

Mixed Review

8. If the circumference of a circle is 20.10 cm, what is the area rounded to the nearest tenth? ____________
(4-8)

9. A large watermelon weighs 14.6 pounds. How many ounces it that? ____________
(4-3)

10. Compare using <, >, or =. 7.23×0.17 ◯ 72.3×1.7
(3-9)

11. Round to the underlined place value. 821. <u>9</u>6 ____________
(3-2)

12. Evaluate $6x$ for $x = 2, 3,$ and 5. ____________
(2-10)

13. Write 5 cubed in standard form. ____________
(2-4)

14. Find the mean, median, and mode(s) for 5, 3, 8, 7, 4, 7, 6, 2, 8, 9, 4, 3, 9, 4, 5
(1-8)

mean ____________ median ____________ mode(s) ____________

Name ______________________

Daily Review 5-3

Daily Cumulative Review

Find the prime factorization. *(Lesson 5-2)*

1. 38 ______________

2. 64 ______________

3. 70 ______________

4. 66 ______________

Tell whether the first number is divisible by the second. *(Lesson 5-1)*

5. 35, 2 ______ **6.** 31, 3 ______ **7.** 88, 11 ______ **8.** 198, 11 ______

Mixed Review

9. Find the area. Use 3.14 for π.
(4-9)

____

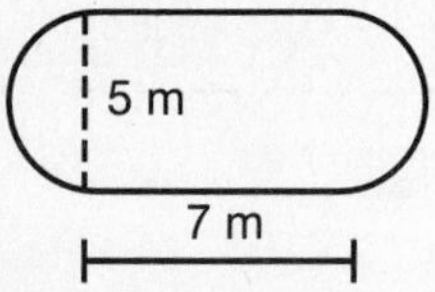

10. Find the circumference.
(4-7)

____

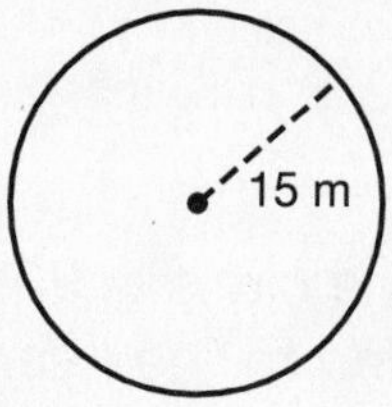

11. Solve. $2.58x = 16.254$
(3-12)

$x =$ ______________

12. Simplify $8.976 + 2.328$
(3-6)

____

13. Write 6.013 in word form. ______________________
(3-1)

14. Solve. $x - 21 = 78$
(2-13)

$x =$ ______________

15. Evaluate. $(2 + 4^3) \div 11$
(2-8)

____

16. Write 3 million in standard form. ______________
(2-1)

17. Make a stem-and-leaf diagram of the data showing scores on a test.
(1-6)
77, 85, 93, 78, 96, 86, 92, 99, 75, 83
75, 91, 86, 77, 95, 82, 94, 72, 81, 77

Stem	Leaf

Name ______________________

Daily Review
5-4

Daily Cumulative Review

Find the least common multiple of each pair. *(Lesson 5-3)*

1. 4, 23 ________ **2.** 5, 35 ________ **3.** 12, 5, ________ **4.** 11, 7 ________

Tell whether the given number is prime or composite. *(Lesson 5-2)*

5. 29 ________ **6.** 63 ________ **7.** 52 ________

Mixed Review

8. Is 95 divisible by 3? ________
(5-1)

9. Is 87 divisible by 3? ________
(5-1)

10. Find the area of a square with sides of length 6.4 ft. ________
(4-4)

11. Divide. 230.92 ÷ 46
((3-10)

____

12. Solve. $6.1 + k = 11.3$
(3-7)

$k =$ ________

13. Solve. $x \div 7 = 6$
(2-13)

$x =$ ________

14. Estimate. 5138 + 4963 + 4874 + 5002 ________
(2-6)

15. Estimate. 6199 + 3100 + 9798 + 3001 ________
(2-6)

16. Find the mean, median, and mode(s) with and without the outliers.
(1-9)

With outlier

mean ________

median ________

mode(s) ________

Without outlier

mean ________

median ________

mode(s) ________

National Preserves (thousands of acres)	
Anigkchak	466
Big Cypress	716
Gates of Arctic	949
Katmai	419
Tall Grass Prairie	11

17. What is the range of the data for Exercise 16?
(1-5)

____

Name ______________________________

Daily Review
5-5

Daily Cumulative Review

For each fraction, draw a model and name an equivalent fraction. *(Lesson 5-4)*

1. $\frac{2}{5}$ __________ **2.** $\frac{6}{12}$ __________

Find the LCM of each pair. *(Lesson 5-3)*

3. 7, 9 __________ **4.** 12, 16 __________ **5.** 14, 11 __________

Mixed Review

6. Find the prime factorization of 120. __________
(5-2)

7. Convert 0.12 km = __________ cm
(4-2)

8. Estimate. $7.31 × 8.27 __________
(3-5)

9. Simplify. 93,715 − 300 __________
(2-5)

10. Order from least to greatest. 17 million; 3 million; 32 thousand; 302,000
(2-3)

____

11. Make a bar graph from the data showing the height of several famous waterfalls.
(1-5)

Waterfall	Height (ft)
Angel Falls, Venezuela	3,212
King George Falls, Guyana	1,600
Takakkaw, Canada	1,200
Silver Strand Falls, USA	1,170

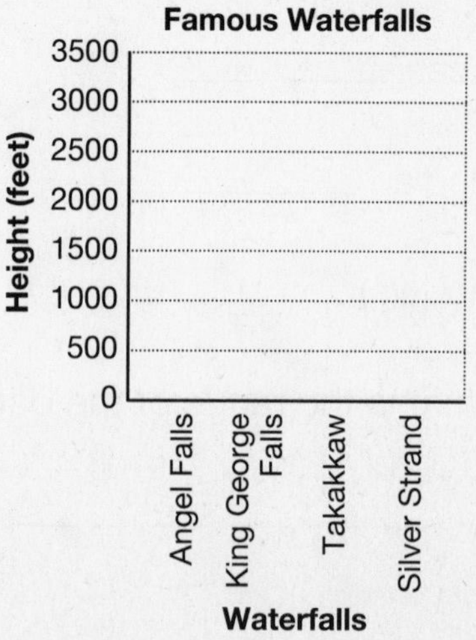

12. From the graph in Exercise 11, about how many times higher is the Angel Falls than the Silver Strand Falls?
(1-1)

____

Name ______________________________

Daily Review
5-6

Daily Cumulative Review

Write in lowest terms. *(Lesson 5-5)*

1. $\frac{8}{16}$ ________ **2.** $\frac{5}{15}$ ________ **3.** $\frac{8}{28}$ ________ **4.** $\frac{4}{20}$ ________

For each fraction, draw a model and name an equivalent fraction. *(Lesson 5-4)*

5. $\frac{3}{10}$ ________ **6.** $\frac{9}{12}$ ________ **7.** $\frac{2}{6}$ ________

Mixed Review

8. Find the LCM of 21 and 5. ________________
(5-3)

9. Is 29 prime or composite? ________________
(5-2)

10. Find the area. Use 3.14 for π.
(4-8)

____

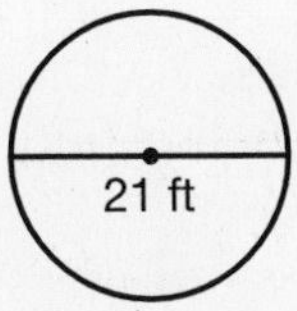

11. Find the area. The dashed line is height.
(4-6)

____

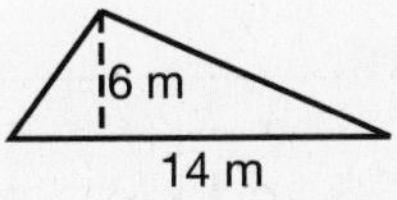

12. Divide. $106.64 \div 12.4$
(3-11)

____

13. Multiply. 6.05×3.8
(3-9)

____

14. Simplify. $123.8 - 11.73$
(3-6)

____

15. Is $x + 2 = 24$ true when $x = 26$? ________________
(2-12)

16. Evaluate $4x$ when $x = 3, 4$, and 7. ________________
(2-10)

17. Make a line plot of the data showing the number of teachers that a set of students have.
(1-4)

2, 6, 3, 6, 2, 4, 5, 3, 5, 3, 4, 5, 6, 4, 5

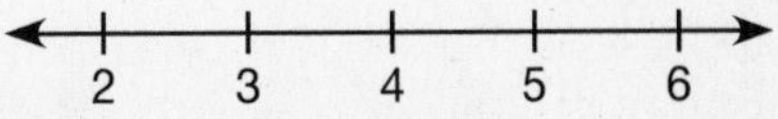

Name ____________________

Daily Review 5-7

Daily Cumulative Review

Write each mixed number as an improper fraction. *(Lesson 5-6)*

1. $3\frac{1}{6}$ ______ **2.** $4\frac{1}{5}$ ______ **3.** $1\frac{3}{8}$ ______ **4.** $14\frac{1}{2}$ ______

Find the greatest common factor of each pair. *(Lesson 5-5)*

5. 18, 10 ______ **6.** 11, 16 ______ **7.** 21, 6 ______ **8.** 10, 6 ______

Mixed Review

9. Find the prime factorization of 450. ______
(5-2)

10. Find the area. ______
(4-5)

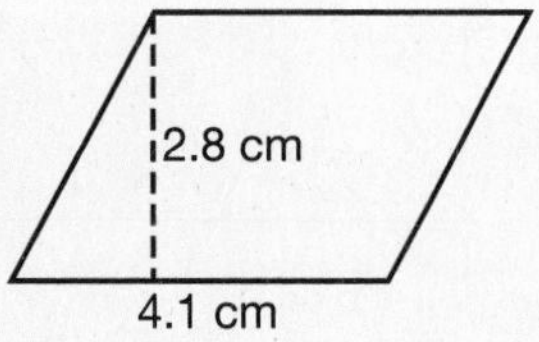

11. Find the perimeter. ______
(4-1)

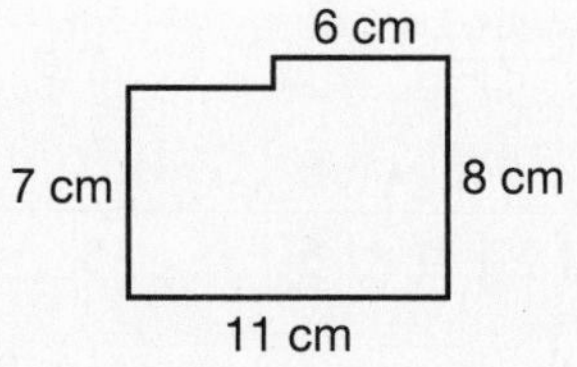

12. Solve. $\frac{x}{9.2} = 5.5$
(3-12)

$x =$ ______

13. Write 6.1×10^5 in standard form.
(3-4)

______

14. Write 1.03 in word form. ______
(3-1)

15. Write "the product of 26 and x" as an expression. ______
(2-11)

Use the scatterplot for Exercises 17 and 18.

16. Determine if there is a trend to the scatterplot. If there is, describe the pattern of the data.
(1-3)

______

______

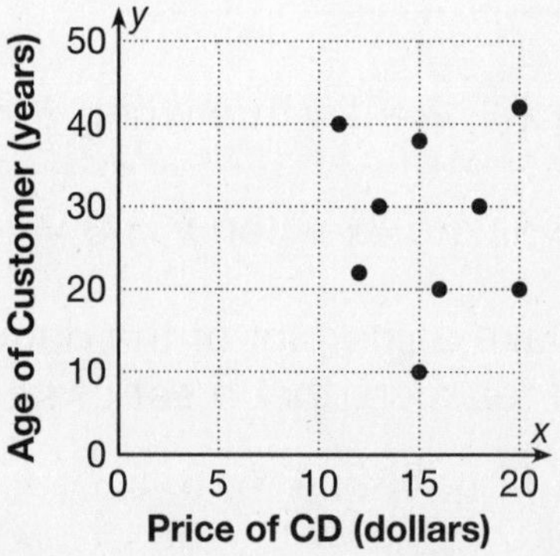

17. How many customers paid $15 for their CD?
(1-3)

______

Name ______________________

Daily Review 5-8

Daily Cumulative Review

Write using bar notation. *(Lesson 5-7)*

1. 0.66666... ______

2. 3.64646464... ______

3. 3.7055555... ______

Write each improper fraction as a mixed number. *(Lesson 5-6)*

4. $\frac{18}{4}$ ______ **5.** $\frac{21}{2}$ ______ **6.** $\frac{35}{3}$ ______ **7.** $\frac{13}{6}$ ______

Mixed Review

8. *(5-5)* Write $\frac{7}{42}$ in lowest terms. ______

9. *(5-3)* Find the LCM of 18, 14. ______

10. *(4-3)* Convert. 12 miles = ______ feet

11. *(4-2)* Convert. 6.2 m = ______ km

12. *(3-10)* Divide. 44.94 ÷ 14

______

13. *(3-5)* Estimate. 121.83 − 10.97

______

14. *(2-13)* Solve. $x + 11 = 33$

x = ______

15. *(2-7)* Estimate. 876 × 11

______

16. *(2-4)* Compare.

10^4 ◯ 10 + 10 + 10 + 10

17. *(2-2)* Round 28,712,380 to the millions place.

______

Use the Cookie Sales graph for Exercises 18 and 19.

18. *(1-2)* About how many times larger do Amy's sales appear to be than Jane's?

______

19. *(1-2)* Could the bar graph be misleading? If so, how would you correct the graph?

______

______

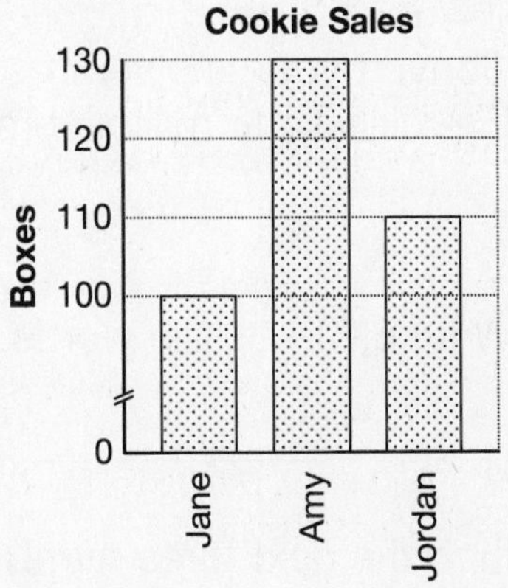

Name ______________________________

Daily Cumulative Review

Compare using <, >, or =. *(Lesson 5-8)*

1. $\frac{1}{4}$ ○ $\frac{4}{14}$ **2.** $\frac{3}{6}$ ○ $\frac{10}{20}$ **3.** $\frac{4}{9}$ ○ $\frac{2}{9}$ **4.** $\frac{4}{10}$ ○ $\frac{3}{5}$

Write each fraction as a decimal. State whether the decimal terminates or repeats. *(Lesson 5-7)*

5. $\frac{1}{3}$ ________ **6.** $\frac{6}{10}$ ________ **7.** $\frac{2}{9}$ ________ **8.** $\frac{6}{15}$ ________

________ ________ ________ ________

Mixed Review

9. Write $7\frac{1}{3}$ as an improper fraction. ________
(5-6)

10. Write $\frac{12}{30}$ in lowest terms. ________
(5-5)

11. The prime factorization of a number is $2 \times 2 \times 3 \times 3 \times 5 \times 5$.
(5-2) What is the number?

____

12. A circle has a circumference of 37.68 in.
(4-8) Find the area of the circle rounded to the nearest tenth. ________

13. Solve. $12.75w = 73.95$ ________
(3-12)

14. Estimate the length to the
(3-2) nearest tenth of a centimeter. ________

15. Convert your answer in
(4-2) Exercise 14 to millimeters. ________

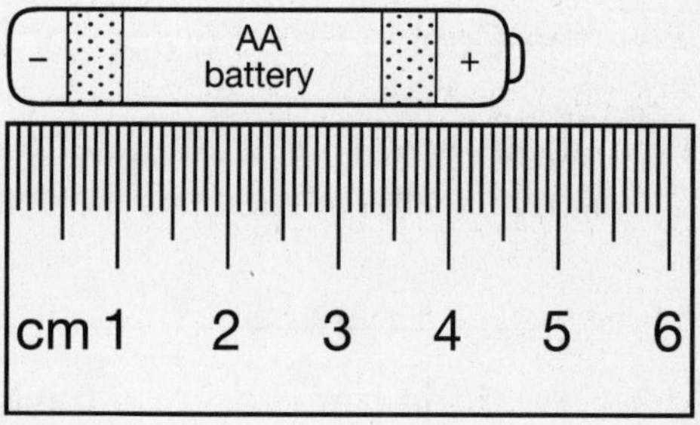

16. Write 6,014,391 in words.
(2-1)

____

17. Find the next three numbers in the pattern.
(2-9)

1, 3, 9, 27, 81, ______, ______, ______

Name ______________________________

Daily Review
6-2

Daily Cumulative Review

Simplify. Write each answer in lowest terms. *(Lesson 6-1)*

1. $\frac{3}{10} - \frac{1}{10}$ **2.** $\frac{7}{15} + \frac{5}{15}$ **3.** $\frac{2}{3} + \frac{2}{3}$ **4.** $\frac{7}{8} - \frac{5}{8}$

__________ __________ __________ __________

Order from smallest to largest. *(Lesson 5-8)*

5. $\frac{5}{8}, \frac{5}{9}, \frac{5}{10}$ **6.** $\frac{3}{5}, \frac{5}{3}, \frac{3}{3}$ **7.** $\frac{9}{10}, \frac{24}{25}, \frac{4}{5}$

__________ __________ __________

Mixed Review

8. Draw a model for $\frac{9}{15}$.
(5-4)

Name an equivalent fraction. ______

9. Find the area. Use 3.14 for π.
(4-9)

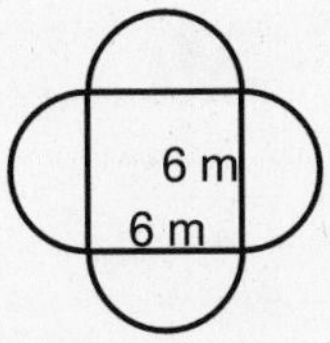

____

10. Convert. 136 ounces = ______________ pounds.
(4-3)

11. Divide. 45.7475 ÷ 7.25
(3-11)

____

12. Simplify. 3.275 + 5.841 + 7.3872
(3-6)

____

13. Solve. $x - 12 = 79$
(2-13)

$x =$ ______________

14. Evaluate. 14 − (8 − 3)
(2-8)

____

15. Simplify. 20 × 81 × 50 ______________
(2-5)

16. Find the median and mode(s).
(1-7)

median ________ mode(s) ________

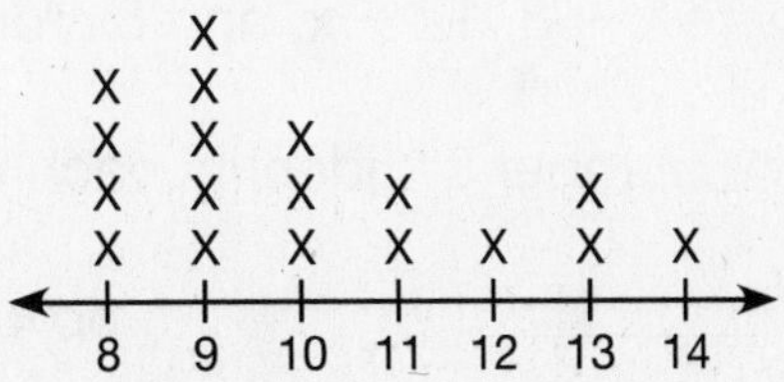

Name ______________________________

Daily Review
6-3

Daily Cumulative Review

Simplify. Write each answer in lowest terms. *(Lesson 6-2)*

1. $\frac{3}{5} - \frac{1}{2}$ **2.** $\frac{3}{8} + \frac{7}{24}$ **3.** $\frac{7}{16} - \frac{1}{8}$ **4.** $\frac{4}{5} - \frac{5}{9}$

________ ________ ________ ________

State whether the answer is greater than, less than, or equal to 1. *(Lesson 6-1)*

5. $\frac{7}{12} - \frac{5}{12}$ **6.** $\frac{7}{9} + \frac{2}{9}$ **7.** $\frac{4}{5} + \frac{2}{5}$

________ ________ ________

Mixed Review

8. Write $\frac{5}{9}$ as a decimal. *(5-7)* ________

9. Is 98 divisible by 6? *(5-1)* ________

10. Find the area. ________ *(4-6)*

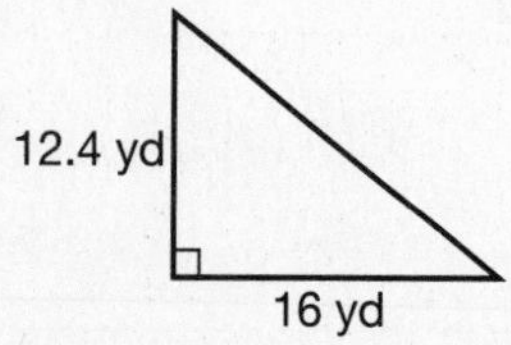

Use the scatterplot for Exercises 11 and 12.

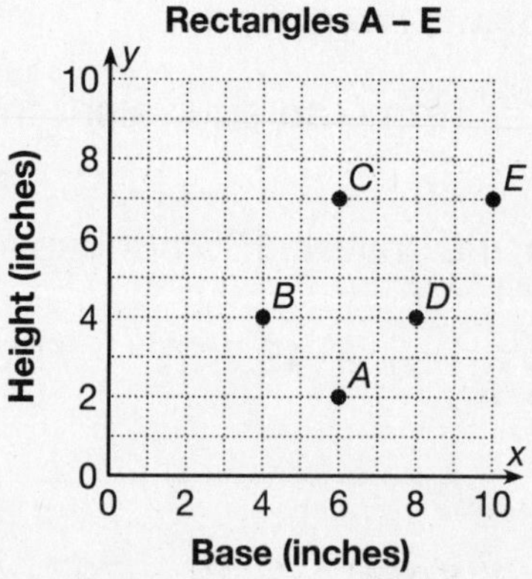

11. Find the area of Rectangle *A*. ________ *(4-4)*

12. Which rectangle is a square? ________ *(4-4)*

13. Compare using <, >, or =. 3.7×8.16 ◯ 3.7×81.6 *(3-9)*

14. Write 650,000,000,000 in scientific notation. ________ *(3-4)*

15. Evaluate $x + 3$, $12 - x$, and $8x$ for $x = 5$. ________ *(2-10)*

16. For the number 3^8, identify each of the following: *(2-4)*

base ________ power ________ exponent ________

Name ______________________

Daily Review 6-4

Daily Cumulative Review

Solve. Write each answer in lowest terms. *(Lesson 6-3)*

1. $\frac{5}{12} + a = \frac{8}{12}$ ________

2. $x - \frac{1}{6} = \frac{3}{4}$ ________

3. $\frac{7}{8} - y = \frac{11}{16}$ ________

4. $g + \frac{1}{4} = \frac{9}{16}$ ________

Simplify. Write each answer in lowest terms. *(Lesson 6-2)*

5. $\frac{1}{5} - \frac{1}{6}$ ________

6. $\frac{1}{2} + \frac{3}{8}$ ________

7. $\frac{4}{7} - \frac{1}{3}$ ________

8. $\frac{1}{4} + \frac{15}{24}$ ________

Mixed Review

9. The bar graph shows the animals in the pet shop. What fraction of the animals are cats and dogs? ________
(6-1)

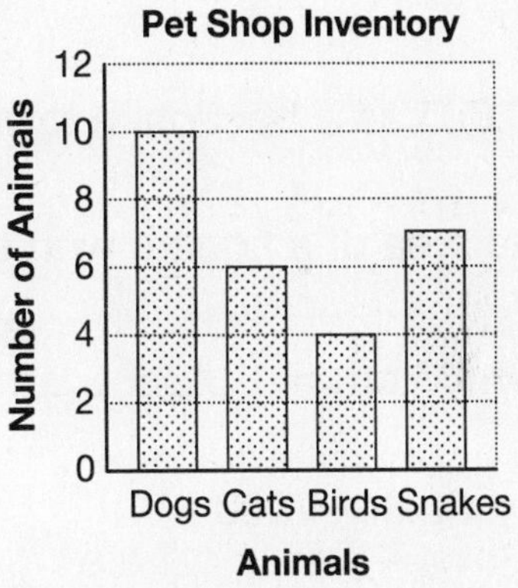

10. Write $\frac{18}{60}$ in lowest terms. ________
(5-5)

11. Write $\frac{102}{7}$ as a mixed number. ________
(5-6)

12. Find the LCM of 15 and 9. ________
(5-3)

13. Find the circumference of a circle whose radius is 7.5 mm. Use 3.14 for π. ________
(4-7)

14. A triangle has a perimeter of 79 m. If two of the sides have lengths 30 m and 25 m, what is the length of the third side? ________
(4-1)

15. Solve. $2.89 + x = 6.2$ $x =$ ________
(3-7)

16. Order from least to greatest. 57.77; 57.777; 57.7 ________
(3-3)

17. Estimate. 57,613 − 12,302 ________
(2-6)

Name ____________________

Daily Review
6-5

Daily Cumulative Review

Round to the nearest whole number. *(Lesson 6-4)*

1. $3\frac{4}{5}$ ______ **2.** $7\frac{21}{34}$ ______ **3.** $9\frac{7}{20}$ ______ **4.** $14\frac{6}{7}$ ______

Write a true equation using the fractions given. *(Lesson 6-3)*

5. $\frac{4}{7}, \frac{2}{5}, \frac{6}{35}$ ______ **6.** $\frac{3}{7}, \frac{2}{7}, \frac{5}{7}$ ______ **7.** $\frac{1}{9}, \frac{5}{6}, \frac{17}{18}$ ______ **8.** $\frac{1}{3}, \frac{3}{8}, \frac{1}{24}$ ______

Mixed Review

9. Simplify. $\frac{5}{8} - \frac{1}{2}$ ______
(6-2)

10. Is 65 prime or composite? ______
(5-2)

11. Write 0.625 as a fraction in lowest terms. ______
(5-7)

12. Find the area of a square with sides of length 6.8 in. ______
(4-4)

13. Convert. 63 cm = ______ m
(4-2)

14. Divide. $130.62 \div 21$ ______
(3-10)

15. Multiply. 52.3×1000 ______
(3-8)

16. Estimate. 29×907 ______
(2-7)

17. Is $x - 9 = 51$ true when $x = 42$? ______
(2-12)

18. Make a stem-and-leaf diagram of the data.
(1-6)

67, 95, 70, 81, 90, 68, 73, 84, 79, 83,

68, 72, 79, 83, 92, 83, 71, 74, 87

Stem	Leaf

19. What is the range of the data in Exercise 18? ______
(1-5)

Name ______________________________

Daily Review
6-6

Daily Cumulative Review

Add. Write the answer as a whole number or mixed number in lowest terms.
(Lesson 6-5)

1. $11\frac{1}{5} + 4\frac{3}{5}$ ________

2. $6\frac{3}{5} + 1\frac{2}{3}$ ________

3. $4 + 6\frac{3}{14}$ ________

Estimate. *(Lesson 6-4)*

4. $2\frac{1}{6} + 6\frac{7}{8}$ ________

5. $9\frac{1}{12} - 6\frac{7}{8}$ ________

6. $18\frac{4}{7} + 6\frac{1}{5}$ ________

Mixed Review

7. Solve. $\frac{5}{6} + x = \frac{23}{24}$ $x =$ ________
(6-3)

8. What fraction does the shaded part represent?
(5-4)

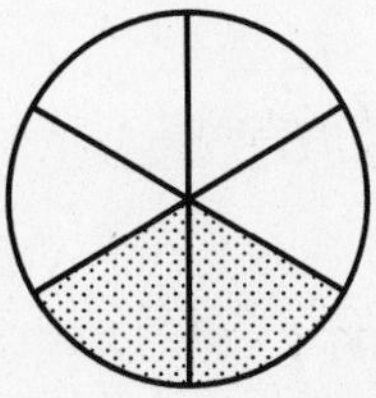

____

9. Find the prime factorization of 630. ________
(5-2)

10. A quilt pattern is made of 12 triangles placed together. If each triangle has a base of 8 cm and a height of 12.5 cm, what is the area of the pattern?
(4-9)

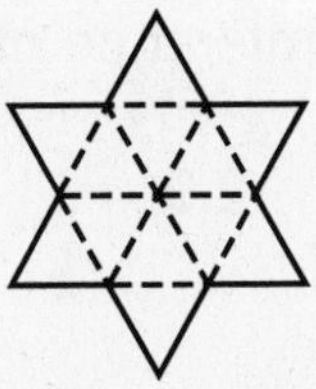

____

11. Estimate. 4.7×7.13
(3-5)

____

12. Write 0.08 in word form.
(3-1)

____

13. Order from least to greatest. 63 thousand; 63 million; 630,000
(2-3)

____

14. Make a line plot with the following data.
(1-4)

2, 2, 5, 5, 7, 7, 9, 9, 8, 2, 2, 3, 4, 5, 5, 6

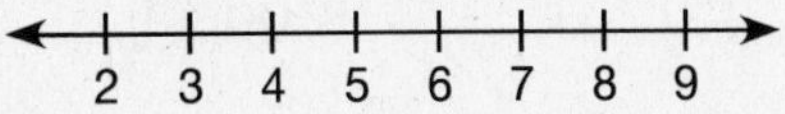

Name ______________________________

Daily Review
7-1

Daily Cumulative Review

Subtract. Write the answer as a whole number or mixed number in lowest terms.
(Lesson 6-6)

1. $6\frac{2}{5} - 5\frac{2}{3}$ ________

2. $12\frac{7}{10} - 8\frac{1}{5}$ ________

3. $7\frac{5}{6} - 5\frac{5}{24}$ ________

4. $4\frac{5}{6} - 4\frac{7}{12}$ ________

Add. Write the answer as a whole number or mixed number in lowest terms.
(Lesson 6-5)

5. $5 + 7\frac{1}{2}$ ________

6. $12\frac{1}{8} + 10\frac{3}{5}$ ________

7. $5\frac{1}{7} + 18\frac{2}{5}$ ________

8. $15\frac{5}{12} + 1\frac{1}{3}$ ________

Mixed Review

9. Estimate. $2\frac{1}{8} + 7\frac{15}{16}$
(6-4)

____

10. Write 0.82 as a fraction in lowest terms.
(5-7)

____

11. Find the LCM of 12 and 28. ________
(5-3)

12. Find the circumference of a circle with diameter of length 18 inches. ________
(4-7)

13. Divide. $9.106 \div 2.9$
(3-11)

____

14. Multiply. 16.5×9
(3-8)

____

15. Compare using $<$, $>$, or $=$. 36.58 ◯ 36.581
(3-3)

16. Solve. $x + 14 = 61$
(2-13)

$x =$ ________

17. Evaluate. $5 + (3^2 - 2)$
(2-8)

____

18. Write 5^4 in expanded form. ________
(2-4)

19. Make a line plot for the data and find the median and mode(s).
(1-7) 25, 26, 24, 21, 25, 21, 23, 20, 25, 22, 21

median ________ mode(s) ________

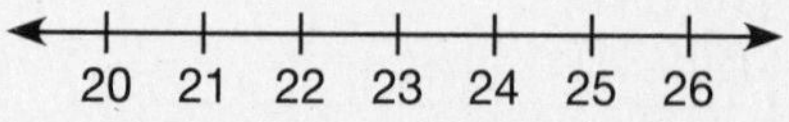

Name ______________________

Daily Review 7-2

Daily Cumulative Review

Estimate. *(Lesson 7-1)*

1. $5\frac{1}{3} \times 9\frac{1}{8}$ ______

2. $8\frac{1}{9} \div 3\frac{7}{8}$ ______

3. $6\frac{2}{3} \times 2\frac{5}{6}$ ______

4. $12\frac{2}{9} \div 4\frac{1}{8}$ ______

Subtract. Write each answer in lowest terms. *(Lesson 6-6)*

5. $5\frac{1}{7} - 3\frac{2}{3}$ ______

6. $18\frac{9}{10} - 12\frac{3}{5}$ ______

7. $8\frac{1}{4} - 6\frac{1}{12}$ ______

8. $16\frac{11}{14} - 14\frac{2}{7}$ ______

Mixed Review

9. Solve. Write answer in lowest terms. $\frac{7}{9} - x = \frac{5}{27}$ $x =$ ______
(6-3)

10. Write $5\frac{3}{4}$ as an improper fraction. ______
(5-6)

11. Find the prime factorization of 819. ______
(5-2)

12. Find the area of circle whose radius is 7 ft. ______
(4-8)

13. Solve. $0.9x = 8.262$
(3-12)

$x =$ ______

14. Simplify. \$5.87 + \$12.32
(3-6)

______

15. Write six hundredths as a decimal. ______
(3-1)

16. Simplify. 200×380 ______
(2-5)

17. Find the mean, median, and mode of the data set.
(1-8)

Mean ______

Median ______

Mode(s) ______

Stem	Leaf
4	6 6 7
5	0 1 3 8 9 9
6	0 0 1 1 4 4 6 9
7	0

Name ______________________________

Daily Review
7-3

Daily Cumulative Review

Simplify. *(Lesson 7-2)*

1. $6\frac{1}{2} \times 4$ ________ **2.** $3 \times 5\frac{2}{3}$ ________ **3.** $10 \times 4\frac{5}{6}$ ________ **4.** $14 \times 4\frac{1}{3}$ ________

Estimate. *(Lesson 7-1)*

5. $7\frac{1}{6} \times 8\frac{1}{9}$ ________ **6.** $13\frac{7}{8} \div 2\frac{1}{12}$ ________ **7.** $7\frac{1}{5} \times 7\frac{1}{3}$ ________ **8.** $14\frac{2}{3} \div 2\frac{7}{8}$ ________

Mixed Review

9. Add. $8\frac{7}{15} + 4\frac{7}{9}$ ________
(6-5)

10. Order $\frac{1}{6}, \frac{1}{7}, \frac{5}{42}$ from smallest to largest. ________
(5-8)

11. Find the area. ________
(4-9)

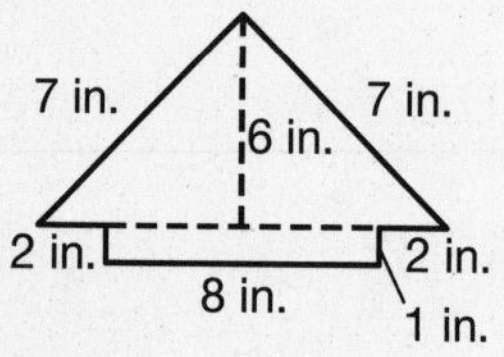

12. Find the perimeter. ________
(4-1)

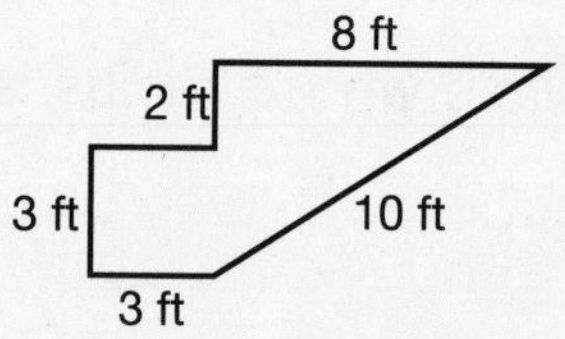

Estimate.

13. 2.78 + 1.91 ________
(3-5)

14. 28.72 × 6.9 ________
(3-5)

15. 15.816 − 5.12 ________
(3-5)

16. 56.125 ÷ 8.1 ________
(3-5)

17. Vance baked 7 loaves of bread, each weighing *w* ounces.
(2-12) The total weight was 84 oz. Write an equation for this situation. ________

18. Find the next three numbers in the pattern.
(2-9)

132, 140, 138, 146, 144, ________, ________, ________

Name ______________________

Daily Review 7-4

Daily Cumulative Review

Find each product. *(Lesson 7-3)*

1. $6\frac{1}{2} \times \frac{1}{2}$ ________

2. $\frac{3}{4} \times \frac{5}{6}$ ________

3. $\frac{8}{9} \times \frac{1}{3}$ ________

4. $\frac{2}{3} \times 5\frac{1}{4}$ ________

Simplify. *(Lesson 7-2)*

5. $5 \times 3\frac{2}{3}$ ________

6. $5 \times 5\frac{1}{7}$ ________

7. $8\frac{1}{2} \times 2$ ________

8. $12\frac{1}{5} \times 4$ ________

Mixed Review

9. Subtract. $12\frac{7}{18} - 5\frac{1}{3}$ *(6-6)* ________

10. Solve. $\frac{1}{6} + w = \frac{19}{24}$ *(6-3)*

$w =$ ________

The bar graph shows the number of jeans, t-shirts, shorts, and sweats in Tim's closet. Use the graph for Exercises **11** and **12**.

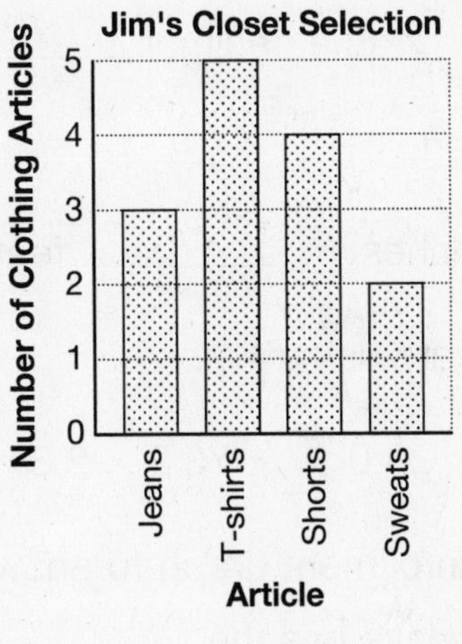

11. What fraction of the clothes are jeans and shorts? *(6-1)* ________

12. What fraction of the clothes are t-shirts and sweats? *(6-1)* ________

13. Find the area. *(4-5)*
The dashed line is the height.

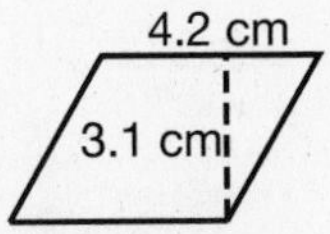

____

14. Write "one-third of x" as an expression. ________ *(2-11)*

15. Write $17,000,000,000 in word-number form. ________ *(2-1)*

Name ________________________________

Daily Review 7-5

Daily Cumulative Review

Simplify. *(Lesson 7-4)*

1. $12 \div \frac{1}{6}$ ______

2. $6 \div \frac{2}{3}$ ______

3. $4 \div 1\frac{5}{8}$ ______

4. $9 \div 2\frac{1}{3}$ ______

Find each product. *(Lesson 7-3)*

5. $\frac{2}{3} \times \frac{3}{8}$ ______

6. $\frac{5}{6} \times \frac{2}{7}$ ______

7. $\frac{3}{8} \times \frac{4}{5}$ ______

8. $\frac{1}{12} \times \frac{3}{7}$ ______

Mixed Review

9. *(7-2)* Multiply. $10 \times 7\frac{1}{5}$ ______

10. *(6-6)* Subtract. $8\frac{4}{5} - 6\frac{3}{20}$ ______

11. *(6-2)* Simplify. $\frac{13}{15} - \frac{7}{10}$ ______

12. *(5-7)* Write $\frac{3}{11}$ as a decimal. ______

13. *(5-1)* Is 117 divisible by 9? ______

14. *(4-3)* Convert.

372 inches = ______ feet

15. *(3-11)* Divide. 3.5584 ÷ 1.112

______

16. *(3-9)* Compare using <, >, or =.

7.32×23.0 ◯ 73.2×2.3

17. *(2-10)* Evaluate $80 \div x$ for $x = 2, 5, 8$.

$x =$ ______

Use the Enrollment graph to answer the questions.

18. *(1-1)* What class has the largest enrollment? ______

19. *(1-1)* If Monroe High has 1,000 students, how many are juniors? ______

Monroe High School Enrollment

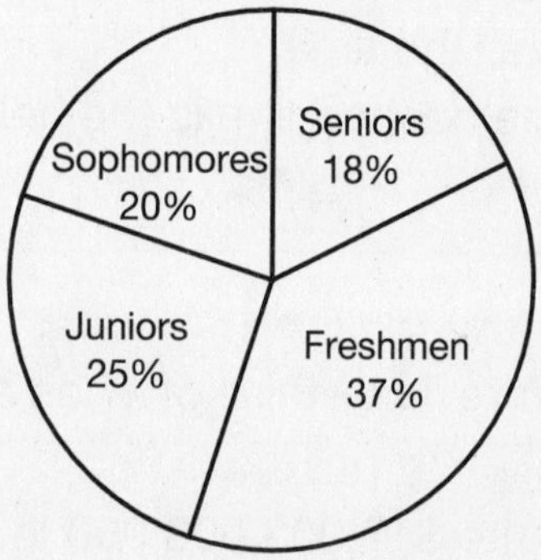

Name ______________________

Daily Review 7-6

Daily Cumulative Review

Simplify. *(Lesson 7-5)*

1. $2\frac{3}{5} \div \frac{1}{3}$ ______

2. $2\frac{2}{3} \div \frac{1}{8}$ ______

3. $\frac{1}{2} \div \frac{2}{3}$ ______

4. $\frac{5}{6} \div 1\frac{1}{3}$ ______

Simplify. *(Lesson 7-4)*

5. $14 \div \frac{1}{3}$ ______

6. $8 \div \frac{1}{4}$ ______

7. $11 \div \frac{5}{6}$ ______

8. $7 \div 1\frac{8}{9}$ ______

Mixed Review

9. Simplify. $\frac{3}{5} \times \frac{3}{7}$ ______
(7-3)

10. Add. $8\frac{1}{2} + 12\frac{1}{7}$ ______
(6-5)

11. Compare using $<$, $>$, or $=$. $\frac{10}{12}$ ◯ $\frac{3}{4}$
(5-8)

12. A class had 12 boys and 8 girls. What fraction of the class was boys?
(5-4)

______

13. Find the area of a rectangle with sides 4.2 cm and 7.3 cm. ______
(4-4)

14. Divide. $7.3 \div 73$
(3-10)

______

15. Write 68 billion in scientific notation.
(3-4)

______

16. Estimate. 163,624 + 4,210
(2-6)

______

17. Determine if there is a trend to the scatterplot. If there is, describe the pattern of the data.
(1-3)

______

______

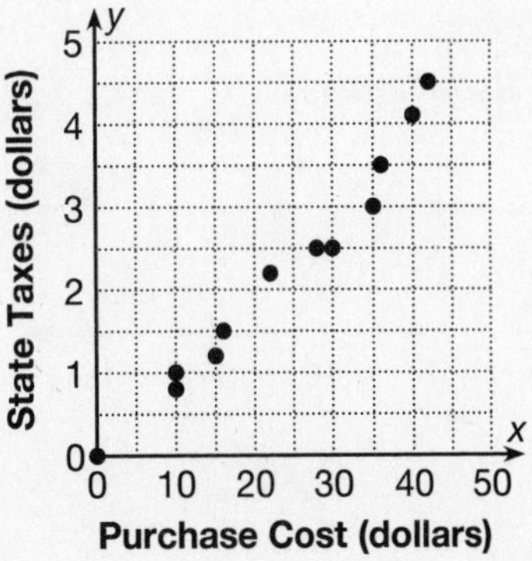

Name ____________________

Daily Review 8-1

Daily Cumulative Review

Solve. *(Lesson 7-6)*

1. $x \div 2\frac{1}{3} = \frac{1}{4}$ **2.** $3\frac{2}{5}m = \frac{1}{2}$ **3.** $f \div 4\frac{1}{3} = \frac{1}{6}$ **4.** $\frac{1}{2}n = 6\frac{3}{4}$

$x =$ ______ $m =$ ______ $f =$ ______ $n =$ ______

Simplify. *(Lesson 7-5)*

5. $\frac{1}{2} \div \frac{3}{5}$ ______ **6.** $1\frac{3}{4} \div 1\frac{1}{8}$ ______ **7.** $\frac{1}{4} \div \frac{5}{9}$ ______

Mixed Review

8. Find the product. *(7-3)*

$\frac{13}{15} \times \frac{1}{10}$ ______

9. Estimate. *(7-1)*

$8\frac{2}{7} \div 4\frac{1}{8}$ ______

10. Add. *(6-5)*

$3\frac{19}{22} + 2\frac{1}{2}$ ______

11. Order from smallest to largest. $\frac{9}{10}, \frac{24}{25}, \frac{4}{5}$ ______ *(5-8)*

12. Is 23 prime or composite? ______ *(5-2)*

13. Find the diameter of a circle whose circumference is 17.27 in. ______ *(4-7)*

14. Convert. 32 cm = ______ mm *(4-2)*

15. Multiply. 0.7×0.013 ______ *(3-9)*

16. Estimate the length of the worm *(3-2)*

to the nearest centimeter. ______

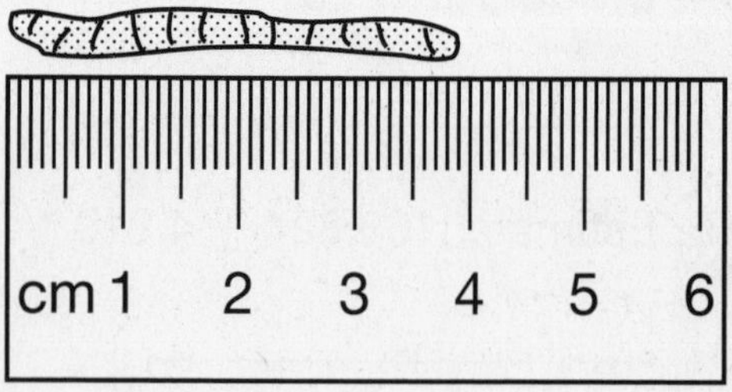

17. Evaluate. $3 + 4 \times 6$ ______ *(2-8)*

18. Compare using <, >, or =. $6^4 \bigcirc 4^6$ *(2-4)*

19. Find the mean. ______ *(1-8)*

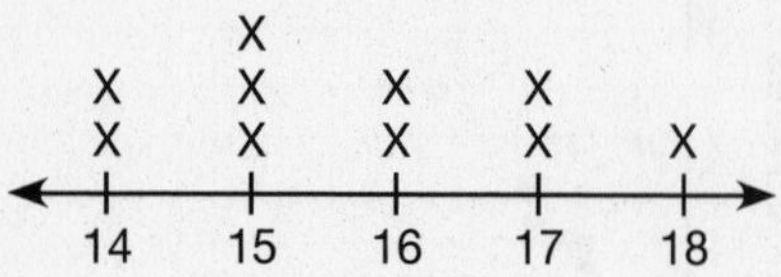

Name ______________________________

Daily Review
8-2

Daily Cumulative Review

Draw an example of each. *(Lesson 8-1)*

1. $\overleftrightarrow{AB}$ **2.** $\overrightarrow{AB}$ **3.** $\overline{AB}$

Solve. *(Lesson 7-6)*

4. $2x = 2\frac{1}{6}$ $x =$ ________

5. $t \div 1\frac{1}{5} = 4$ $t =$ ________

6. $3\frac{1}{4}p = \frac{1}{8}$ $p =$ ________

7. $k \div \frac{9}{10} = \frac{1}{5}$ $k =$ ________

Mixed Review

8. Simplify. $\frac{2}{5} \div 3\frac{1}{5}$ ________ *(7-5)*

9. Solve. $\frac{2}{5} + p = \frac{4}{5}$; $p =$ ________ *(6-3)*

10. Write 0.125 as a fraction in lowest terms. ________ *(5-7)*

11. Is 192 divisible by 8? ________ *(5-1)*

12. Convert. 112 quarts = ________ gallons *(4-3)*

13. Solve. $\frac{k}{3.72} = 10.6$ *(3-12)*

$k =$ ________

14. Solve. $5.61 - x = 3.102$ *(3-7)*

$x =$ ________

15. Write 6.23×10^8 in standard form. ________ *(3-4)*

16. Complete the table. *(2-10)*

One pizza will serve 5 children.

Number of Pizzas	Number of Servings
2	
3	
4	
p	

17. Find the median and mode(s). *(1-7)*

median ________ mode(s) ________

Stem	Leaf
2	3 5 5 7
3	1 2 5 6
4	0 1 2 2 2 8
5	1 2 5

Name ______________________________

Daily Review
8-3

Daily Cumulative Review

Classify each angle as acute, right, obtuse, or straight. *(Lesson 8-2)*

1. __________ **2.** __________ **3.** __________ **4.** __________

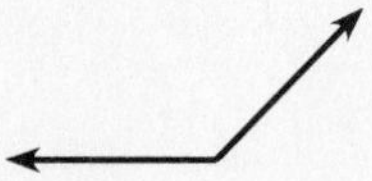

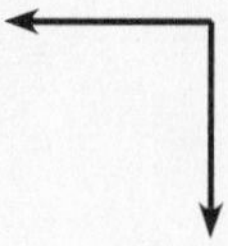

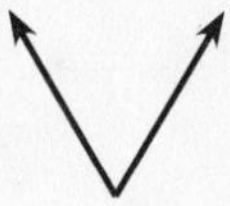

Describe the relationship between the lines, rays, or segments. *(Lesson 8-1)*

5. ______________ **6.** ______________ **7.** ______________

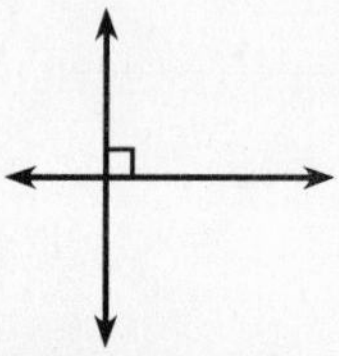

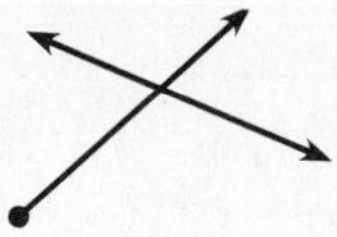

Mixed Review

8. Divide. $8 \div 1\frac{1}{7}$ __________
(7-4)

9. Subtract. $7 - 1\frac{3}{8}$ __________
(6-6)

10. Write $9\frac{7}{8}$ as an improper fraction. __________
(5-6)

Use the scatterplot for Exercices 11 and 12.

Plate Comparison

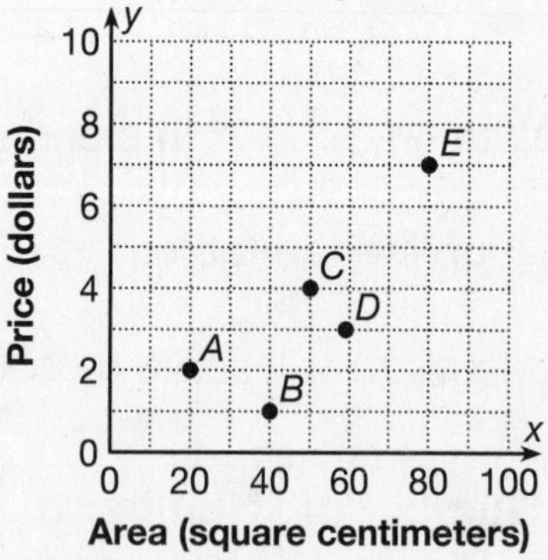

11. Find the cost of the plate with diameter 8 cm.
(4-8)

____

12. Find the plate with the smallest circumference.
(4-8)

____

Estimate.

13. $5.79 + 2.81$
(3-5)

____

14. 39.13×6.8
(3-5)

____

15. $68.1 - 12.13$
(3-5)

____

16. Solve. $12t = 132$
(2-13)

$t =$ ______________

17. Simplify. 210×30
(2-5)

____

Name ____

Daily Review
8-4

Daily Cumulative Review

Measure each angle with a protractor. *(Lesson 8-3)*

1. __________ **2.** __________ **3.** __________ **4.** __________

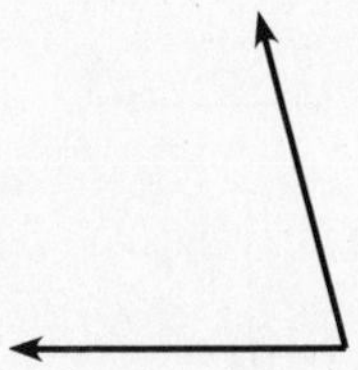

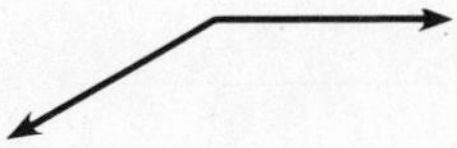
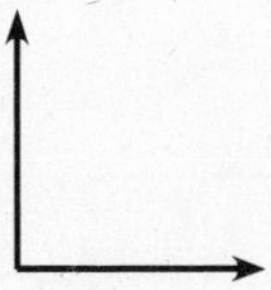

Classify the angle made by the hands of a clock at each time. *(Lesson 8-2)*

5. 3:00 ____________ **6.** 10:00 ____________ **7.** 4:45 ____________

Mixed Review

8. State whether the figure is a line, ray, or segment. __________
(8-1)

9. Multiply. $10 \times 5\frac{1}{6}$ __________
(7-2)

10. Simplify. $\frac{5}{6} + \frac{1}{16}$ __________
(6-2)

11. Write $\frac{18}{32}$ in lowest terms. __________
(5-5)

12. Find the area of a triangle whose base is 7.32 ft and height is 10.2 ft.
(4-6)

____

13. Find the area of a parallelogram whose base is 12.3 cm and height is 2.5 cm.
(4-5)

____

14. Simplify. $65.683 - 21.43$
(3-6)

____

15. Is $56 \div n = 14$ true when $n = 6$?
(2-12)

____

16. Estimate. 42,681 + 42,798 + 42,902 + 42,987 + 43,100 ____________________
(2-6)

17. Write 6,312,105 in words. ____
(2-1)

____

Name ______________________________

Daily Review 8-5

Daily Cumulative Review

Classify each triangle as acute, right, or obtuse. *(Lesson 8-4)*

1. ____________ **2.** ____________ **3.** ____________ **4.** ____________

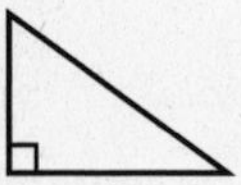
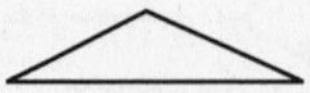

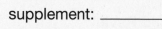

Measure each angle. Find its complement and supplement *(Lesson 8-3)*

5. measure: ________
complement: ________
supplement: ________

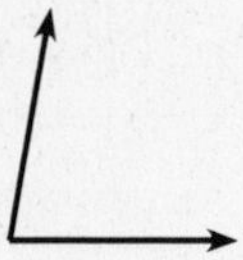

6. measure: ________
complement: ________
supplement: ________

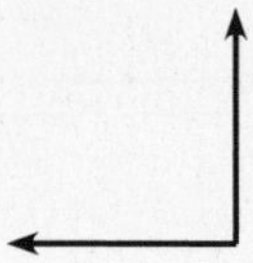

7. measure: ________
complement: ________
supplement: ________

Mixed Review

8. Describe the relationship between the lines shown.
(8-1)

____

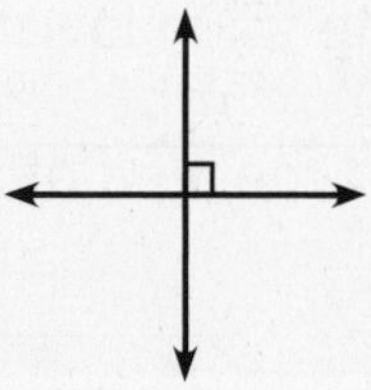

9. Estimate. $5\frac{1}{8} + 2\frac{22}{25}$ ____________
(6-4)

10. The gumball machine had 5 red balls, 3 green, 6 blue,
(5-4) and 1 white ball. What fraction of the gumballs were green? ____________

11. Find the area of a square with sides 7.3 meters long. ____________
(4-4)

12. Divide. $2.2545 \div 0.835$ ____________
(3-11)

13. Make a stem-and-leaf diagram of the data showing
(1-6) the number of candy bars sold in a fundraiser.
52, 49, 31, 57, 68, 35, 40, 38, 47, 31,
55, 64, 55, 33, 48, 42, 56, 60, 62, 55

Stem	Leaf

Name ______________________________

Daily Review
8-6

Daily Cumulative Review

Classify each triangle as scalene, equilateral, or isosceles. *(Lesson 8-5)*

1. ____________

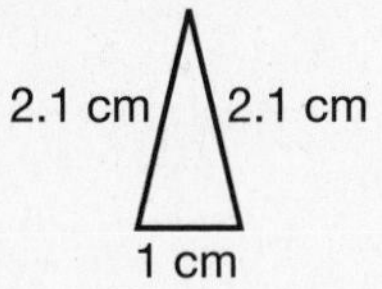

2. ____________

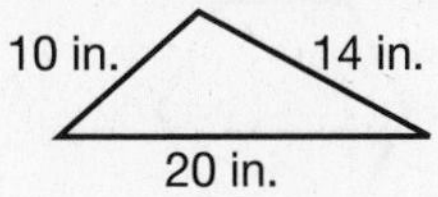

3. ____________

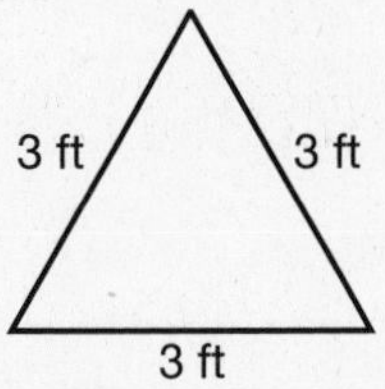

4. ____________

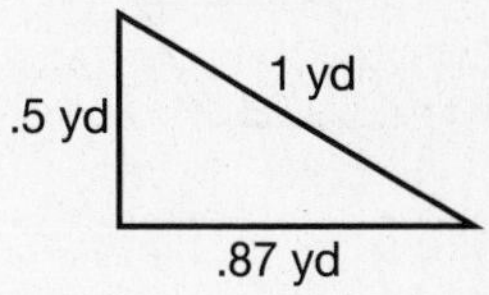

Classify each triangle as acute, right, or obtuse. *(Lesson 8-4)*

5. $m\angle T = 43°, m\angle U = 85°, m\angle V = 52°$

____

6. $m\angle A = 60°, m\angle R = 15°, m\angle F = 105°$

____

Mixed Review

7. Solve. $k \div \frac{1}{5} = 2\frac{1}{3}$ ____________
(7-6)

8. Simplify. $\frac{9}{13} + \frac{1}{6}$ ____________
(6-2)

9. Find the area. Use 3.14 for π.
(4-9)

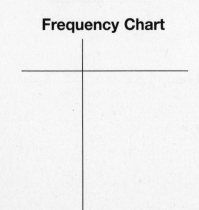

____

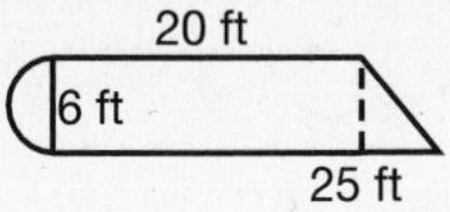

10. Find the lengths of the unknown sides.
(4-1)

$a =$ ____________ $b =$ ____________

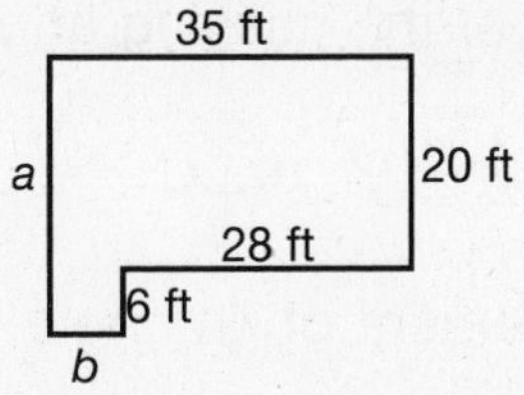

11. Divide. $193.44 \div 62$ ____________
(3-10)

12. Make a frequency chart for the data in the line plot showing scores on a 10 point quiz.
(1-4)

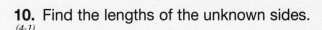

Frequency Chart

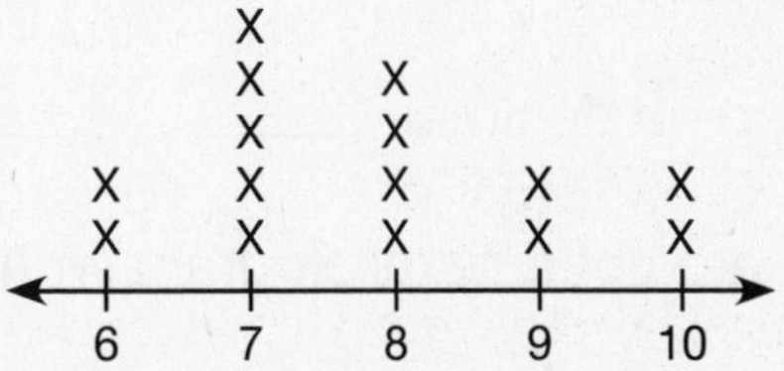

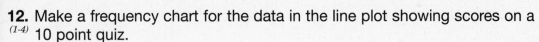

Name ______________________________

Daily Review 8-7

Daily Cumulative Review

Name each polygon and tell if it is regular or irregular. *(Lesson 8-6)*

1. ______________________

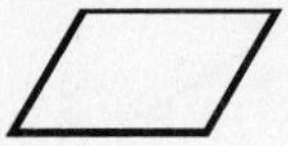

2. ______________________

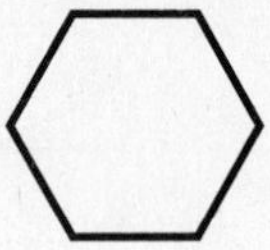

3. ______________________

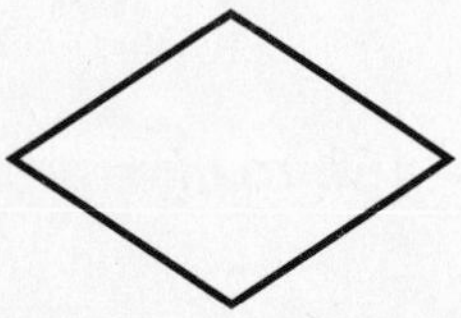

4. ______________________

State whether the given lengths can form a triangle. *(Lesson 8-5)*

5. 8 in., 4 in., and 11 in. ______________

6. 30 cm, 20 cm, 10 cm ______________

7. 8 m, 8m, 18 m ______________

Mixed Review

8. Find the measure of the missing angle in triangle *ABC*.
(8-4)

$m\angle A = 92°, m\angle B = 49°, m\angle C =$ ________

9. What is the supplement of an angle with measure 118°? ______________
(8-3)

10. Simplify. $\frac{8}{9} \div \frac{1}{3}$ ________
(7-5)

11. Multiply. $\frac{3}{4} \times \frac{2}{7}$ ________
(7-3)

12. Simplify. $\frac{14}{18} + \frac{7}{18}$ ________
(6-1)

13. Write $\frac{11}{9}$ as a decimal. ______________
(5-7)

14. Find the area of a parallelogram with base 7 cm and height 8.9 cm. ________
(4-5)

15. Write 7.036 in word form. ______________________________
(3-1)

16. Find the next three numbers in the pattern.
(2-9)

6, 13, 20, 27, 34, ________, ________, ________

Name ________________________________

Daily Review
8-8

Daily Cumulative Review

Classify each figure in as many ways as possible. *(Lesson 8-7)*

1. ______________________
____

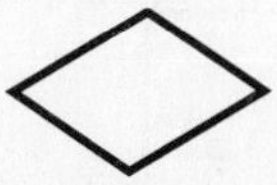

2. ______________________
____

What kind of polygon is each quilt piece? *(Lesson 8-6)*

3. ____________

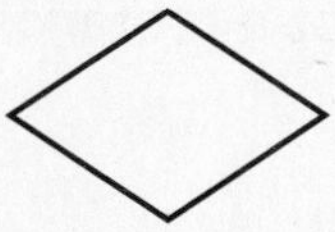

4. ____________

5. ____________

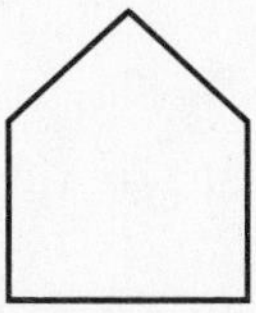

6. ____________

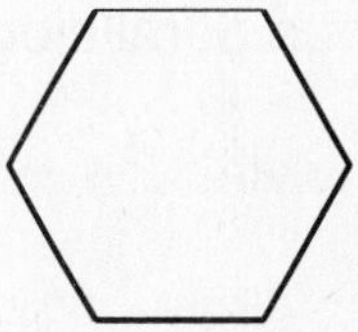

Mixed Review

7. Draw an example of $\overrightarrow{XY}$.
(8-1)

8. The circle graph shows the number of hours Peter plays sports. How many more hours did Peter spend jogging than playing tennis?
(6-6)

____

Weekly Sports (hours)

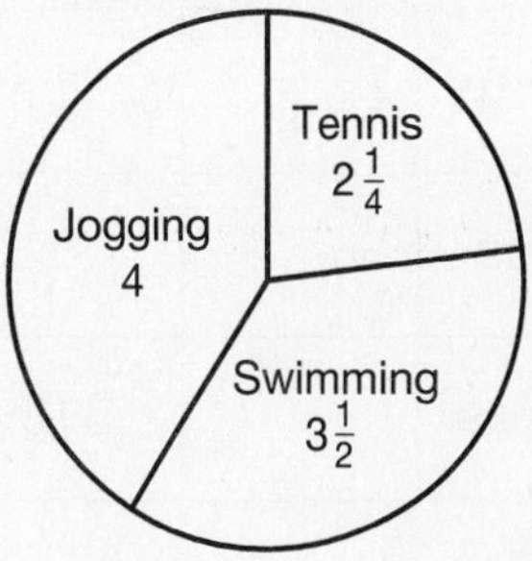

9. Multiply. 15×18.13
(3-8)

____

10. Write a phrase for "*x* increased by 15."
(2-11)

____

11. Round 62,293,635,811 to the hundred-millions place.
(2-2)

____

12. Identify the outlier. ____________
(1-9)

72, 85, 91, 77, 76, 22, 88, 92, 95

Name ______________________________

Daily Review 8-9

Daily Cumulative Review

Tell if the picture has line symmetry. If it does, tell how many lines of symmetry it has. *(Lesson 8-8)*

1. ____________ **2.** ____________ **3.** ____________ **4.** ____________

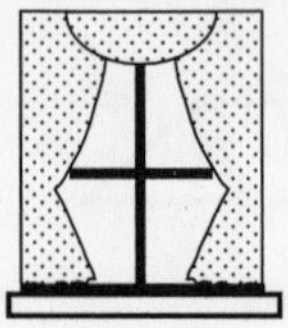

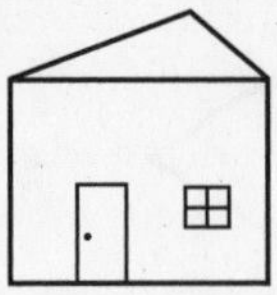

Draw an example of each figure. *(Lesson 8-7)*

5. A quadrilateral that is not a parallelogram

6. A rhombus

7. A parallelogram that is not a rectangle

Mixed Review

8. Name the angle three ways. ______________________
(8-2)

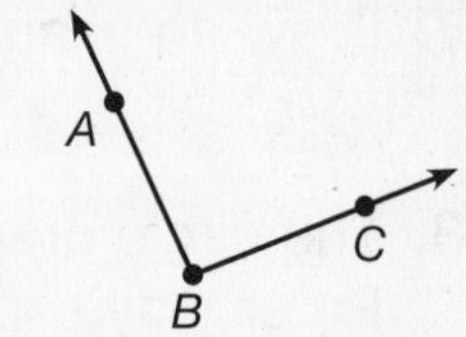

9. Complete the table for calories in a certain ice cream.
(7-2)

Servings	$\frac{2}{3}$	1	$1\frac{1}{3}$	$2\frac{1}{2}$
Ounces		8		
Calories		310		

10. The graph shows the normal monthly rainfall for Denver, CO. On average, how much rain does Denver receive during the first six months of the year?
(1-1)

____

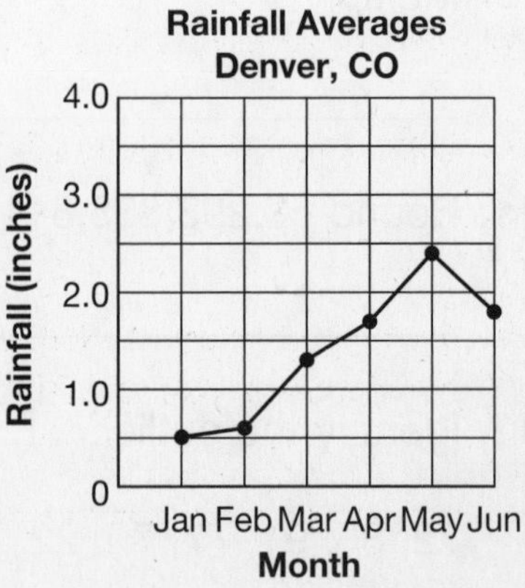

11. Colorado is about 378 miles long and about 283 miles wide. About how many square miles does this rectangular shaped state have?
(2-7)

____

Name ______________________________

Daily Review
8-10

Daily Cumulative Review

What is the least rotation that will land the figure on top of itself? *(Lesson 8-9)*

1. ____________

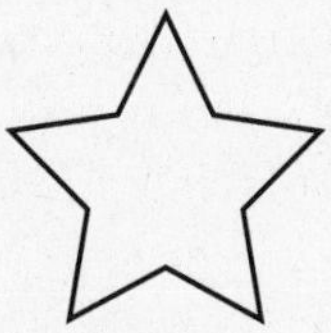

2. ____________

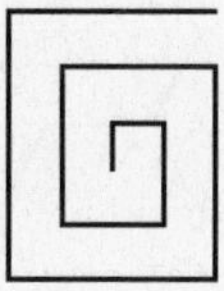

3. ____________

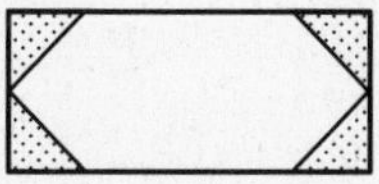

4. ____________

Tell if each pair of figures are congruent. *(Lesson 8-8)*

5. ____________

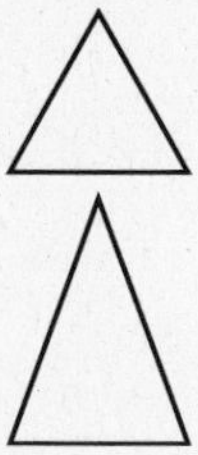

6. ____________

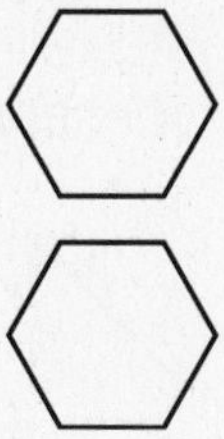

7. ____________

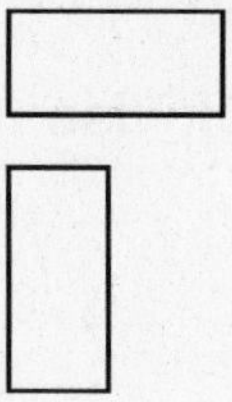

Mixed Review

8. Classify a triangle with sides of length 6 cm, 8 cm, 6 cm. ____________
(8-5)

9. Solve. $\frac{1}{4}x = 18$
(7-6)

$x =$ ____________

10. Write a true equation using $\frac{1}{6}, \frac{3}{4}, \frac{11}{12}$.
(6-3)

____

11. Find the prime factorization of 162. ____________
(5-2)

12. Solve. $4.61 + p = 4.98$
(3-7)

$p =$ ____________

13. Evaluate. $(3^2 - 1) + 12$
(2-8)

____

Use the Popcorn Sales graph for Exercises 14 and 15.

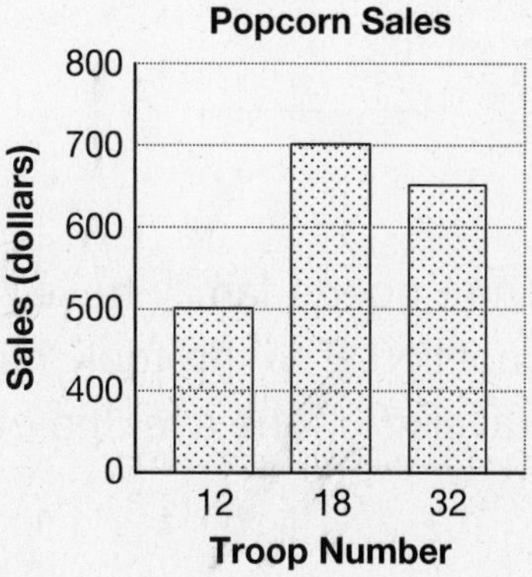

14. Give the total sales of the three troops.
(1-2)

____

15. If the bar graph is misleading, how would you correct it?
(1-2)

____

Name ______________________

Daily Review
9-1

Daily Cumulative Review

Name the polygon that is tessellated in each design. *(Lesson 8-10)*

1. ______________________

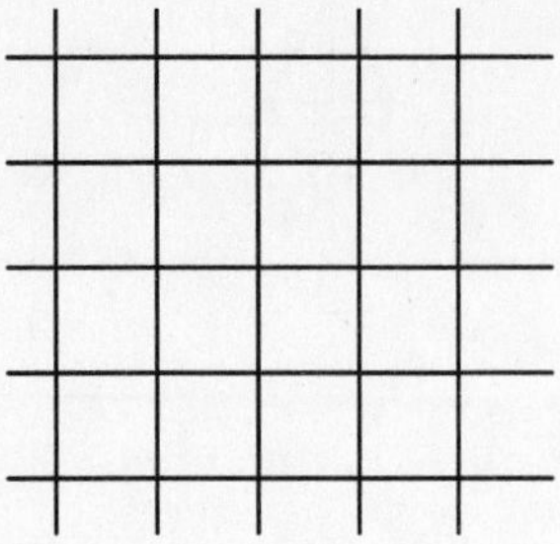

2. ______________________

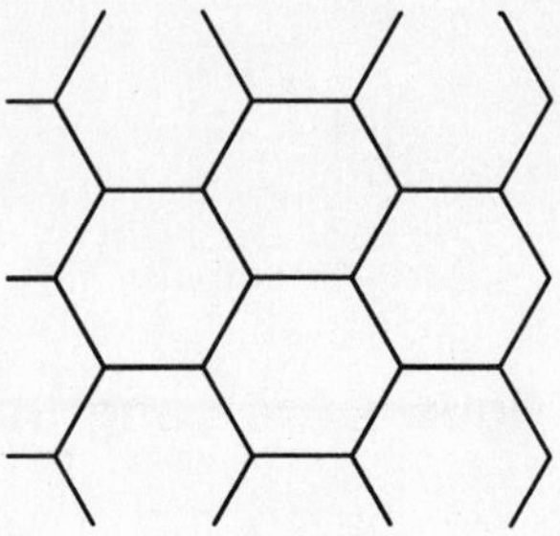

Draw a 45° clockwise rotation of the figure. *(Lesson 8-9)*

3. 

4. 

Mixed Review

5. Simplify.
(7-5)

$5\frac{4}{7} \div 2\frac{1}{3}$ ____________

6. Subtract.
(6-6)

$7\frac{2}{3} - 2\frac{9}{10}$ ____________

7. If a rhombus has a perimeter of of 48 inches, what is the length of each side?
(8-7)

____

8. State the angle measure that is complementary to an angle of 48°.
(8-3)

____

9. If the circumference of a circle is 18.2 yards, what is the circle's radius and area rounded to the nearest tenth?
(4-8)

$r =$ ____________ $A =$ ____________

10. Estimate the length to the nearest tenth of a centimeter. ____________
(3-2)

11. The Roberts family traveled 2,389 miles on a summer vacation. The trip took 11 days. Estimate how far they traveled on the average each day.
(2-7)

____

Name ______________________________

Daily Review 9-2

Daily Cumulative Review

Locate each integer on the number line. *(Lesson 9-1)*

1. 2

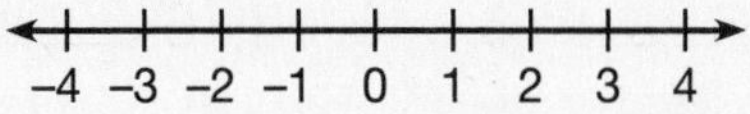

2. −2

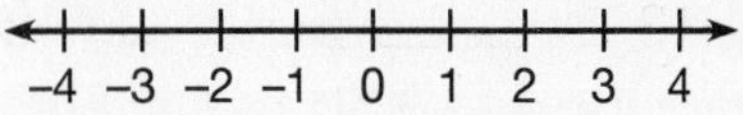

3. −4

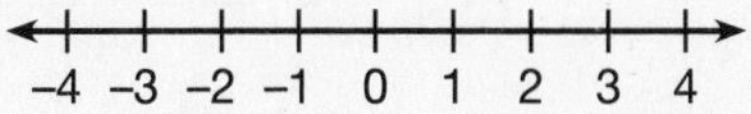

4. 3

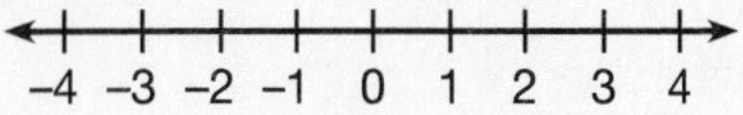

State if each figure will tessellate. Make a drawing to show your answer. *(Lesson 8-10)*

5. ______________________

6. ______________________

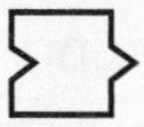

Mixed Review

7. Solve. *(7-6)*

$x \div 2\frac{1}{3} = 8$

$x =$ __________

8. Solve. *(6-3)*

$m + \frac{1}{4} = \frac{9}{16}$

$m =$ __________

9. Write $\frac{5}{6}$ as a decimal. *(5-7)*

__________.

Does $\frac{5}{6}$ repeat or terminate?

____

10. Solve. *(3-7)*
$x - 10.6 = 1.8$

$x =$ __________

11. Evaluate. *(2-8)*
$6^2 - 3^3$

____

12. Write 13 squared in standard form. *(2-4)*

____

13. Make a line plot for the data. Then find the median and mode(s). *(1-7)*

26, 32, 28, 27, 30, 32, 28, 29, 31, 28, 27, 30, 31

median __________ mode(s) __________

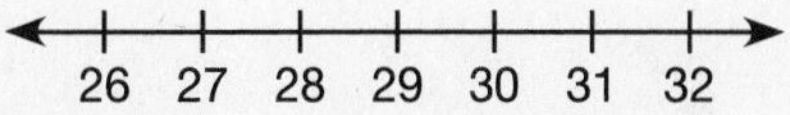

14. Find the area. *(4-9)*

____

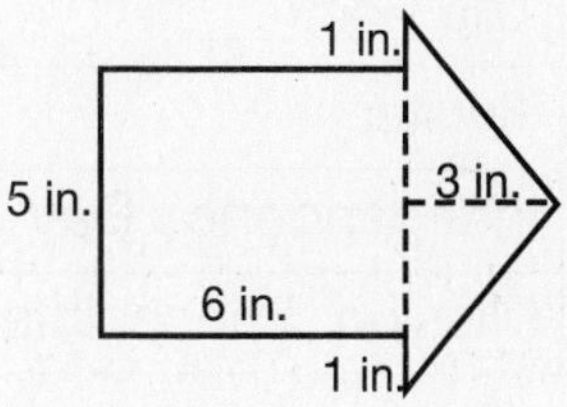

15. If gasoline costs \$1.059 per gallon, how much would you pay for 14.73 gallons? (Round your answer to the nearest cent.) *(3-9)* ______________

Name ______________________

Daily Review 9-3

Daily Cumulative Review

Add. *(Lesson 9-2)*

1. $-8 + 13$ ______ **2.** $43 + (-2)$ ______ **3.** $-5 + (-6)$ ______

4. $0 + (-5)$ ______ **5.** $-8 + 3$ ______ **6.** $7 + 2$ ______

Compare using > or <. *(Lesson 9-1)*

7. -6 ◯ 6 **8.** -3 ◯ -4 **9.** 0 ◯ -5 **10.** 18 ◯ -19

Mixed Review

11. Find the product. *(7-3)*

$\frac{1}{3} \times \frac{6}{13}$ ______

12. Round to the nearest whole number. *(6-4)*

$6\frac{17}{20}$ ______

13. Write in lowest terms. *(5-5)*

$\frac{40}{56}$ ______

14. Convert. *(4-3)*

27 mi = ______ ft

15. Divide. *(3-10)*

$246.79 \div 29$ ______

16. Round 531,692 to the ten-thousands place. *(2-2)*

______

17. Is the line a line of symmetry? *(8-8)*

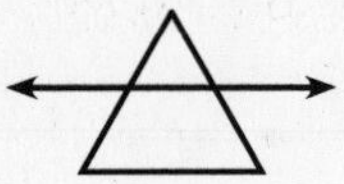

______

18. Measure each angle of the triangle. *(8-4)*

$m\angle A$ ______

$m\angle B$ ______

$m\angle C$ ______

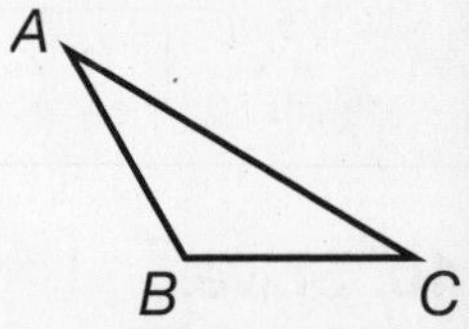

19. Make a bar graph showing the following top four movies in 1996. *(1-5)*

Movie	Gross (millions)
The Rock	$134
Twister	$242
Independence Day	$306
Mission: Impossible	$181

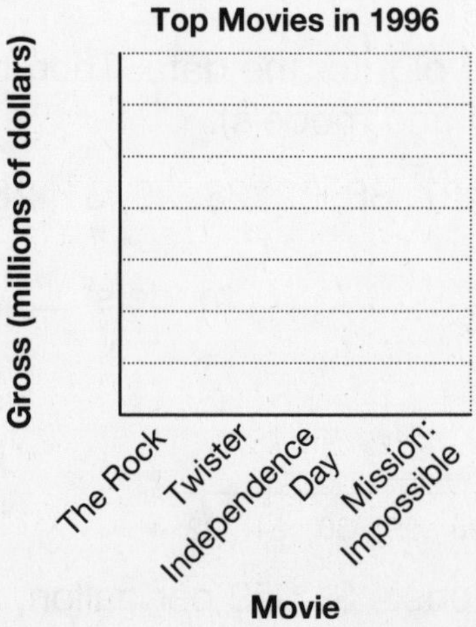

Name ______________________

Daily Review
9-4

Daily Cumulative Review

Subtract. *(Lesson 9-3)*

1. $-1 - (-5)$ ________ **2.** $12 - (-5)$ ________ **3.** $18 - 5$ ________

4. $0 - (-8)$ ________ **5.** $-3 - 22$ ________ **6.** $-27 - 0$ ________

Add. *(Lesson 9-2)*

7. $9 + (-12)$ ________ **8.** $-63 + 27$ ________ **9.** $26 + 8$ ________

10. $-2 + (-6)$ ________ **11.** $15 + (-15)$ ________ **12.** $-26 + 8$ ________

Mixed Review

Simplify.

13. *(7-4)* $8 \div 2\frac{1}{6}$ ________

14. *(6-5)* $12\frac{7}{15} + 14\frac{2}{3}$ ________

15. *(2-5)* $250{,}000 \div 5{,}000$ ________

16. *(4-2)* Convert.

376 mL = ________ L

17. *(3-8)* Multiply.

$9 \times \$11.74$ ________

18. *(5-2)* Is 83 prime or composite?

____

19. *(9-1)* Order from greatest to least.
16, −14, −18, 19

____

20. *(8-6)* Draw a regular pentagon.

21. *(8-2)* Give one name for the angle.

____

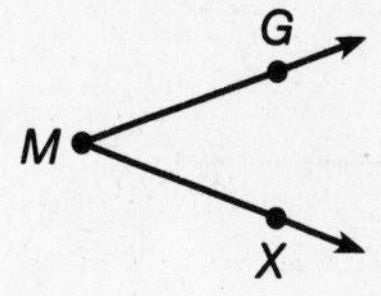

22. *(1-7)* Find the median of 16, 44, 71, 77, 22, 30. ________

23. *(4-4)* Use the scatterplot to answer the following.

a. What is the area of rectangle A? ________

b. Which rectangle has the greatest height? ________

c. Which rectangle has the greatest area? ________

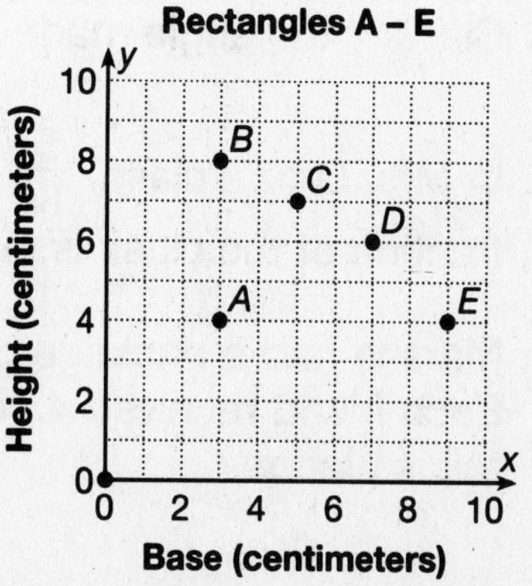

Name ____________________

Daily Review 9-5

Daily Cumulative Review

Multiply or divide. *(Lesson 9-4)*

1. -3×4 ________ **2.** $44 \div (-4)$ ________ **3.** $-1 \times (-11)$ ________

4. $2 \times (-8)$ ________ **5.** $-56 \div (-7)$ ________ **6.** $-35 \div 5$ ________

Subtract. *(Lesson 9-3)*

7. $-3 - (-7)$ ________ **8.** $18 - (-3)$ ________ **9.** $15 - 7$ ________

10. $0 - (-9)$ ________ **11.** $-7 - 21$ ________ **12.** $-18 - 0$ ________

Mixed Review

13. *(9-2)* Add.

$-32 + 5$ ________

14. *(7-2)* Simplify.

$12\frac{3}{7} \times 5$ ________

15. *(3-12)* Solve. $5.6x = 16.24$

$x =$ ________

16. *(5-3)* Find the LCM of 6 and 20.

____

17. *(4-2)* Convert.

27 mm = ______ cm

18. *(4-3)* Convert.

24 qt = ______ gal

Estimate.

19. *(3-5)* $4.71 + 1.86$

____

20. *(3-5)* $11.838 - 2.15$

____

21. *(3-5)* 36.17×7.837

____

22. *(8-5)* Classify a triangle with sides of length 8 ft, 14 ft, and 8 ft. ________

23. *(8-2)* Classify the angle made the hands of a clock at 4:00. ________

24. *(6-1)* In Mrs. Ortiz's class, $\frac{5}{12}$ of the students are male. What fraction of the class is female? ________

25. *(2-12)* Marsha had a package of 48 cookies to give to k friends. Each friend received 4 cookies. Write an equation for this situation. ________

Name ____________________

Daily Review 9-6

Daily Cumulative Review

Give the coordinate of each point. *(Lesson 9-5)*

1. *A* ________ 2. *B* ________

3. *C* ________ 4. *D* ________

5. *E* ________ 6. *F* ________

7. *G* ________ 8. *H* ________

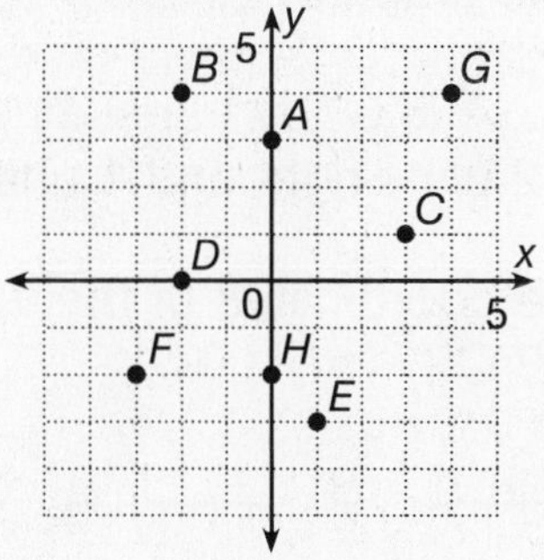

Multiply or divide. *(Lesson 9-4)*

9. $-25 \div 5$ ________ 10. $3 \times (-7)$ ________ 11. $-5 \times (-11)$ ________

12. $27 \div (-3)$ ________ 13. 7×15 ________ 14. $-18 \div (-2)$ ________

Mixed Review

Add or subtract.

15. $-56 - 10$ *(9-3)* ________

16. $\frac{4}{5} - \frac{1}{25}$ *(6-2)* ________

17. \$49.23 – \$26.74 *(3-6)* ________

18. Write $\frac{43}{9}$ as a mixed number. *(5-6)* ________

19. Round $5\frac{4}{7}$ to the nearest whole number. *(6-4)* ________

20. Solve. *(6-3)* $\frac{3}{4} + n = \frac{5}{6}$ ________

21. True or false. Perpendicular lines intersect at right angles. *(8-1)* ________

22. A CD box measures $5\frac{5}{8}$ inches across. A music store manager wants to display 9 CDs side-by-side on a 49-inch shelf. Is there enough room for the display? *(7-1)* ________

23. a. Identify the outlier in the data at the right. *(1-9)*

____

b. Find the mean without the outlier.

____

Stem	Leaf
1	4
3	5 7 8
4	0 2 2 3 5 7 9
5	2

Name ______________________________

Daily Review
9-7

Daily Cumulative Review

Consider $\triangle ABC$ with vertices at $A(-2, 3)$, $B(3, 1)$, and $C(0, -2)$. *(Lesson 9-6)*

1. Draw the graph of $\triangle ABC$.

2. Create $\triangle A'B'C'$ by translating $\triangle ABC$ 2 units right and 1 unit down.

3. Give the coordinates of the vertices of $\triangle A'B'C'$.

A' ________ B' ________ C' ________

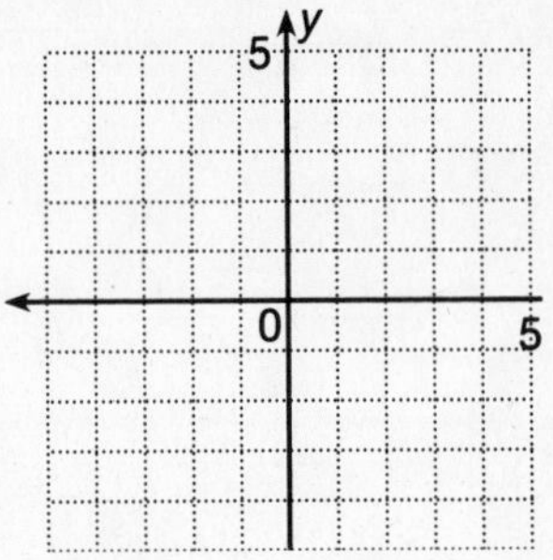

State which quadrant each point is in. *(Lesson 9-5)*

4. $(4, -10)$ ____________ **5.** $(-15, -30)$ ____________ **6.** $(-12, 20)$ ____________

Mixed Review

Simplify.

7. $-48 \div -6$ ________ (9-4)

8. $(-2)^4$ ________ (9-4)

9. $-18 - 13$ ________ (9-3)

10. Solve. (7-6)

$1\frac{3}{10}m = 1\frac{19}{20}$

$m =$ ____________

11. Solve. (6-3)

$x + \frac{5}{13} = \frac{25}{26}$

$x =$ ____________

12. Write 0.125 as a fraction in lowest terms. (5-7)

____

13. If the star shown is rotated 360°, how many times will it land on its original position? (8-9)

____

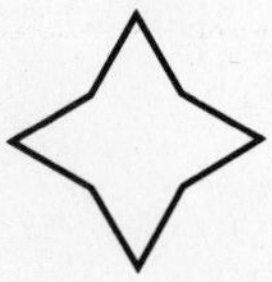

14. Find the perimeter. (4-1)

____

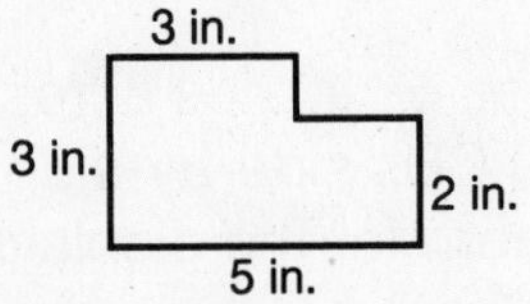

15. Write 34,900,000 in scientific notation. ____________ (3-4)

16. Note pads are priced at \$0.49. Estimate how many you could buy for \$5.00. (3-5) ____________

Name ______________________________

Daily Review
10-1

Daily Cumulative Review

Make a T-table with five (x, y) pairs. Graph the equation. *(Lesson 9-7)*

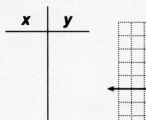

1. $y = x + 3$

x	y

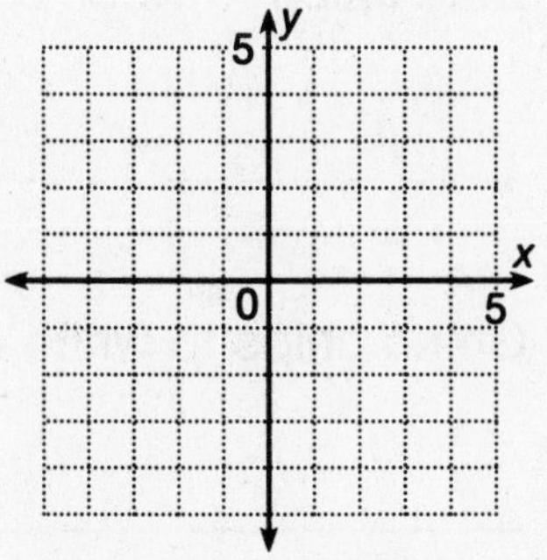

2. $y = -2x$

x	y

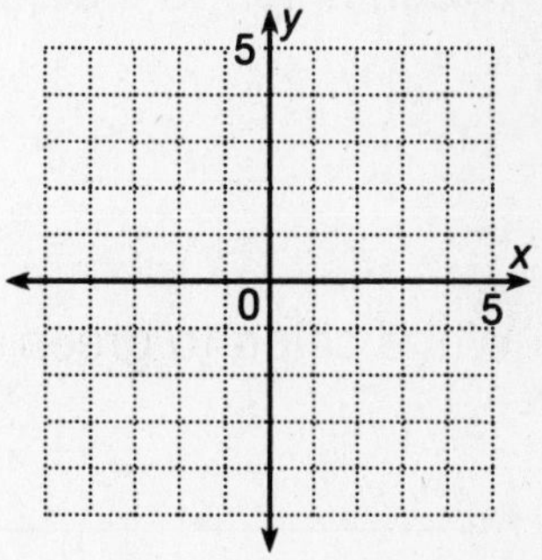

Plot the image of quadrilateral *GHIJ*. *(Lesson 9-6)*

3. Translate *GHIJ* 3 units right and 2 units down.

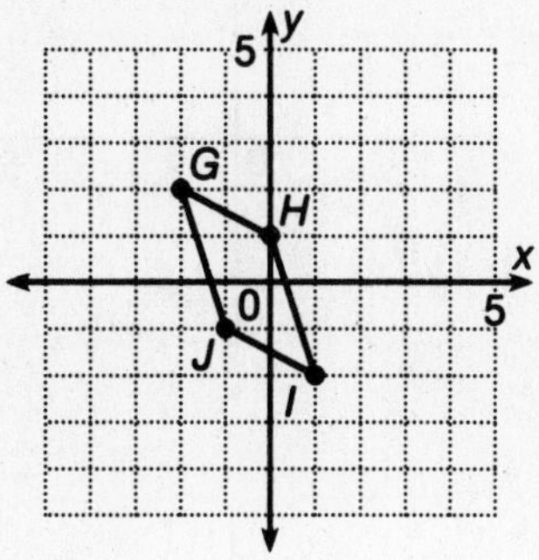

4. Slide *GHIJ* 2 units right and 2 units up.

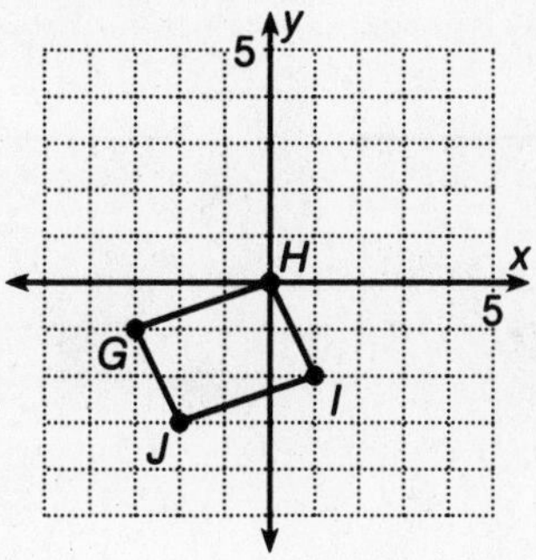

Mixed Review

Simplify.

5. $-9 \div (-3)$ ____________
(9-4)

6. $8 - 12$ ____________
(9-3)

7. $-9 + (-8)$ ____________
(9-2)

8. $6\frac{1}{7} \div 2\frac{1}{3}$ ____________
(7-5)

9. $3 \times 12\frac{5}{8}$ ____________
(7-2)

10. $\frac{5}{6} + \frac{1}{24}$ ____________
(6-2)

11. Find the GCF of 60 and 42. ____________
(5-5)

12. Find the area of a circle with diameter 11 cm, rounded to the nearest tenth of a centimeter. ____________
(4-8)

13. Compare using >, <, or =. 8.34×17.0 ◯ 83.4×0.17
(3-9)

14. Karen earns \$75 per day at her job. If she works 20 days in a month, how much will she earn? ____________
(2-5)

Name ______________________

Daily Review 10-2

Daily Cumulative Review

A box contains 10 green chips, 6 blue chips, and 5 white chips. Give each ratio in three ways. *(Lesson 10-1)*

1. Green chips to blue chips. ______________

2. Blue chips to white chips. ______________

3. White chips to green chips. ______________

4. Green chips to white chips. ______________

Graph each equation. *(Lesson 9-7)*

5. $y = 3x$

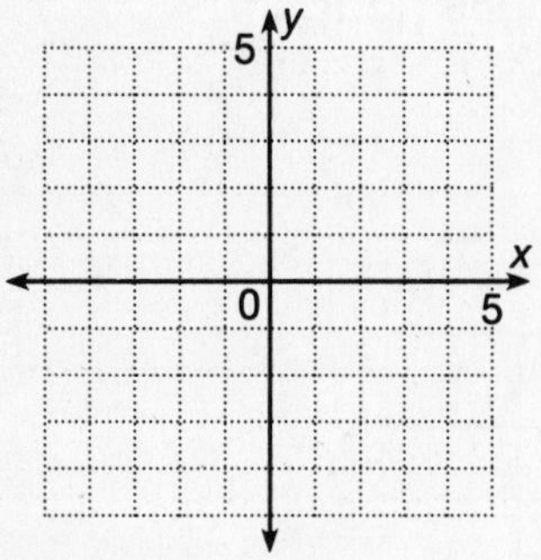

6. $y = x + 1$

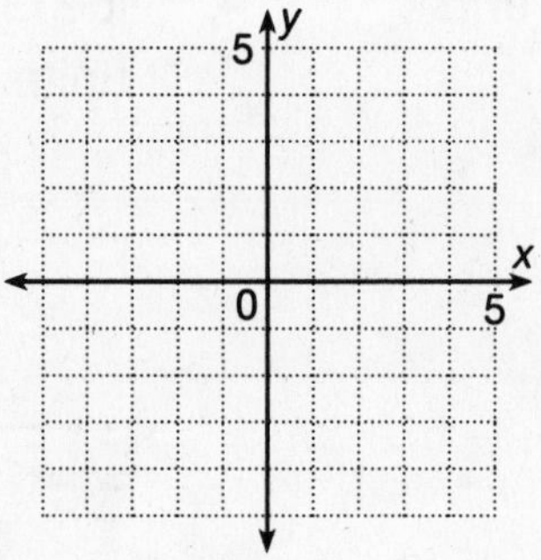

7. $y = 2$

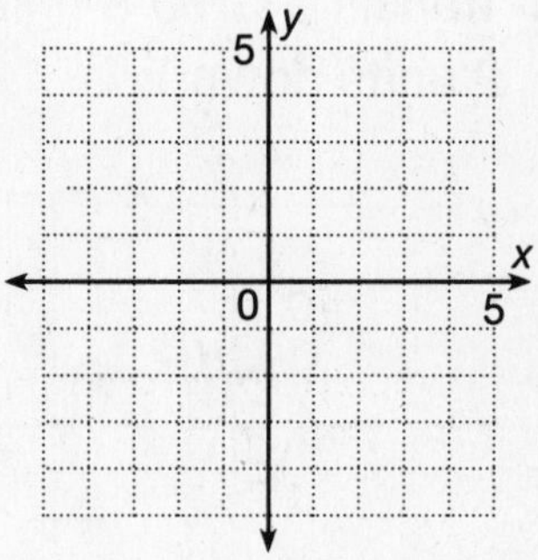

Mixed Review

Simplify.

8. $-48 \div 12$ *(9-4)* ______________

9. $-12 + 12$ *(9-2)* ______________

10. $8 \div \frac{2}{9}$ *(7-4)* ______________

11. $6\frac{1}{8} - 1\frac{3}{4}$ *(6-6)* ______________

12. *(5-2)* Find the prime factorization of 225. ______________

13. *(9-6)* If the point $X(3, 1)$ is reflected across the x-axis, what would be the coordinate of X'? ______________

14. *(4-5)* The base of a parallelogram is 1.8m and its height is 0.6m. What is the area of the parallelogram? ______________

15. *(4-8)* The circumference of a circle is 50.24 cm. What is its area rounded to the nearest tenth? Use 3.14 for π. ______________

Name ______________________________

Daily Review
10-3

Daily Cumulative Review

State if the ratios are equal. *(Lesson 10-2)*

1. 6:10; 3:5 ________ **2.** $\frac{4}{8}, \frac{5}{6}$ ________ **3.** 3:15, $\frac{1}{5}$ ________

Use the shapes to find the ratio. *(Lesson 10-1)*

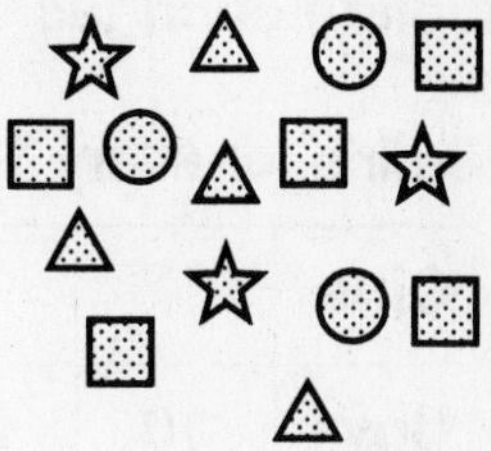

4. What is the ratio of stars to squares? ________

5. What is the ratio of circles to stars? ________

6. What is the ratio of circles to the whole group? ________

Mixed Review

7. *(9-7)* Graph the line $y = -4x$.

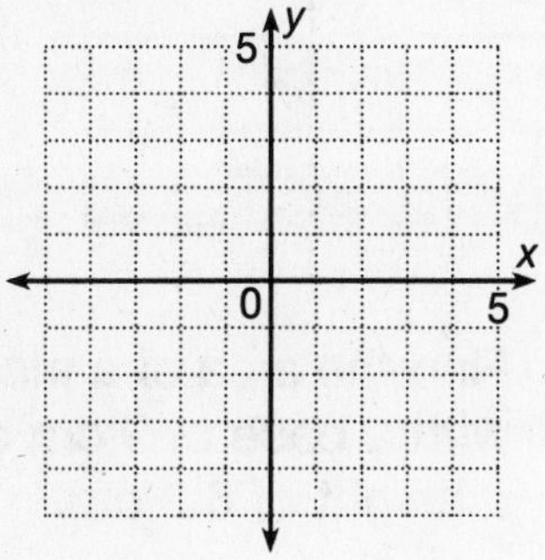

8. *(8-7)* Classify the figure in as many ways as possible.

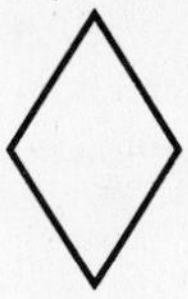

____
____
____

9. *(8-3)* Measure the angle at the right with a protractor.

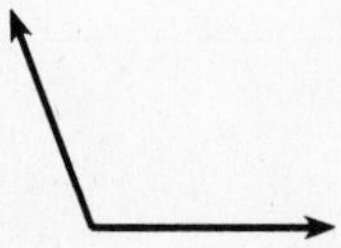

____

10. *(4-3)* Convert.

73 yards = ______ feet

11. *(3-11)* Divide.
72.576 ÷ 11.52

____

12. *(3-4)* Write 6.25×10^5 in standard form.

____

13. *(2-8)* Evaluate.
$(48 \div 6)^2 - 5$

____

14. *(2-4)* Compare.

3^5 ◯ 5×3

15. *(2-1)* Write 79 trillion in standard form.

____

Name ______________________

Daily Review 10-4

Daily Cumulative Review

State if the ratio is a unit rate. *(Lesson 10-3)*

1. $\frac{4 \text{ cats}}{5 \text{ dogs}}$ ______ 2. $\frac{20 \text{ miles}}{1 \text{ minute}}$ ______ 3. $\frac{5 \text{ pounds}}{1 \text{ dollar}}$ ______ 4. $\frac{12 \text{ yards}}{1 \text{ yard}}$ ______

Complete each table of equal ratios. *(Lesson 10-2)*

5. 8 girls for every 10 boys

Girls				
Boys	10	20	30	40

6. 5 trucks for every 3 cars

Cars	3	6		
Trucks			15	20

Mixed Review

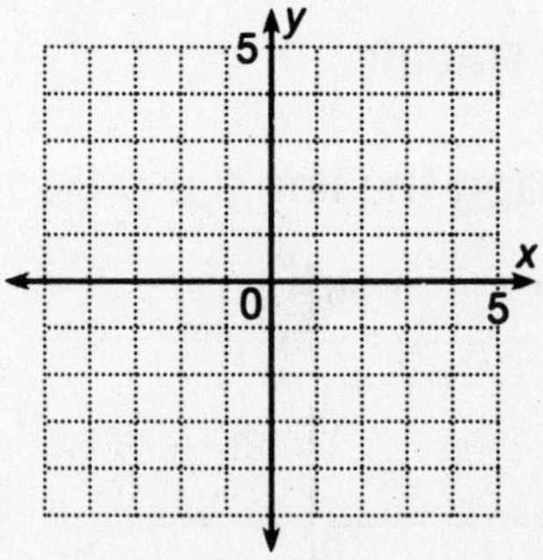

7. *(9-5)* Plot and label each point.
$W(-2, 3)$, $X(1, -2)$, $Y(3, 0)$, $Z(-2, -3)$

8. *(9-1)* Compare using > or <.

$-6 \bigcirc 8$

9. *(6-5)* Simplify. $12\frac{8}{9} + 7$

______

10. *(5-7)* Write 0.48 as a fraction in lowest terms.

______

11. *(4-6)* Find the area of a triangle with a base of 9 cm and a height of 6.2 cm.

______

Solve.

12. *(3-12)* $6.55x = 7.86$

$x =$ ______

13. *(3-7)* $21.5 - m = 9.72$

$m =$ ______

14. *(2-13)* $\frac{a}{7} = 15$

$a =$ ______

15. *(8-5)* Classify a triangle with sides of length 7 cm, 7 cm, and 7 cm. ______

16. *(7-3)* A recipe calls for $4\frac{1}{2}$ cups of flour. How much flour would you need to make $\frac{2}{3}$ of the original recipe? ______

17. *(9-3)* On Tuesday, the low temperature was –4°F and the high temperature was 11°F. What is the difference between these temperatures? ______

Name ________________________________

Daily Review
10-5

Daily Cumulative Review

State whether or not each pair of ratios forms a proportion. *(Lesson 10-4)*

1. $\frac{5}{12} \stackrel{?}{=} \frac{10}{14}$ ________ **2.** $\frac{7}{20} \stackrel{?}{=} \frac{6}{10}$ ________ **3.** $\frac{12}{20} \stackrel{?}{=} \frac{18}{30}$ ________

For each situation give two equal rates. *(Lesson 10-3)*

4. Joan drove 30 miles in 40 minutes. ________________

5. Mike earned $21 for working 3 hours. ________________

Mixed Review

Simplify.

6. -9×11 ________ *(9-4)*

7. $-8 - (-8)$ ________ *(9-3)*

8. $-12 + 22$ ________ *(9-2)*

9. *(8-10)* State if the figure tessellates. Make a drawing to show your answer.

____

10. *(4-9)* Find the area. Use 3.14 for π.

____

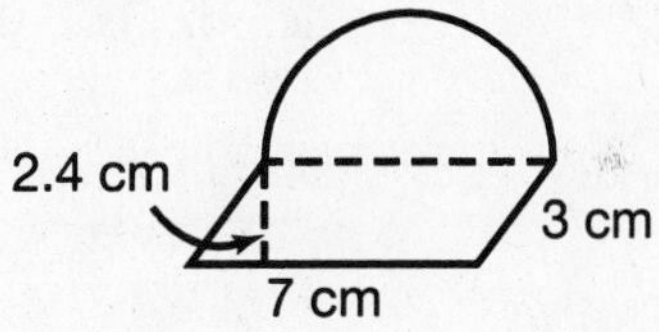

11. *(4-1)* Find the perimeter of the figure in Exercise 10.

____

12. *(3-2)* Round to the underlined place value.
816.<u>9</u>2

____

13. *(2-13)* Write an equation for this situation and solve it.
A section of the auditorium has 12 rows of x chairs. There are 108 chairs all together. How many chairs are in each row?

____

14. *(1-8)* Find the mean, median, and mode(s) of the data showing the number of home runs hit by leading ball players.
25, 32, 40, 28, 42, 30, 45, 28, 41, 34, 27

mean ________ median ________ mode(s) ________

Name ______________________________

Daily Review
10-6

Daily Cumulative Review

Solve each proportion. *(Lesson 10-5)*

1. $\frac{8}{a} = \frac{2}{15}$ **2.** $\frac{3}{9} = \frac{t}{27}$ **3.** $\frac{b}{2} = \frac{15}{5}$ **4.** $\frac{4}{3.5} = \frac{1.6}{d}$

$a =$ ________ $t =$ ________ $b =$ ________ $d =$ ________

Determine if the proportion is written correctly. *(Lesson 10-4)*

5. $\frac{\text{8 pies}}{\text{3 cakes}} = \frac{\text{6 cakes}}{\text{16 pies}}$ **6.** $\frac{\text{15 gal}}{\text{5min}} = \frac{\text{6 gal}}{\text{2 min}}$ **7.** $\frac{\text{19 chairs}}{\text{2 rows}} = \frac{\text{6 rows}}{\text{57 chairs}}$

________ ________ ________

Mixed Review

For Exercises 8–12, estimate.

8. $8\frac{3}{4} \times 10\frac{1}{6}$ *(7-1)* **9.** $11\frac{1}{9} + 4\frac{5}{9} + 3\frac{1}{7}$ *(6-4)* **10.** $52.91 – $12.12 *(3-5)*

________ ________ ________

11. 450,123 ÷ 897 *(2-7)* **12.** 62,163 + 59,920 + 60,125 + 58,685 *(2-6)*

________ ________

13. *(10-3)* Is $\frac{\text{5 bananas}}{\$1}$ a unit rate? ________________

14. *(8-4)* A triangle has two angles with measures of 68° and 46°. What is the measure of the third angle? ________________

15. *(1-6)* Make a stem-and-leaf diagram of the data showing the number of stuffed animals owned by some students.

6, 15, 22, 18, 8, 23, 12, 8, 11, 22, 19, 28, 9, 29, 21, 4, 28

Stem	Leaf

16. *(1-5)* What is the range of the data in Exercise 15? ________

17. Rosie's gas tank was $\frac{3}{4}$ full when she left home. After driving all morning, the tank was $\frac{1}{3}$ full. What fraction of a tank of gas did she use? ________

Name ______________________

Daily Review 10-7

Daily Cumulative Review

Find the unit rate for each. *(Lesson 10-6)*

1. $\frac{\text{15 books}}{\text{3 shelves}}$ ________ 2. $\frac{\text{180 mi}}{\text{4 hr}}$ ________ 3. $\frac{\text{21 boys}}{\text{21 girls}}$ ________

Solve each proportion. *(Lesson 10-5)*

4. $\frac{a}{6} = \frac{5}{15}$ 5. $\frac{40}{y} = \frac{16}{6}$ 6. $\frac{8}{36} = \frac{m}{90}$ 7. $\frac{18}{24} = \frac{3}{K}$

$a =$ ________ $y =$ ________ $m =$ ________ $K =$ ________

Mixed Review

8. Graph $y = x - 2$.
(9-7)

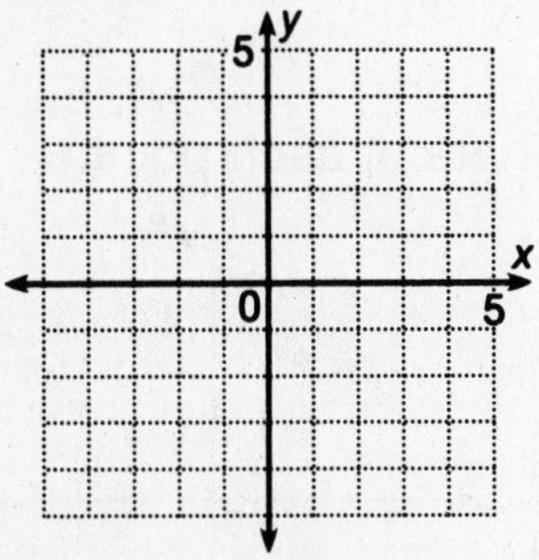

9. Draw a 45° clockwise rotation of the figure.
(8-9)

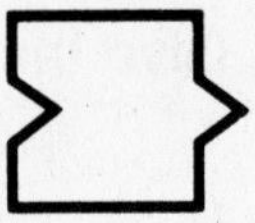

10. Draw an example of $\overrightarrow{JK}$.
(8-1)

11. Solve. $x \div 3\frac{1}{4} = 6$
(7-6)

$x =$ ________

12. Solve. $g + \frac{1}{3} = \frac{4}{9}$
(6-3)

$g =$ ________

13. Write $2\frac{3}{5}$ as an improper fraction.
(5-6)

____

14. Find the area of a parallelogram with base 3.5 in. and height 2.7 in.
(4-5)

____

15. Multiply. 1000×3.802
(3-8)

____

16. Write $45,000,000 in word form and in number-word form.
(2-1)

____

17. Write in standard form.
(2-1) Six million, seven hundred twenty-eight thousand, sixty

____

Name ______________________________

Daily Review
10-8

Daily Cumulative Review

In each pair of similar figures, find the missing side lengths. *(Lesson 10-7)*

1. A = _____ B = _____ C = _____

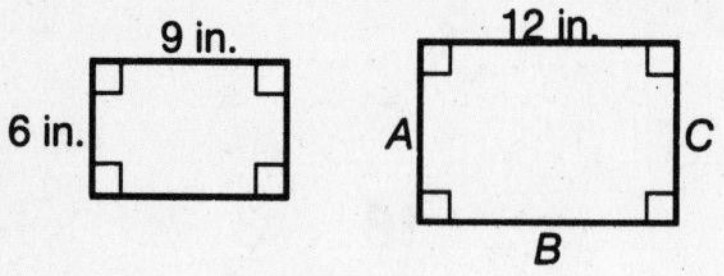

2. A = _____ B = _____

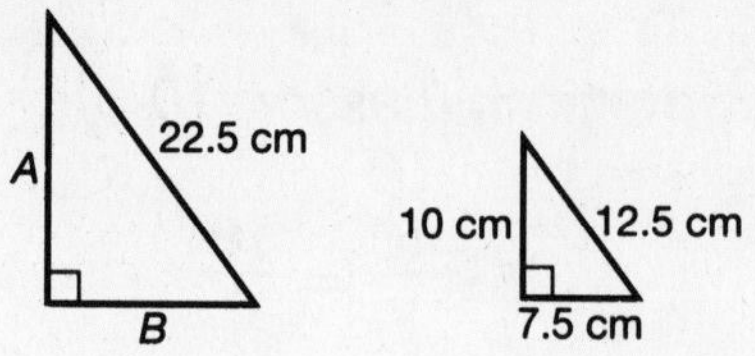

Find the unit rate for each. *(Lesson 10-6)*

3. $\frac{12\text{ tsp}}{3\text{ gal}}$ __________ **4.** $\frac{24\text{ CDs}}{6\text{ tapes}}$ __________ **5.** $\frac{625\text{ ft}^2}{25\text{ people}}$ __________

Mixed Review

6. Solve.
(10-5)

$\frac{50}{5} = \frac{a}{2}$

a = _______

7. Give the coordinate of each point.
(9-5)

A __________

B __________

C __________

D __________

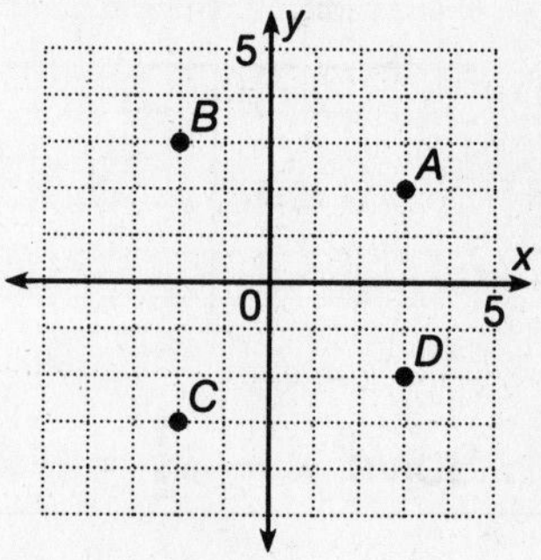

8. Classify the following angle.
(8-2)

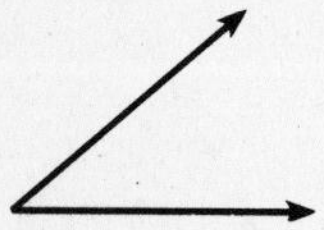

____

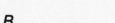

9. Order from least to greatest.
(5-8)

$\frac{1}{2}, \frac{3}{8}, \frac{1}{3}$ __________

10. Is 585 divisible by 9?
(5-1)

____

11. Convert.
(4-2)

23.5 kg = _______ g

12. Divide. 17.71 ÷ 7
(3-10)

____

13. Add. 7.23 + 11.7 + 6.74
(3-6)

____

14. Write 17 million in scientific notation.
(3-4)

____

15. Solve the equation.
(2-13)

$14m = 98$ _______

Name ____________________

Daily Review
10-9

Daily Cumulative Review

Give the percent of each figure that is shaded. *(Lesson 10-8)*

1. ________ **2.** ________ **3.** ________

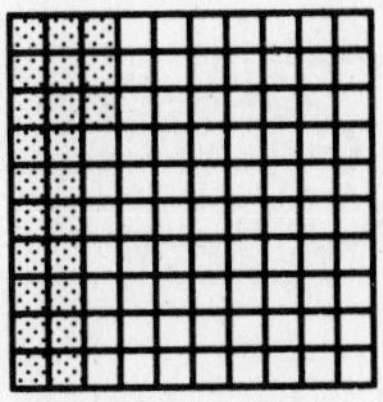
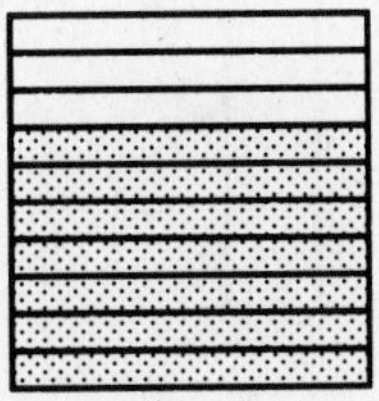

Find the missing side lengths of the similar figures. *(Lesson 10-7)*

4. *A* = ________ *B* = ________

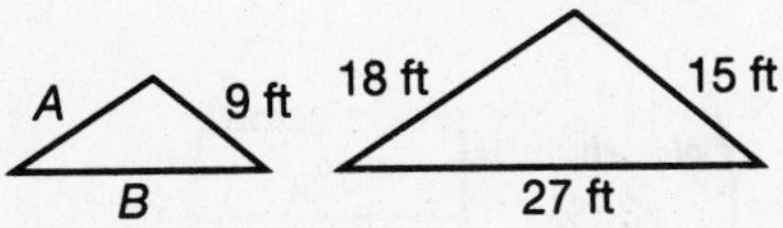

5. *A* = ________ *B* = ________

C = ________

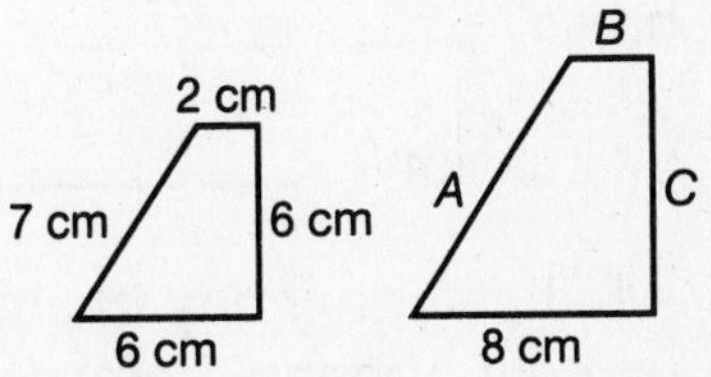

Mixed Review

6. *(10-2)* Complete the table of equal ratios. 32 children for every 2 teachers.

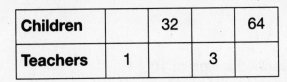

Children		32		64
Teachers	1		3	

7. *(8-8)* How many lines of symmetry does this figure have?

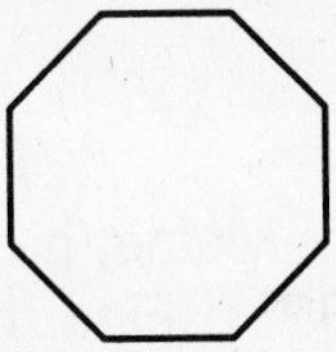

____

8. *(5-3)* Find the LCM of 8 and 32

____

9. *(3-3)* Compare using <, >, or =.

54.37 ◯ 54.371

10. *(2-8)* Evaluate. $(18 - 6)^2 \div 9$ ________

11. *(2-3)* Order from least to greatest. 12 million; 1 billion; 12 thousand

____

12. *(1-9)* Identify the outlier in this data. ________
7, 12, 23, 15, 8, 95, 23, 16, 9, 14, 24, 29, 6

Name ______________________________

Daily Review 10-10

Daily Cumulative Review

Estimate what percent of each figure is shaded. *(Lesson 10-9)*

1. ________

2. ________

3. ________

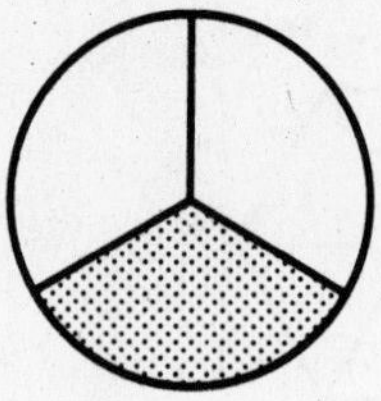

The circle graph shows the makeup of a local high school band. Use the graph for Exercises 4–6. *(Lesson 10-8)*

4. What percent of the band is

brass? ____________

percussion? ____________

Band Composition

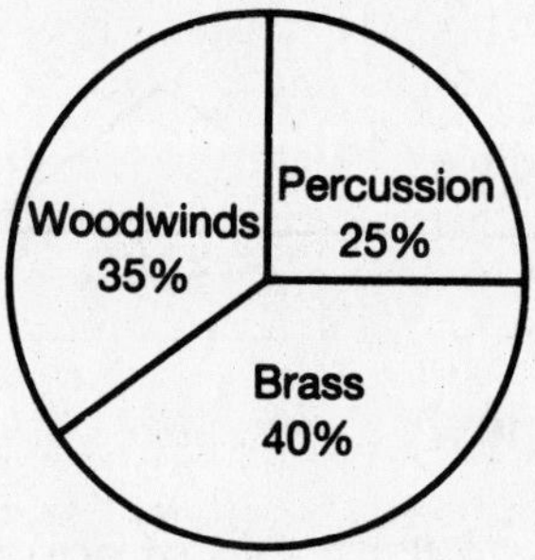

5. What category has the highest percent of band members. __________

6. What two categories combine to make up 75% of the band?

____

Mixed Review

7. *(9-3)* Temperatures in Portland, Maine, have reached a high of 103° F and an all time low of −39° F. Find the difference between these temperatures. ________

8. *(2-9)* Find the next three numbers in the pattern.

123, 175, 227, 279, 331, ______, ______, ______

9. *(1-3)* For the scatterplot, determine if there is a trend. If there is, describe the pattern of the data.

____

____

____

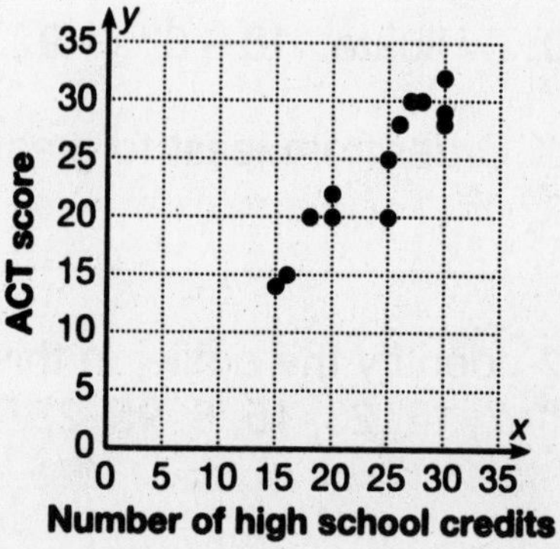

Name ______________________

Daily Review 10-11

Daily Cumulative Review

Convert to a fraction in lowest terms. *(Lesson 10-10)*

1. 90% ______ **2.** 28% ______ **3.** 75% ______ **4.** 115% ______

5. 15% ______ **6.** 98% ______ **7.** 4% ______ **8.** 125% ______

Estimate the percent. *(Lesson 10-9)*

9. 12 out of 65 ______ **10.** 22 out of 108 ______ **11.** $\frac{58}{73}$ ______

Mixed Review

12. *(10-5)* Solve. $\frac{x}{2} = \frac{45}{10}$

$x =$ ______

13. *(10-1)* Write 12 out of 38 as a ratio in lowest terms. ______

14. *(9-4)* Divide. $48 \div (-6)$ ______

15. *(8-5)* Can the lengths of 9 in., 4 in., and 3 in. form a triangle? ______

16. *(7-1)* Estimate. $3\frac{3}{4} \times 4\frac{1}{10}$ ______

17. *(6-2)* Simplify. $\frac{7}{25} - \frac{1}{8}$ ______

18. *(5-7)* Write $\frac{5}{11}$ as a decimal. ______

19. *(5-3)* Find the LCM of 24 and 36. ______

20. *(5-2)* Find the prime factorization of 44. ______

21. *(4-2)* Name an appropriate metric unit for the weight of a thumb tack. ______

22. *(3-8)* In a typical day, Mike works for 8 hours at the rate of \$8.41 per hour. He also buys lunch for \$6.50. How much does he have at the end of the day? ______

23. *(3-4)* Uranus is about 1,698,800,000,000 miles from the sun. Write this number in scientific notation. ______

24. *(2-4)* Write 12^3 in standard form. ______

25. *(2-1)* Write 3 million in standard form. ______

Name ____________________

Daily Cumulative Review

Simplify. Round your answer to the nearest hundredth. *(Lesson 10-11)*

1. 28% of 14 ________ **2.** 33% of 48 ________ **3.** 95% of 59 ________

4. 2% of 85________ **5.** 15% of \$8.96 ________ **6.** 30% of 98 ________

Convert to a percent. *(Lesson 10-10)*

7. $\frac{8}{10}$ ________ **8.** $\frac{29}{50}$ ________ **9.** 0.43 ________ **10.** 0.05 ________

Mixed Review

Give the percent of each figure that is shaded.

11. ________ *(10-8)*

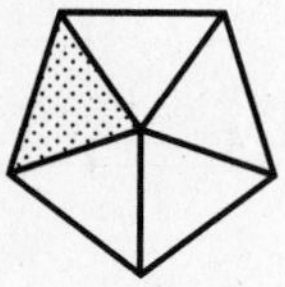

12. ________ *(10-8)*

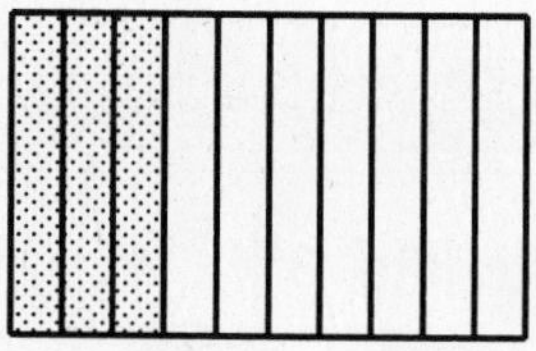

13. ________ *(10-8)*

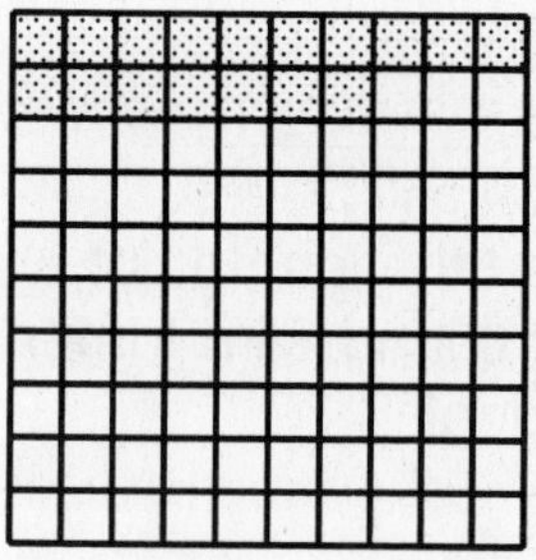

Order from greatest to least.

14. 6, 0, −9, 4, −6 *(9-1)*

____

15. −1, 5, 3, −6, 1 *(9-1)*

____

16. If a triangle has two angles with measures 51° and 68°, what is the measure of the third angle? *(8-4)* ________

Solve.

17. $x \div 2\frac{1}{2} = 6\frac{1}{4}$ *(7-6)*

$x =$ ________

18. $\frac{6}{7} - K = \frac{13}{21}$ *(6-3)*

$K =$ ________

19. $5.7b = 20.406$ *(3-12)*

$b =$ ________

Insert parentheses to make the following true.

20. 36 ÷ 12 × 3 = 1 *(2-8)*

21. 4 × 5 + 3 × 2 = 44 *(2-8)*

Name ______________________________

Daily Review
11-2

Daily Cumulative Review

Classify each solid. If it is a polyhedron, tell how many vertices, edges, and faces it has. *(Lesson 11-1)*

1. ______________________ **2.** ______________________

V: ___ *E*: ___ *F*: ___ *V*: ___ *E*: ___ *F*: ___

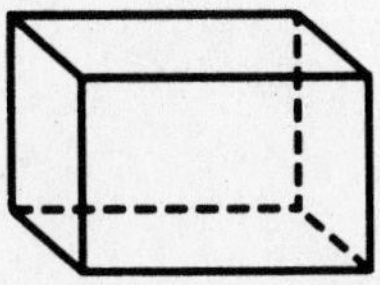

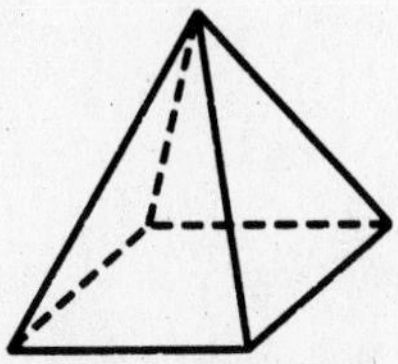

Simplify. Round your answers to the nearest hundredth. *(Lesson 10-11)*

3. 36% of 11.4 ________ **4.** 8% of \$64.75 ________ **5.** 91% of 98 ________

Mixed Review

Solve each problem.

6. *(10-5)* $\frac{14}{36} = \frac{f}{54}$ $f =$ ________

7. *(10-5)* $\frac{1}{8} = \frac{t}{10}$ $t =$ ________

8. *(10-5)* $\frac{a}{64} = \frac{8}{32}$ $a =$ ________

9. *(10-5)* $\frac{36}{x} = \frac{18}{4}$ $x =$ ________

Give two ratios equal to the given ratio.

10. *(10-2)* $\frac{21}{35}$ ______________________

11. *(10-2)* 12:30 ______________________

Simplify.

12. *(9-4)* -7×6 ________ **13.** *(9-3)* $-12 - (-5)$ ________ **14.** *(9-2)* $-8 + (-21)$ ________

15. *(8-8)* How many lines of symmetry does the figure have?

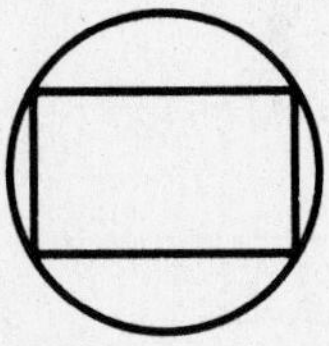

____

16. *(4-9)* Find the area.

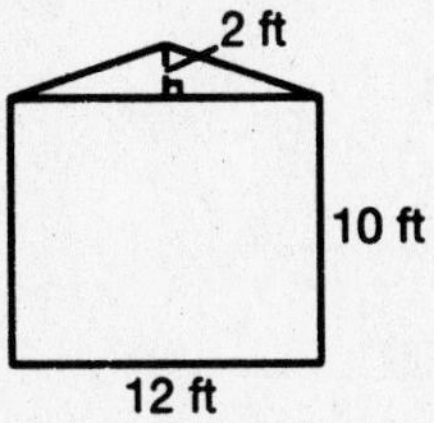

____

17. *(3-4)* Write 6,953,000,000,000 in scientific notation. ______________________

Name ______________________

Daily Review
11-3

Daily Cumulative Review

Find the area of each net. Classify the solid. *(Lesson 11-2)*

1. SA: ______________________

____

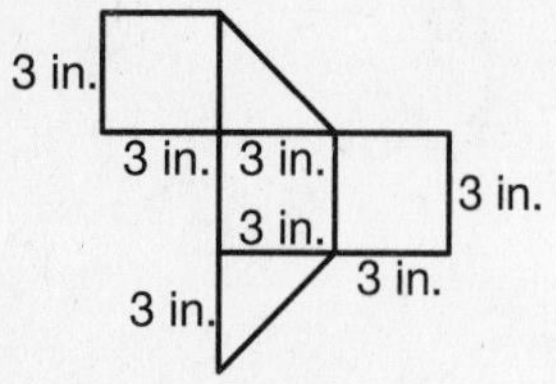

2. SA: ______________________

____

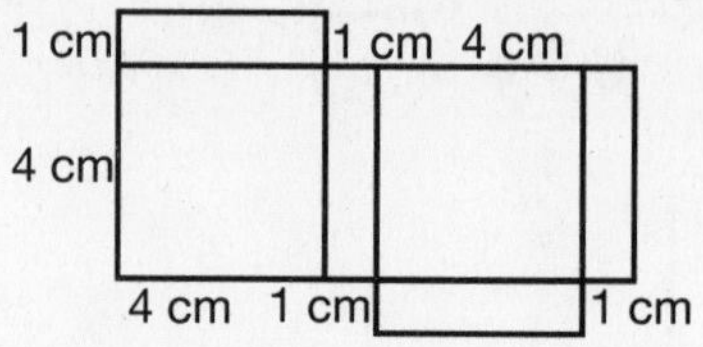

Draw an example of each. *(Lesson 11-1)*

3. Rectangular pyramid

4. Sphere

5. Cone

Mixed Review

6. *(10-7)* Find the missing side lengths. in the similar triangles

A = ________ *B* = ________

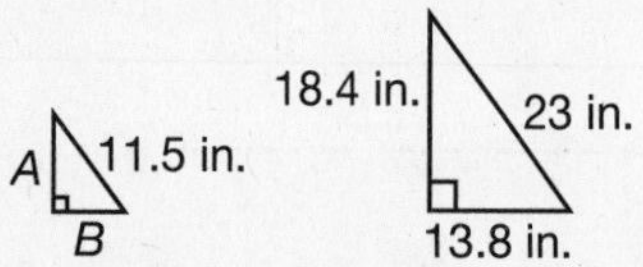

7. *(9-5)* Plot and label each point.

M (−2, 2)
A (3, 2)
T (2, −1)
H (−1, −1)

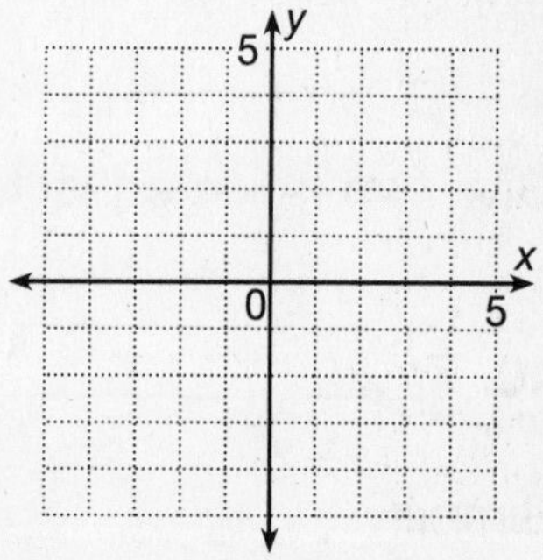

8. *(8-7)* Connect the points in Exercise 7. Classify the figure in as many ways as possible.

____

Simplify.

9. *(7-5)* $\frac{3}{4} \div \frac{5}{2}$ ________

10. *(7-3)* $3\frac{1}{10} \times 6$ ________

11. *(6-6)* $5\frac{5}{6} - 3\frac{5}{7}$ ________

12. *(6-2)* $\frac{2}{5} + \frac{3}{10}$ ________

13. *(7-6)* Bob said, "I'm thinking of a number. If I divide it by $1\frac{3}{4}$, I get $\frac{4}{7}$." What number is Bob thinking of? ________

Name ______________________

Daily Review
11-4

Daily Cumulative Review

Find the surface area. *(Lesson 11-3)*

1. ________

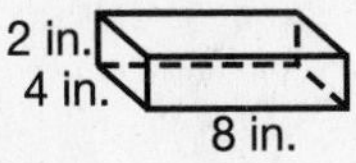

2. ________

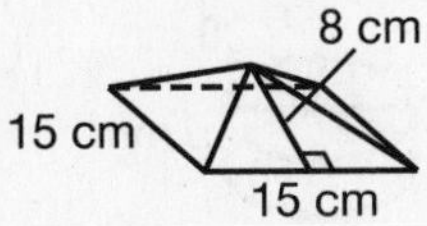

3. ________

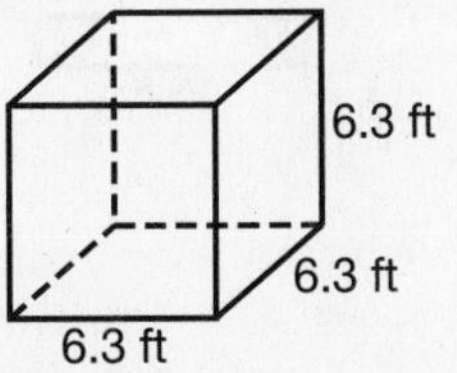

4. ________

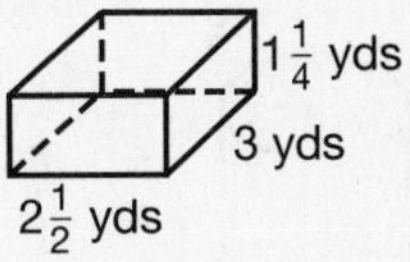

State the number of faces. Then classify each face and find the total surface area. *(Lesson 11-2)*

5. ______________________

SA: ______________________

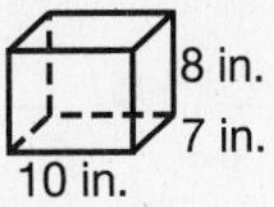

6. ______________________

SA: ______________________

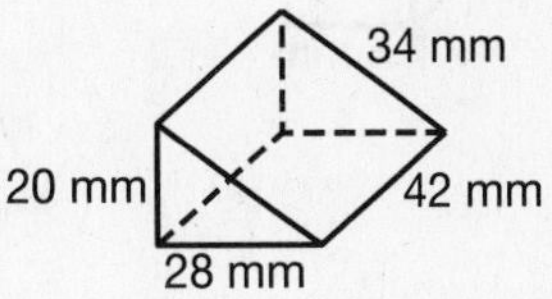

Mixed Review

Find the unit rate.

7. $\frac{\$304}{38 \text{ hours}}$ ________ *(10-6)*

8. $\frac{6 \text{ pt}}{2 \text{ min}}$ ________ *(10-6)*

9. $\frac{400 \text{ mi}}{8 \text{ hr}}$ ________ *(10-6)*

Simplify.

10. $9 \div \frac{3}{7}$ *(7-4)* ________

11. $3\frac{19}{22} + 5\frac{1}{2}$ *(6-5)* ________

12. $5 \times 3\frac{1}{8}$ *(7-2)* ________

Find the prime factorization.

13. 540 *(5-2)* ________

14. 280 *(5-2)* ________

15. 148 *(5-2)* ________

16. Divide. 871.2 ÷ 16.5 *(3-11)* ________

17. Simplify. 3.275 + 7.541 + 8.3984 *(3-6)* ________

Name ____________________

Daily Review
11-5

Daily Cumulative Review

Find the surface area of each cylinder. Use 3.14 for π. *(Lesson 11-4)*

1. ________ **2.** ________ **3.** ________ **4.** ________

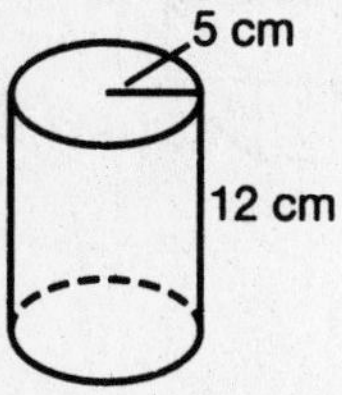

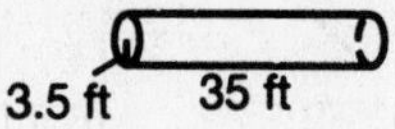

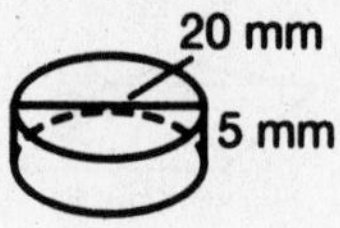

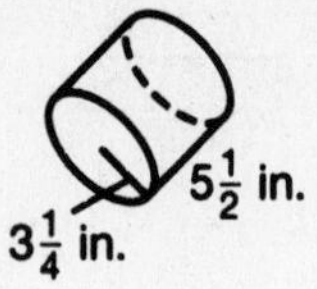

Find the surface area. *(Lesson 11-3)*

5. ________ **6.** ________ **7.** ________ **8.** ________

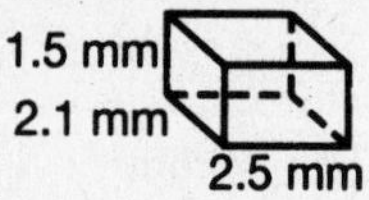

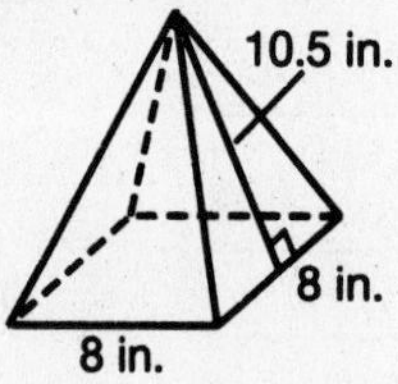

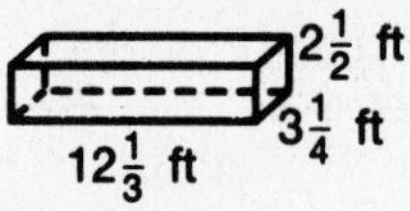

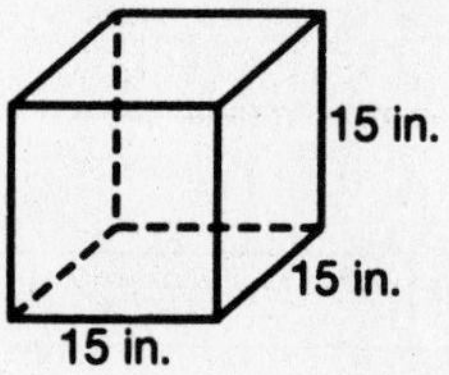

Mixed Review

9. *(10-1)* In a recent survey, 12 out of 18 students liked Brand A over Brand B. Write this ratio in lowest terms. ________

10. *(8-5)* Classify a triangle with sides of length 12 yd, 14 yd, and 12 yd.

____

Estimate.

11. *(7-1)* $11\frac{5}{6} \times 10\frac{2}{9}$ ________

12. *(6-4)* $34\frac{3}{5} - 27\frac{19}{20}$ ________

13. *(3-5)* \$95.86 − \$51.02 ________

14. *(2-6)* 7265 − 2105 ________

15. *(2-3)* Order from least to greatest.

38,280; 38,276; 38,308; 38,380 ____________________

16. *(1-4)* The following data set shows the scores on a 25 point quiz. Make a line plot for the data.

20, 18, 23, 24, 19, 18, 24, 25, 18,
17, 22, 24, 18, 21, 17, 25, 23, 18

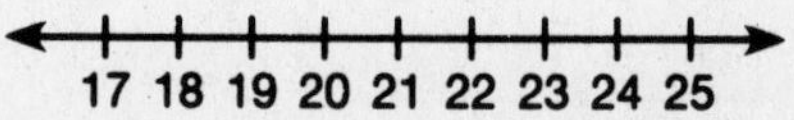

Name ____________________

Daily Review 11-6

Daily Cumulative Review

Use the three-dimensional figure. *(Lesson 11-5)*

1. Each cube in the solid is 3 cm by 3 cm by 3 cm. There are no hidden cubes.

a. How many cubes are in the solid? ________

b. How tall is the solid at its highest point? ________

c. How wide is the solid at its widest point? ________

Given the radius and height of each cylinder, find the surface area. Use 3.14 for π. *(Lesson 11-4)*

2. $r = 4.6$, $h = 12$

SA ≈ ________

3. $r = 11$, $h = 6$

SA ≈ ________

4. $r = 9.1$, $h = 30$

SA ≈ ________

Mixed Review

5. *(11-1)* How many vertices, edges, and faces does the solid have?

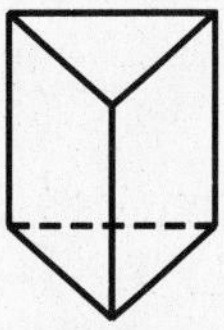

V: ________ *E*: ________ *F*: ________

For Exercises 6-8, Use the bar graph.

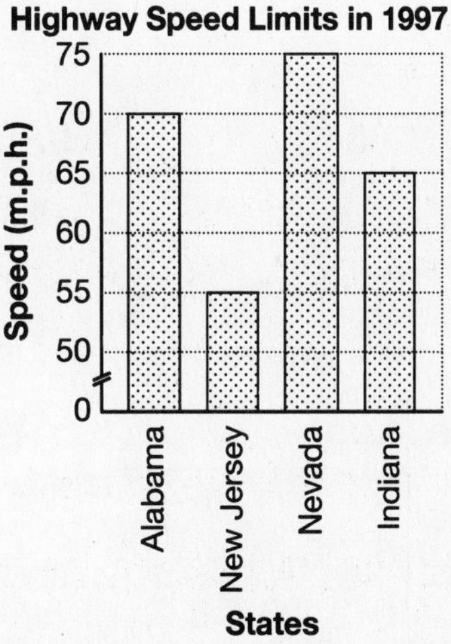

6. *(10-3)* Give a rate that uses the number 75.

State: ________ Rate: ________

7. *(10-3)* Give three different rates that describe the speed limit in Alabama.

____

8. *(10-3)* Use the speed limit in Nevada to give a rate that compares a distance to $\frac{1}{3}$ hour. ________

9. *(5-6)* Write $9\frac{1}{8}$ as an improper fraction.

____

10. *(4-3)* Convert.

833.6 oz = ________ lb.

Name ______________________________

Daily Review
11-7

Daily Cumulative Review

Find the volume of each solid. *(Lesson 11-6)*

1. ____________ **2.** ____________ **3.** ____________

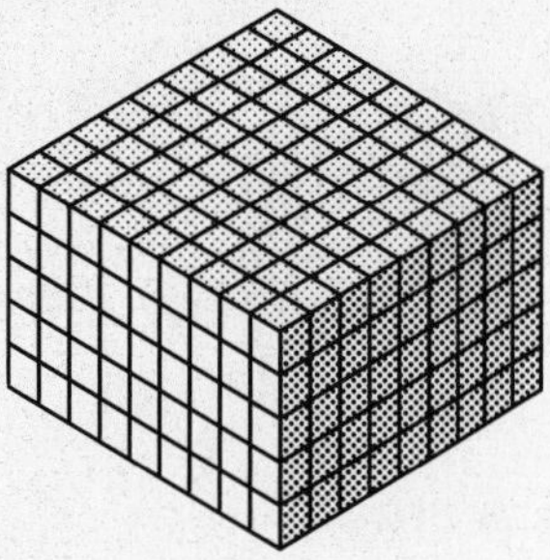

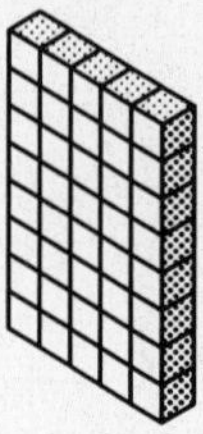

Draw the front, side, and top view of this solid. *(Lesson 11-5)*

4.

Mixed Review

Compare using >, <, or =.

5. *(5-8)* $\frac{7}{11}$ ◯ $\frac{11}{12}$ **6.** *(3-3)* 6.823 ◯ 6.283 **7.** *(2-4)* 4^4 ◯ 3^5

Simplify.

8. *(3-10)* 17.64 ÷ 63 ________

9. *(3-9)* 0.4 × 38.6 ________

10. *(2-5)* 25 × 39 × 40 ________

11. *(1-9)* Identify the outlier. ________

Stem	Leaf
1	0
4	5 7 8
5	0 2 2 3 5 8 9
6	0 1

12. *(1-8)* Find the mean of the data in Exercise 11.

____

13. *(9-6)* Plot the image of the quadrilateral *GHIJ* translated 3 units right and 2 units down.

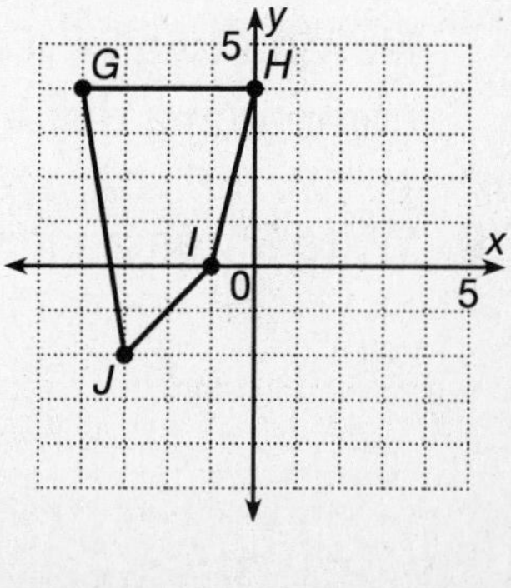

Name ____________________

Daily Review 12-1

Daily Cumulative Review

Find the volume of each solid. *(Lesson 11-7)*

1. ________

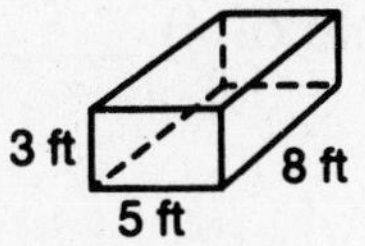

2. ________

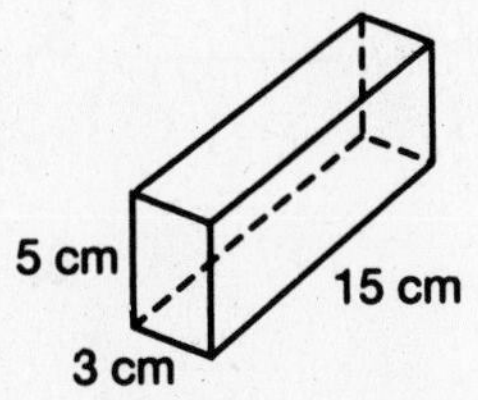

3. ________

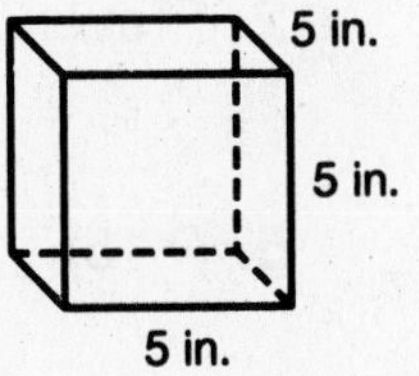

4. ________

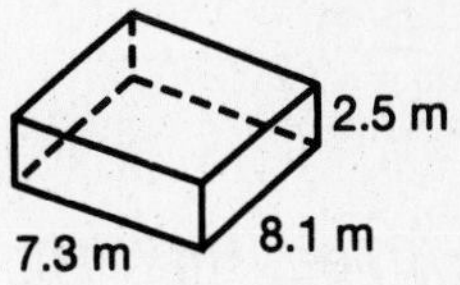

Find the volume of each solid. *(Lesson 11-6)*

5. ________

6. ________

7. ________

Mixed Review

8. Find the surface area of the cylinder shown below. Use 3.14 for π.
(11-4)

____

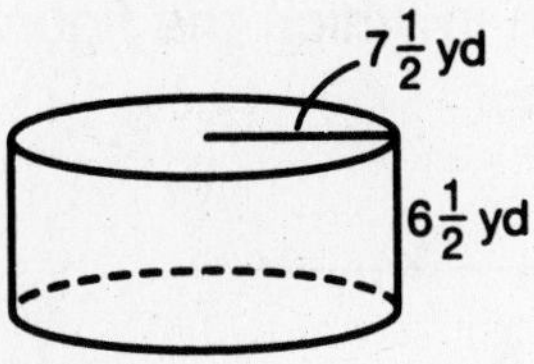

9. Give the shaded part of the figure as a percent, fraction, and decimal.
(10-10)

Percent: ________

Fraction: ________

Decimal: ________

Simplify.

10. $-12 \div (-3)$
(9-4)

____

11. $8 - 15$
(9-3)

____

12. $-12 + (-12)$
(9-2)

____

13. $\frac{4}{5} \div 2\frac{1}{5}$
(7-5)

____

14. $10\frac{1}{8} + 7\frac{7}{8}$
(6-5)

____

15. $\frac{13}{15} - \frac{3}{10}$
(6-2)

____

16. $6.53 + 20.194$
(3-6)

____

17. 70×800
(2-5)

____

Name ______________________________

Daily Review
12-2

Daily Cumulative Review

A set of 15 cards is labeled 1 through 15. Suppose you choose one card at random. Find the probability of each event. *(Lesson 12-1)*

1. $P(3)$ ______ **2.** P(even number) ______ **3.** P(multiple of 4) ______

4. P(less than 10) ______ **5.** $P(15)$ ______ **6.** P(multiple of 5) ______

Find the volume of each solid. *(Lesson 11-7)*

7. __________ **8.** __________ **9.** __________ **10.** __________

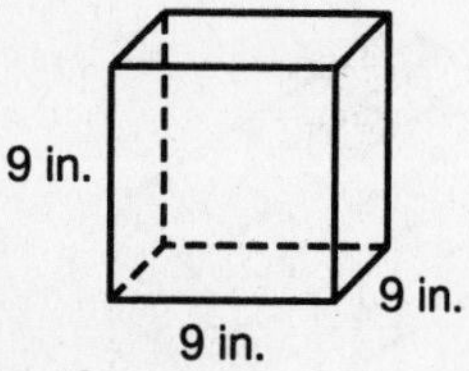

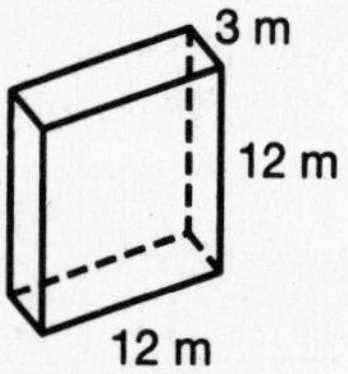

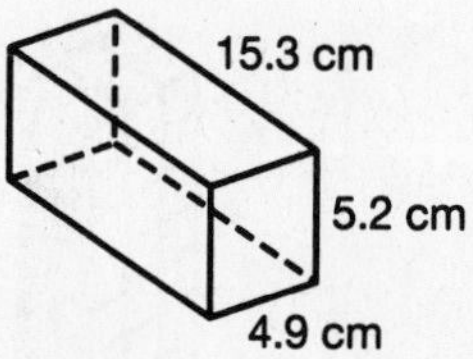

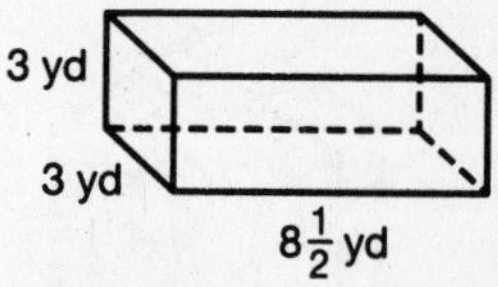

Mixed Review

11. Find the surface area of the prism in Exercise 8.
(11-3)

____

12. Solve the proportion $\frac{30}{x} = \frac{20}{22}$
(10-5)

$x =$ __________

13. Graph $y = 3 - x$
(9-7)

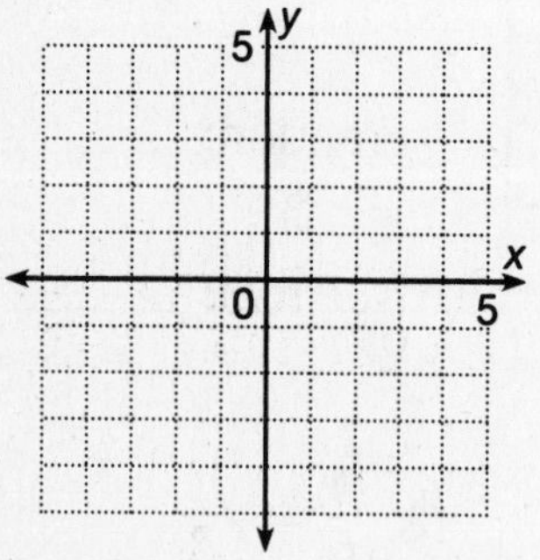

14. Estimate the number of degrees and state the direction in which the figure has been rotated.
(8-9)

____

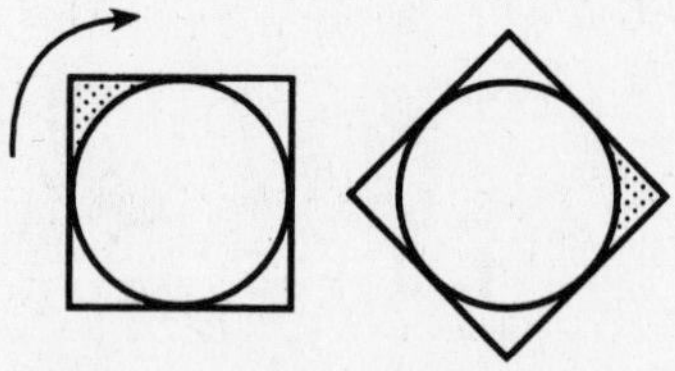

Solve.

15. $2\frac{1}{3}x = 8\frac{1}{6}$
(7-6)

16. $k - \frac{5}{6} = \frac{1}{12}$
(6-3)

17. $\frac{m}{2.901} = 6$
(3-12)

18. $p + \$18.03 = \$21$
(3-7)

__________ __________ __________ __________

Name ______________________________

Daily Review 12-3

Daily Cumulative Review

Use the data recorded in the chart for Exercises 1–3. *(Lesson 12-2)*

Trial	1	2	3	4	5	6	7	8
Outcome	blue	red	yellow	red	red	blue	yellow	green

1. How many different outcomes were there? ________

2. How many times was the outcome blue? ________

3. What is the probability of the outcome being red? ______

There are 10 cards that spell out S U M M E R T I M E. Suppose you choose one card. Find the probability of the event. *(Lesson 12-1)*

4. *P*(M) ______ **5.** *P*(consonant) ______ **6.** *P*(vowel) ______

Mixed Review

7. Classify the solid. *(11-1)*

____

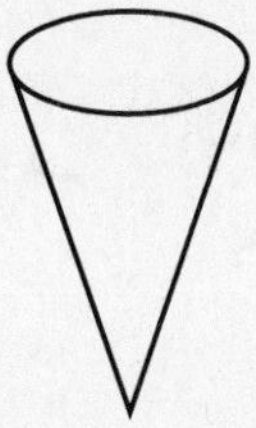

8. Find the total amount. *(10-11)*

55% of ______ is 47.3

Compare using <, >, or =.

9. -12 ◯ -10 *(9-1)* **10.** $\frac{2}{5}$ ◯ $\frac{2}{9}$ *(5-8)* **11.** 4^3 ◯ 3^4 *(2-4)* **12.** 6.03 ◯ 6.030 *(3-3)*

13. Each class period is 50 minutes. On Friday each period is shortened *x* minutes so they are 40 minutes. Write an equation for this situation. *(2-12)*

____

14. Find the next three numbers in this pattern. *(2-9)*

1, 3, 9, 27, 81, ______, ______, ______

Name ______________________________

Daily Review
12-4

Daily Cumulative Review

Suppose you drop a token on each shape in Exercises 1–4. Find the probability of the token landing on the shaded area. *(Lesson 12-3)*

1. ____________

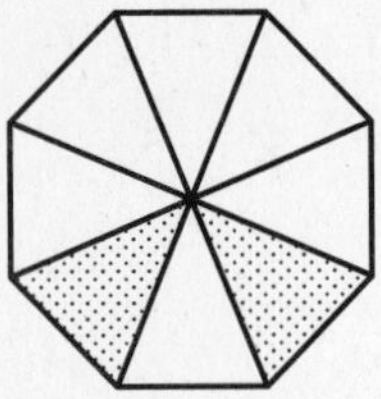

2. ____________

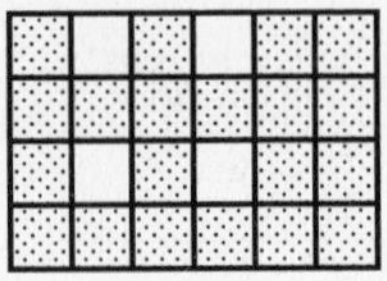

3. ____________

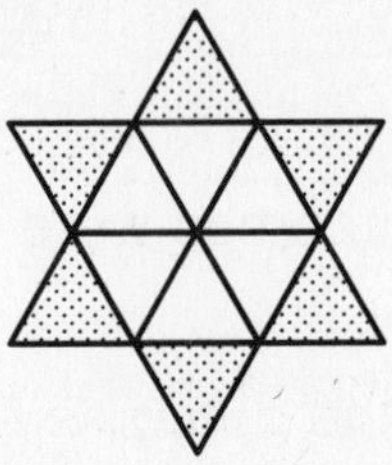

4. ____________

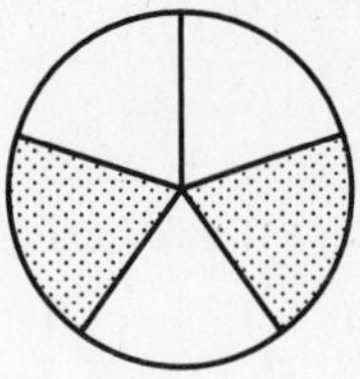

Make predictions using the chart for Exercises 5–7 *(Lesson 12-2)*

Trial	1	2	3	4	5	6	7	8
Outcome	square	circle	circle	triangle	square	triangle	circle	triangle

5. How many different outcomes were there? __________

6. What is the probability of the outcome being a square? ______

7. What is the probability of the outcome being a pentagon? __________

Mixed Review

8. *(11-7)* Find the volume of a rectangular prism which has a length of 21 in., a width of 11 in., and a depth of 8 in. ____________

9. *(10-2)* Give three equal ratios. A pet store has 4 cats for every 3 dogs. ____________

10. *(8-5)* Classify the triangle that has sides of length 8 ft, 7 ft, 6 ft.____________

11. *(5-5)* Write $\frac{16}{24}$ as a fraction in lowest terms.

____

12. *(4-8)* Find the area of a circle rounded to the nearest tenth whose circumference is 24.1 yd.

____

13. *(1-8)* Find the mean of the data set.
6, 4, 8, 7, 5, 6, 8, 3, 9, 9, 4, 3, 9, 4, 5

Mean ____________

Name ______________________________

Daily Review
12-5

Daily Cumulative Review

Draw a tree diagram for the situation. *(Lesson 12-4)*

1. A combo meal at a local restaurant has the following choices: pick one meat from beef, pork, chicken; and pick one side-dish from coleslaw, french fries, or beans.

Suppose you drop a token on each shape. To the nearest percent, find the probability of the token landing on the shaded area. *(Lesson 12-3)*

2. ________ 3. ________ 4. ________ 5. ________

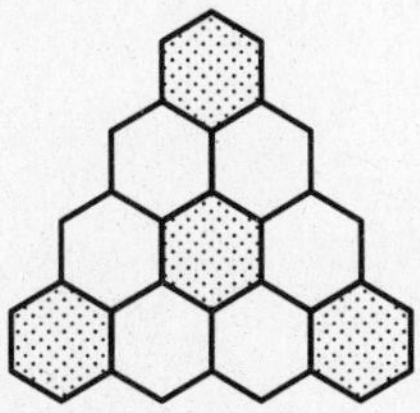

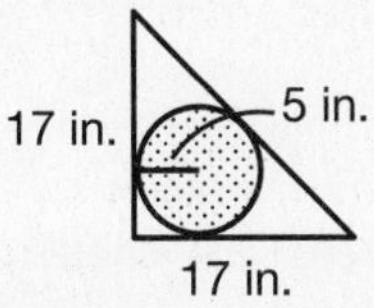

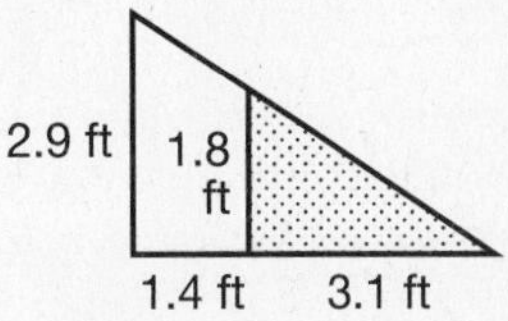

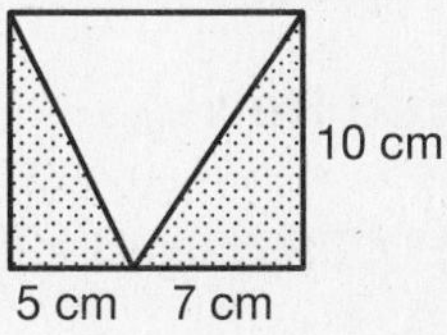

Mixed Review

6. Find the missing side lengths. in the similar triangles. *(10-7)*

$A =$ ________ $B =$ ________

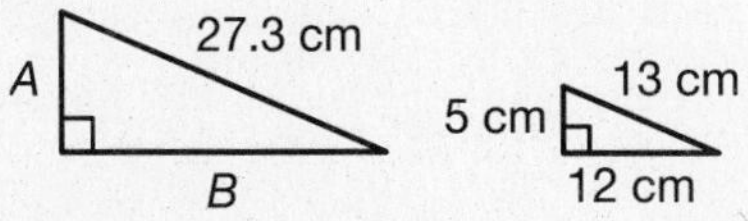

7. Name the polygon that is tessellated in Exercise 2. *(8-10)*

____

Simplify.

8. $9 \div 1\frac{5}{9}$ *(7-4)* ________

9. $6\frac{3}{5} \times 10$ *(7-2)* ________

10. $120.48 \div 48$ *(3-10)* ________

11. 9×4.713 *(3-8)* ________

12. Write 6,305,120 in words. *(2-1)*

____

____

Name ______________________________

Daily Review
12-6

Daily Cumulative Review

Six cards numbered 1, 2, 3, 4, 5, and 6 are in a paper bag. Each time a card is drawn it is replaced. Find the probability of each event. *(Lesson 12-5)*

1. *P*(even, then even) ___ **2.** *P*(even, then odd) ___ **3.** *P*(odd, even, odd) ___

Draw a tree diagram for the following situation. *(Lesson 12-4)*

4. Jane has 2 skirts, 2 vests, and 3 blouses to make an outfit. (Use Skirt A, Skirt B, Vest A, Vest B, Blouse A, Blouse B, Blouse C)

5. How many different outfits are possible?

____

Mixed Review

6. Is 78 divisible by 4? ________
(5-1)

7. Draw an example of $\overline{AB}$.
(8-1)

8. The bar graph shows Jim's clothing selections. What fraction of the clothes are T-shirts or sweatshirts?
(6-1)

____

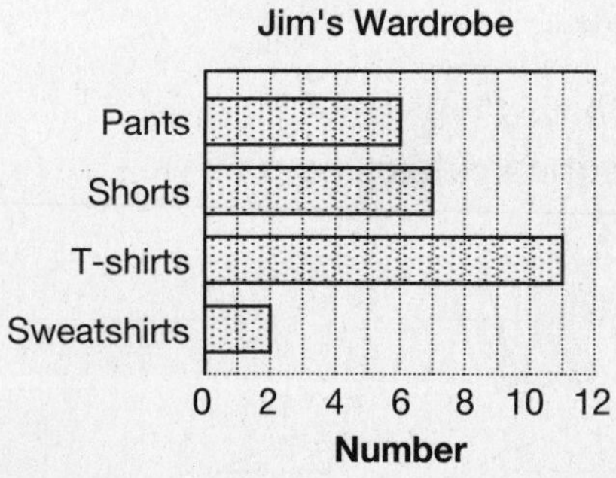

9. Use a protractor to measure the angle. Then classify the angle.
(8-3)

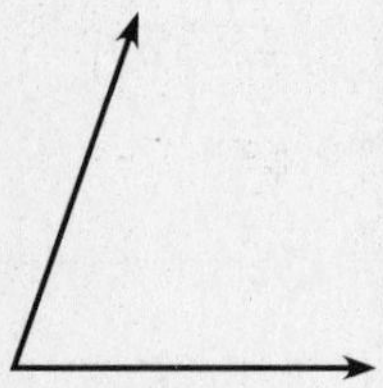

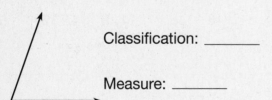

Classification: ________

Measure: ________

10. Measure the nail to the nearest centimeter. ________
(3-2)

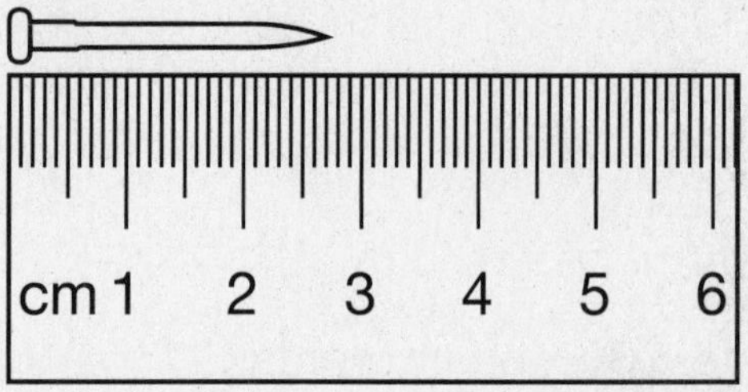

Name ____________________

Daily Review 1-1

Daily Cumulative Review

Mixed Review *(From Last Year)*

Write each number in word form.

1. 2,083,706 two million, eighty three-thousand, seven hundred six

2. 417,209,512 four hundred seventeen million, two hundred nine thousand, five hundred twelve

Find each product. Estimate to check.

3. 216×5 = 1,080 4. 37×46 = 1,702 5. 72×39 = 2,808 6. 548×17 = 9,316

Classify each triangle as equilateral, isosceles, or scalene.

7. Scalene

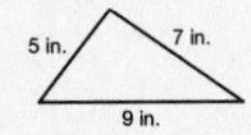

8. Equilateral

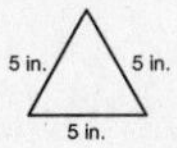

9. Isosceles

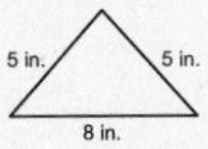

10. Four classes worked together and earned $219 on a newspaper drive. They agreed to split the money equally. How much should each class get? $54.75

11. One class collected 843 pounds of newspaper. Another class collected 971 pounds. How much more did the second class collect than the first one? 128 pounds

12. If each of 24 students in one class worked 6 hours on the newspaper drive, how many hours did the class work altogether? 144 hours

Name ____________________

Daily Review 1-2

Daily Cumulative Review

Use the Expenses graph for 1–5 *(Lesson 1-1)*

1. What is the most costly expense for Mathco? Salaries
2. For each $100 spent, how much did Mathco spend on computers? $15
3. Which expense is about 5 times as much as the telephone expense? Rent
4. For each $100 spent, how much more is spent on utilities and salaries than on rent? $30
5. For each $500 spent, how much would be spent on telephones? $25

Mathco Expenses

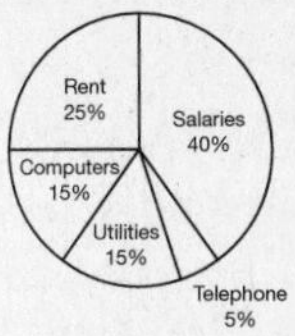

Mixed Review *(From Last Year)*

Find each sum or difference. Then estimate to check.

6. $465 + 279$ = 744 7. $803 - 214$ = 589 8. $928 - 327$ = 601 9. $507 + 236$ = 743

Find each sum or difference. Simplify.

10. $\frac{11}{12} - \frac{5}{12}$ = $\frac{1}{2}$ 11. $\frac{3}{5} + \frac{4}{5}$ = $1\frac{2}{5}$ 12. $\frac{9}{10} - \frac{3}{10}$ = $\frac{3}{5}$

Find the perimeter and area of each room.

13.

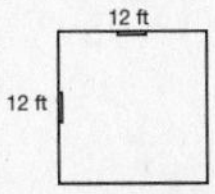

P = 48 ft
A = 144 ft^2

14.

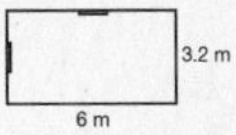

P = 18.4 m
A = 19.2 m^2

15. If a square yard of carpet costs $5.75, how much would it cost to carpet a room that has an area of 35 square yards? $201.25

Name ____________________

Daily Review 1-3

Daily Cumulative Review

Use the Miles Driven bar graph for Exercises 1–4. *(Lesson 1-2)*

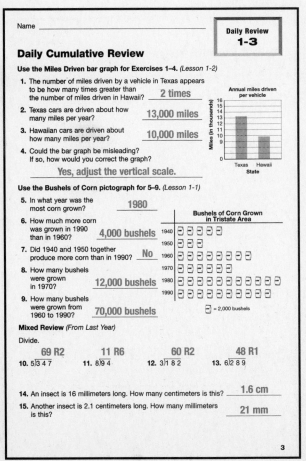

1. The number of miles driven by a vehicle in Texas appears to be how many times greater than the number of miles driven in Hawaii? 2 times
2. Texas cars are driven about how many miles per year? 13,000 miles
3. Hawaiian cars are driven about how many miles per year? 10,000 miles
4. Could the bar graph be misleading? If so, how would you correct the graph? Yes, adjust the vertical scale.

Annual miles driven per vehicle

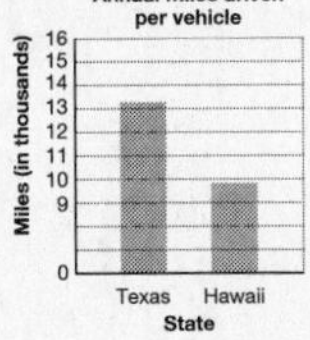

Use the Bushels of Corn pictograph for 5–9. *(Lesson 1-1)*

5. In what year was the most corn grown? 1980
6. How much more corn was grown in 1990 than in 1960? 4,000 bushels
7. Did 1940 and 1950 together produce more corn than in 1990? No
8. How many bushels were grown in 1970? 12,000 bushels
9. How many bushels were grown from 1960 to 1990? 70,000 bushels

Bushels of Corn Grown in Tristate Area

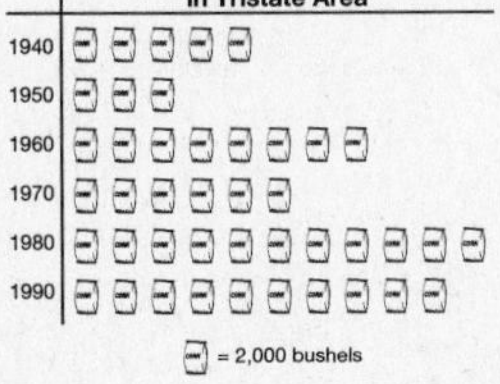

Mixed Review *(From Last Year)*

Divide.

10. $5\overline{)347}$ = 69 R2 11. $8\overline{)94}$ = 11 R6 12. $3\overline{)182}$ = 60 R2 13. $6\overline{)289}$ = 48 R1

14. An insect is 16 millimeters long. How many centimeters is this? 1.6 cm
15. Another insect is 2.1 centimeters long. How many millimeters is this? 21 mm

Name ____________________

Daily Review 1-4

Daily Cumulative Review

For each scatterplot, determine if there is a trend. If there is, describe the pattern of the data. *(Lesson 1-3)*

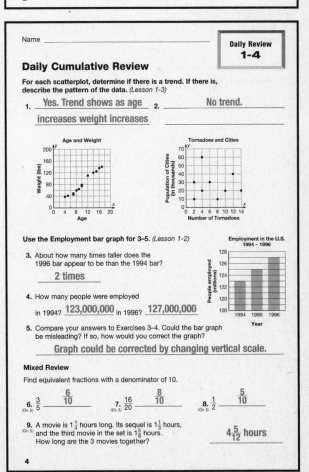

1. Yes. Trend shows as age increases weight increases 2. No trend.

Age and Weight

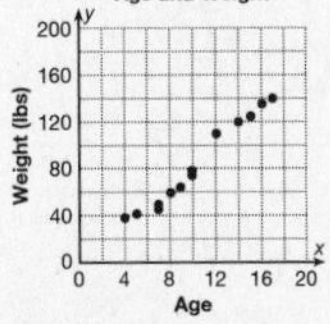

Tornadoes and Cities

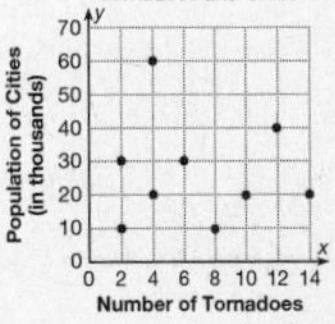

Use the Employment bar graph for 3–5. *(Lesson 1-2)*

3. About how many times taller does the 1996 bar appear to be than the 1994 bar? 2 times
4. How many people were employed in 1994? 123,000,000 in 1996? 127,000,000
5. Compare your answers to Exercises 3–4. Could the bar graph be misleading? If so, how would you correct the graph? Graph could be corrected by changing vertical scale.

Employment in the U.S. 1994 – 1996

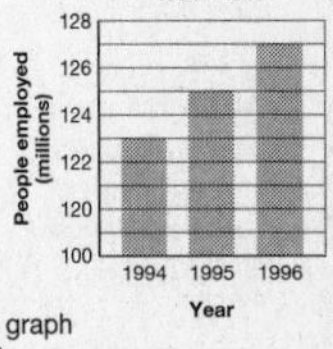

Mixed Review

Find equivalent fractions with a denominator of 10.

6. (Gr. 5) $\frac{3}{5}$ = $\frac{6}{10}$ 7. (Gr. 5) $\frac{16}{20}$ = $\frac{8}{10}$ 8. (Gr. 5) $\frac{1}{2}$ = $\frac{5}{10}$

9. (Gr. 5) A movie is $1\frac{1}{4}$ hours long. Its sequel is $1\frac{1}{3}$ hours, and the third movie in the set is $1\frac{5}{6}$ hours. How long are the 3 movies together? $4\frac{5}{12}$ hours

Name ______________________

Daily Review 1-5

Daily Cumulative Review

Make a frequency chart and line plot for the following data. *(Lesson 1-4)*

Hours of Television Students Watched Last Week:

10, 9, 14, 7, 12, 11, 8, 9, 12, 7

1. Frequency Chart

Hours of TV	Frequency
7	2
8	1
9	2
10	1
11	1
12	2
13	0
14	1

2. Line Plot

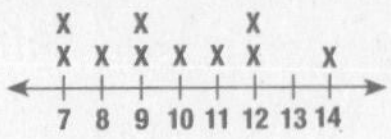

Give the approximate weight and price represented by each point in the scatterplot. *(Lesson 1-3)*

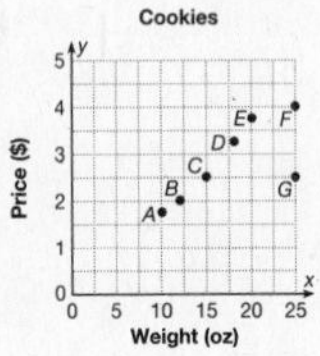

3. *A*: weight 10 oz price $1.75
4. *B*: weight 12 oz price $2
5. *E*: weight 20 oz price $3.75
6. *G*: weight 25 oz price $2.50

Mixed Review

Find each quotient.

7. 91 ÷ 7 (Gr. 5) 13
8. 75 ÷ 5 (Gr. 5) 15
9. 67 ÷ 2 (Gr. 5) 33.5
10. 124 ÷ 3 (Gr. 5) 41 R1

11. A factory packs 15 pens in a box. (Gr. 5) How many boxes will be needed for 1680 pens? 112

5

Name ______________________

Daily Review 1-6

Daily Cumulative Review

Use the data for Exercises 1 and 2. *(Lesson 1-5)*

1. Make a bar graph from the data showing the revenues of the leading U.S. telecommunication businesses in 1996.

Company	Billions of Revenue
A	$74.5
B	21.3
C	19.0
D	18.5

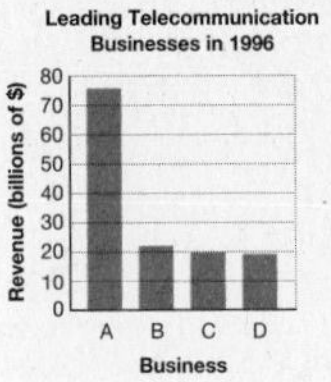

2. What is the range of the data for the revenues in Exercise 1? $56 billion

Record each set of data in a tally chart. *(Lesson 1-4)*

3. 15, 16, 16, 14, 13, 15, 16, 13 14, 15, 16, 14, 13, 15, 16

Number	Tally
13	|||
14	|||
15	||||
16	~~||||~~

4. 3, 5, 3, 6, 5, 3, 6, 7, 6, 3, 6, 7, 5, 3, 4

Number	Tally
3	~~||||~~
4	|
5	|||
6	||||
7	||

Mixed Review

5. (1-3) For the scatterplot shown, determine if there is a trend. If there is, describe the pattern of the data.

No trend

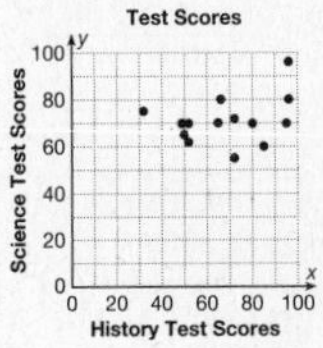

6. (Gr. 5) Write the fractions in order from least to greatest.

$\frac{3}{9}, \frac{3}{4}, \frac{3}{5}$ $\frac{3}{9}, \frac{3}{5}, \frac{3}{4}$

6

Name ______________________

Daily Review 1-7

Daily Cumulative Review

Use the stem-and-leaf diagram for Exercises 1–4. *(Lesson 1-6)*

Stem	Leaf
5	6 7 7
6	0 1 3 4 8 8
7	1 4 4 4 7 9
8	0 2 6

1. What is the range of the values? 30
2. What value appears most often? 74
3. How many times does the value 68 appear? 2
4. What is the largest number in the data that is less than 80? 79

Make a bar graph of the data. *(Lesson 1-5)*

5. The data shows the average shoe size for middle school age girls.

Age	Average Shoe Size
11	4
12	5.5
13	6.5
14	8

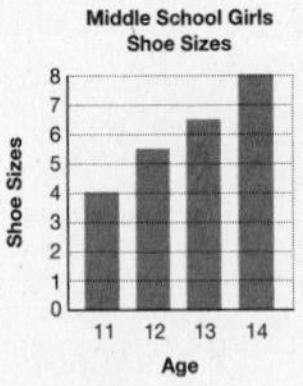

Mixed Review

6. (1-4) Make a line plot of the number of movies watched last week by a group of students.

Movies	Frequency
0	4
1	8
2	4
3	1

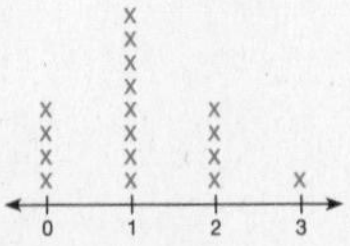

7. (1-2) About how many times taller does the bar showing Mr. Ortiz's sales appear to be than the bar showing Mr. Jones' sales? 2 times

Is the bar graph misleading? If so, how would you correct the graph?

No, graph scale is fine.

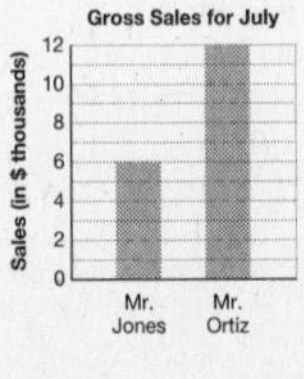

7

Name ______________________

Daily Review 1-8

Daily Cumulative Review

Find the median and mode(s). *(Lesson 1-7)*

1. median 19

mode(s) 18

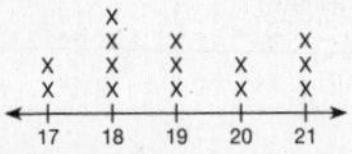

2. median 36

mode(s) 27 and 35

Stem	Leaf
2	7 7 9
3	0 3 5 5 7
4	2 5 8
5	3 5 6

3. 14, 20, 21, 23, 25, 20, 15, 19, 21, 20, 33, 18, 41, 28, 26, 36, 29

median 21 mode(s) 20

Make a stem-and-leaf diagram. *(Lesson 1-6)*

4. Make a stem-and-leaf diagram of the data showing the number of videos owned by some students.

6, 12, 9, 3, 17, 24, 0, 4, 10, 20, 13, 4, 9, 15

Stem	Leaf
0	0 3 4 4 6 9 9
1	0 2 3 5 7
2	0 4

Mixed Review

5. (1-5) What is the range of the data for Exercise 3? 27

Use the scatterplot for Exercises 6 and 7.

6. (1-3) How many people exercised 7 hours per week? 2

7. (1-3) For the scatterplot shown, determine if there is a trend. If there is, describe the pattern.

The trend indicates that as you increase your exercise you lose more weight.

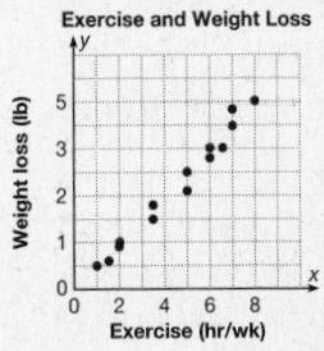

8. (Gr. 5) Write $\frac{3}{10}$ as a percent. 30%

8

Name ______________________

Daily Review 1-9

Daily Cumulative Review

Find the mean of each set of data. *(Lesson 1-8)*

1. mean 14

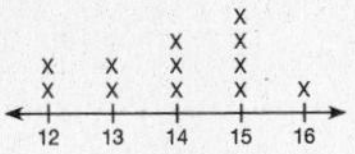

2. mean 19

Stem	Leaf
0	6 6 7
1	0 1 4 7 8 8
2	0 0 1 4 4 6 7 9
3	0 3

3. mean 46

23, 28, 36, 36, 42, 42, 49, 64, 94

Find the median and mode(s) of each data set. *(Lesson 1-7)*

4. median 7
mode(s) 10

7, 4, 9, 8, 6, 8, 7, 3, 10, 10, 5, 4, 10

5. median 47
mode(s) 43 and 51

Stem	Leaf
3	4 7 8
4	0 1 3 3 7 9
5	1 1 4 6
6	0 1

Mixed Review

6. *(1-6)* Make a stem-and-leaf diagram of the data showing the number of members of local scout troops.

40, 74, 31, 70, 66, 53, 49, 70, 35, 57, 62, 39

Stem	Leaf
3	1 5 9
4	0 9
5	3 7
6	2 6
7	0 0 4

Use the Children in U.S. Families graph to answer Exercises 7 and 8.

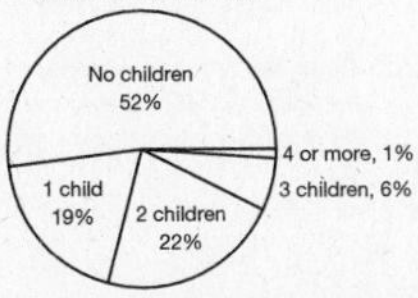

7. *(1-1)* What category represents about $\frac{1}{2}$ of U.S. families? No children

8. *(1-1)* What percent of familes have 2 or more children? 29%

Name ______________________

Daily Review 2-1

Daily Cumulative Review

Identify the outlier in each data set. *(Lesson 1-9)*

1. 85

22, 35, 21, 32, 85, 28, 30, 29

2. 31

Stem	Leaf
3	1
4	7 9 9 8 9
5	0 1 1 2 5 8 9
6	0 1

3. 15

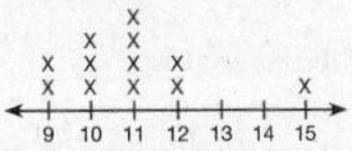

Find the mean of each set of data. *(Lesson 1-8)*

4. 41, 18, 62, 24, 38, 72, 81, 48

5. 87, 102, 98, 92, 79, 80, 88, 82, 90, 93 89.1

Mixed Review

6. *(1-4)* Make a line plot for 12, 21, 17, 14, 19, 12, 17, 14, 21, 17, 14, 13

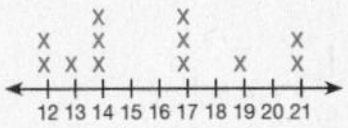

7. *(1-7)* Find the median and mode(s) for the data in Exercise 6.
median 15.5 mode 14 and 17

Use the scatterplot for Exercises 8 and 9.

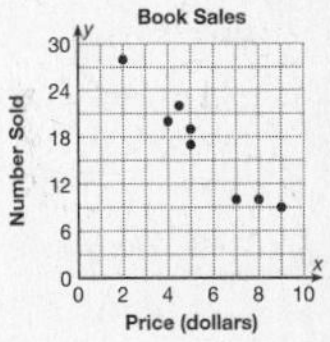

8. *(1-3)* Is there a trend? If so, describe the pattern of data.
As price increases, the number sold decreases.

9. *(1-3)* At what prices do the number of books sold remain the same? 7 and 8 dollars

Name ______________________

Daily Review 2-2

Daily Cumulative Review

Write the number in words. *(Lesson 2-1)*

1. 6,895 six thousand, eight hundred ninety-five

2. 943,201 nine hundred forty-three thousand, two hundred one

3. 51,207,050 fifty-one million, two hundred seven thousand, fifty

Identify the outlier in each data set. *(Lesson 1-9)*

4. 100, 125, 200, 400, 225, 210 400

5. 80

Stem	Leaf
2	0 0 2 2 5
3	0 2 6 7
4	0 5 6 7
8	0

Mixed Review

6. *(1-8)* Using the table, find the mean ACT score.
21

7. *(1-7)* Using the table, find the median and mode(s).
median 21 mode(s) 21

Midville High School ACT Scores			
14	17	21	30
22	20	21	22
25	15	24	21

Use the pictograph for Exercises 8 and 9.

8. *(1-1)* Which grade filled the most recycling bins?
Grade 7

9. *(1-1)* How many recycling bins did Grade 8 fill?
20 bins

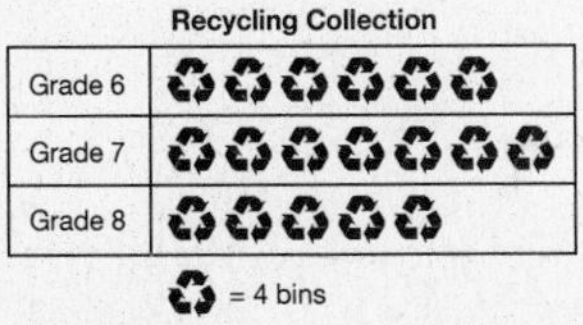

Name ______________________

Daily Review 2-3

Daily Cumulative Review

Round to the given place. *(Lesson 2-2)*

1. 47,621,920; ten millions
50,000,000

2. 342,392; ten thousands
340,000

3. 1,591,327; tens
1,591,330

4. 73,273,736,903; hundred millions
73,300,000,000

Write each number in standard form. *(Lesson 2-1)*

5. 3 million 3,000,000

6. 27 thousand 27,000

7. six billion, seven hundred twenty-three million, nine hundred sixteen thousand
6,723,916,000

8. four million, nineteen thousand, two hundred fifty-seven
4,019,257

Mixed Review

Use the table at the right to answer Exercises 9–12.

1996 Population of Selected States (thousands)	
WA	5,533
AR	2,510
SC	3,699
MN	4,658
WY	481
KY	3,884

9. *(1-9)* Identify the outlier. 481,000

10. *(1-8)* Find the mean with and without the outlier. Round to the nearest one.
with 3,460,833 without 4,056,800

11. *(1-7)* Find the median with and without the outlier.
with 3,791,500 without 3,884,000

12. *(1-5)* What is the range of the data? 5,052,000

Name ____________________

Daily Review 2-4

Daily Cumulative Review

Order each group of numbers from least to greatest. *(Lesson 2-3)*

1. 2,000; 70,000; 300; 80 **80; 300; 2,000; 70,000**
2. 2,123; 2,213; 2,312; 2,231 **2,123; 2,213; 2,231; 2,312**
3. 72,270; 73,100; 72,200; 72,160 **72,160; 72,200; 72,270; 73,100**
4. 10 billion, 100 million, 10 thousand **10 thousand, 100 million, 10 billion**

In 1996 the United States population was 265,283,783. Round the population to the given place. *(Lesson 2-2)*

5. thousands **265,284,000** 6. millions **265,000,000**
7. hundred thousands **265,300,000** 8. hundred millions **300,000,000**

Mixed Review

9. (2-1) Write the 1996 United States population (given above) in word form.
two hundred sixty-five million, two hundred eighty-three thousand, seven hundred eighty-three

10. (2-1) Write 6 trillion in standard form.
6,000,000,000,000

Use the Rainfall graph for Exercises 11 and 12.

11. (1-1) How many inches of rain did Maysville receive in May 1995? **7.5 in.** May 1996? **10 in.**

12. (1-2) Could the bar graph be misleading? If so, how would you correct the graph?
Yes. It looks like the 1996 rainfall was twice the 1995 rainfall. Change the vertical scale.

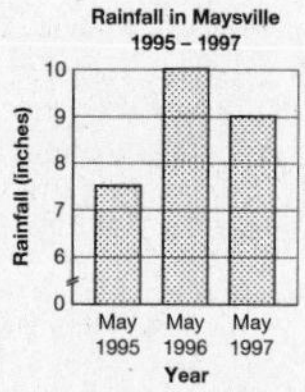

Name ____________________

Daily Review 2-5

Daily Cumulative Review

In Exercises 1–4, answer the questions about exponents. *(Lesson 2-4)*

1. What is the base of 11^4? **11**
2. What is the power of 11^4? **4**
3. What is the exponent of 11^4? **4**
4. Use a calculator to write 11^4 in standard form. **14,641**

Order each group of numbers from greatest to least. *(Lesson 2-3)*

5. 57,000; 56,940; 57,010 **57,010; 57,000; 56,940**
6. 2,222; 22,222; 22; 222 **22,222; 2,222; 222; 22**
7. 66,606; 66,000; 66,600; 60,000 **66,606; 66,600; 66,000; 60,000**
8. 12 thousand; 12 million; 120,000 **12 million; 120,000; 12 thousand**

Mixed Review

9. (2-1) In 1996 Chicago O'Hare Airport had 69,133,189 arrivals and departures. Write this number in words.
sixty-nine million, one hundred thirty-three thousand, one hundred eighty-nine

10. (1-1) Round the number given in Exercise 9 to the nearest million. **69,000,000**

Exercises 11 and 12 refer to the scatterplot on the right which shows the number of boys and girls in several classes.

11. (1-3) Which point represents the class with the most boys? **C** most girls? **G**

12. (1-3) Three classes have the same number of boys. How many boys are in each of these classes?
12

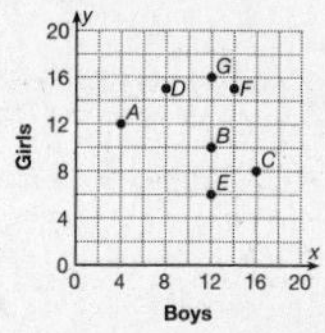

Name ____________________

Daily Review 2-6

Daily Cumulative Review

Simplify using mental math. *(Lesson 2-5)*

1. 30×80 **2400** 2. $20 \times 53 \times 50$ **53,000** 3. $3{,}600 \div 9$ **400**
4. $152 + 47$ **199** 5. $725 + 523 + 275$ **1,523** 6. $152 - 98$ **54**
7. $2{,}600 \div 13$ **200** 8. $287 - 195$ **92** 9. 69×4 **276**

Compare using <, >, or =. *(Lesson 2-4)*

10. 3^4 (>) 4^3 11. 4^7 (<) 4^8 12. 4^3 (=) $4 \times 4 \times 4$
13. 10^5 (>) 5×10 14. 10^5 (>) $10 + 10 + 10 + 10 + 10$
15. 6^3 (>) $3 \times 3 \times 3 \times 3$

Mixed Review

16. (2-3) One major company made 22,641,502 bolts one year. Another company made 21,963,212 bolts during the same year. Compare these numbers using < or >.
22,641,502 > 21,963,212

17. (2-1) Write $12,000,000,000 in word form **twelve billion** number-word form **12 billion**

18. (1-5) Make a bar graph showing the number of dogs registered in the American Kennel Club.

Dog	Thousands Registered in 1996
Golden Retriever	69
Beagle	57
Dalmation	33
Collie	13
Dachshund	48

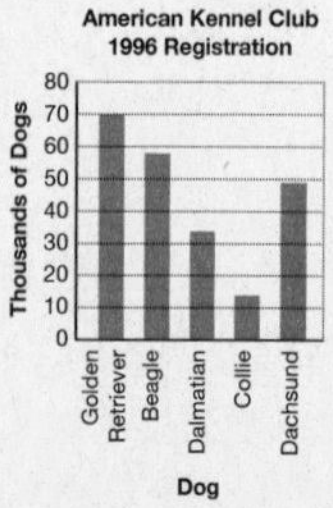

Name ____________________

Daily Review 2-7

Daily Cumulative Review

Estimate the following sums and differences. *(Lesson 2-6)*
Possible answers are given.

1. $28{,}724 + 93{,}201$ **122,000** 2. $37{,}723 - 11{,}389$ **26,300** 3. $47 + 51 + 53$ **150**
4. $285 + 315 + 306$ **900** 5. $723{,}468 + 316{,}728$ **1,000,000** 6. $827{,}157 - 362{,}206$ **465,000**

Simplify using mental math. *(Lesson 2-5)*

7. 70×80 **560** 8. $272 + 27$ **299** 9. $2 \times 23 \times 5$ **230**
10. $3{,}200 \div 40$ **80** 11. $53{,}625 - 200$ **53,425** 12. 37×9 **333**
13. $491 + 209$ **700** 14. $48{,}000 \div 120$ **400** 15. 21×7 **147**

Mixed Review

16. (2-4) Compare using <, >, or =. 4^3 (<) 3^4
17. (2-3) Compare using <, >, or =. 5,000,000,000 (<) 5 trillion
18. (2-2) Round 36,852,706,079,821 to the nearest ten thousand.
36,852,706,080,000
19. (2-1) Write six million, seven hundred twenty thousand, two hundred three in standard form. **6,720,203**
20. (1-8) Find the mean, median, and mode(s) of the following set of data:

33, 38, 36, 36, 42, 49, 64, 73, 84

mean **50.6** median **42** mode(s) **36**

Name ______________________

Daily Review 2-8

Daily Cumulative Review

Estimate the following products and quotients. *(Lesson 2-7)*

1. 48 × 37 2000 2. 78 × 51 4000 3. 657 × 11 7000

4. 152 ÷ 29 5 5. 796 ÷ 192 4 6. 6,315 ÷ 69 90

7. 120,985 ÷ 108 1100 8. 31 × 68 × 99 210,000

For 1–12, possible answers are given.

Estimate the following sums and differences. *(Lesson 2-6)*

9. 57,823 + 64,184 122,000 10. 28 + 51 + 32 110

11. 725,167 − 263,198 460,000 12. 5425 − 2880 2500

Mixed Review

13. (2-4) Write 3 × 3 × 3 × 3 × 3 × 3 using exponents. 3^6

14. (2-3) Compare using <, >, or =. three thousand, twenty-five (<) 32,500

15. (1-4) The following data set shows the quiz scores for Mrs. Hanson's 10 point math quiz: 8, 7, 8, 6, 8, 7, 9, 7, 9, 10, 6, 8, 10, 9, 7.

a. Make a frequency chart

scores	frequency
6	2
7	4
8	4
9	3
10	2

b. Make a line plot

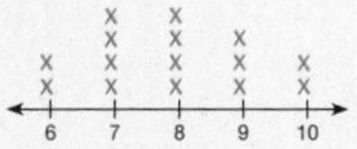

16. (1-7) Find the median, mode, and range of 22, 12, 16, 20, 12, 20, 21.

median 20 mode 12 and 20 range 10

Name ______________________

Daily Review 2-9

Daily Cumulative Review

Evaluate the expression. *(Lesson 2-8)*

1. 7 × 6 ÷ 3 14 2. 3 + 4 × 6 27

3. 16 ÷ 4 + 3 7 4. 35 − (22 − 10) 23

5. 5×2^3 40 6. $(24 \div 12)^4$ 16

7. $8^2 - 2^4$ 48 8. 64 ÷ (16 ÷ 4) 16

9. 128 ÷ 8 − 8 × 2 0 10. $(9 \div 3)^4$ 81

For 11–17, possible answers are given.

Estimate the following products and quotients. *(Lesson 2-7)*

11. 182 ÷ 31 6 12. 389 × 31 12,000

13. 888 ÷ 91 10 14. 9 × 12 × 19 2000

15. 3258 × 5 × 9 150,000 16. 4825 ÷ 69 70

Mixed Review

17. (2-6) In 1996 the population for Cook County in Illinois was 5,096,540. The population in Los Angeles County, California was 9,127,751. Estimate the combined population of these two cities.

14,000,000

Simplify mentally.

18. (2-5) 74 + 101 175 19. (2-5) 1653 − 101 1552 20. (2-5) 31 × 5 155

Write using exponents.

21. (2-4) 4×4×4 = 4^3 22. (2-4) 6×2×2×2 = 6×2^3 23. (2-4) 82×82 = 82^2

24. (2-1) The Dallas-Ft. Worth Airport handled over 58,000,000 arrivals and departures in 1996. Write this number in word-number form.

58 million

Name ______________________

Daily Review 2-10

Daily Cumulative Review

Find the next three numbers in the pattern. *(Lesson 2-9)*

1. 4, 7, 10, 13, 16, 19, 22, 25

2. 124, 112, 100, 88, 76, 64, 52, 40

3. 98, 99, 101, 104, 108, 113, 119, 126

4. 110, 100, 91, 83, 76, 70, 65, 61

5. 16, 26, 24, 34, 32, 42, 40, 50

Evaluate each expression. *(Lesson 2-8)*

6. 8 − 3 − 2 3 7. 8 − (3 − 2) 7

8. $8^2 - 3^2$ 55 9. 4 × (5 − 3) 8

10. (4 × 5) − 3 17 11. $(4 + 5)^2 \div 3$ 27

Mixed Review

Estimate.

12. (2-7) 2895 ÷ 511 6 13. (2-7) 206 × 9 2,000

Simplify mentally.

14. (2-5) 54 + 105 159 15. (2-5) 250 − 151 99 16. (2-5) 56,000 ÷ 800 70

Use the circle graph for Exercices 17 and 18.

17. (1-1) How much of the family budget is spent on clothing and food for each $100 of the budget.

$29

18. (1-1) For each $100, how much money is left over after food, housing, and clothes?

$38

Family Budget (for each $100)

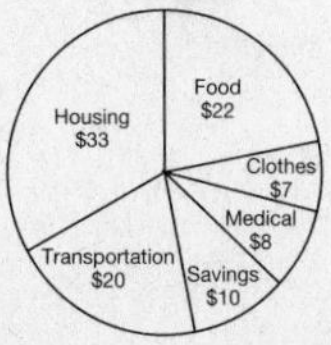

Name ______________________

Daily Review 2-11

Daily Cumulative Review

Complete the table by evaluating each expression for x = 2, 3, 4, and 5. *(Lesson 2-10)*

1.

x	$x + 7$	$20 - x$	$8x$	$\frac{120}{x}$	$x \times x$	$x \div x$	x^3
2	9	18	16	60	4	1	8
3	10	17	24	40	9	1	27
4	11	16	32	30	16	1	64
5	12	15	40	24	25	1	125

Find the next three numbers in the pattern. *(Lesson 2-9)*

2. 5, 7, 11, 17, 25, 35, 47, 61

3. 3, 6, 12, 24, 48, 96, 192, 384

4. 1, 3, 9, 27, 81, 243, 729, 2187

5. 31, 36, 33, 38, 35, 40, 37, 42

Mixed Review

6. (2-6) Estimate. 891 + 921 + 889 + 906 + 875 + 902 5400

Compare using <, >, or =.

7. (2-4) 3^5 (=) 3 × 3 × 3 × 3 × 3 8. (2-4) 5 × 10 (<) 10^5

9. (1-6) Make a stem-and-leaf diagram of the data showing the number of badges earned by a local girl scout troop.
8, 12, 9, 3, 18, 24, 0, 3, 10, 20, 12, 3, 6, 5, 15

Stem	Leaf
0	0 3 3 3 5 6 8 9
1	0 2 2 5 8
2	0 4

10. (1-7) Find the median and mode(s) for the data in Exercise 9.

median 9 mode(s) 3

Name ______________________

Daily Review 2-12

Daily Cumulative Review

Write the phrase as an expression. *(Lesson 2-11)*

1. 8 more than x $x + 8$
2. x less than 23 $23 - x$
3. one-fourth of b $\frac{1}{4}b$
4. a multiplied by 5 $5a$
5. c squared c^2
6. d increased by 10 $d + 10$
7. e doubled $2e$
8. f divided by 12 $f \div 12$

Complete the table by evaluating each expression for x = 2, 5, and 8. *(Lesson 2-10)*

9.

x	$12 + x$	$x - 2$	$15 \times x$	$120 \div x$	$7x$	x^2
2	14	0	30	60	14	4
5	17	3	75	24	35	25
8	20	6	120	15	56	64

Mixed Review

10. Find the next three numbers in the pattern. (2-9)
13, 18, 23, 28, 33, 38, 43, 48

Simplify.

11. $(4 + 4^2) \div 5$ 4 (2-8)
12. $(2^3 + 6) \div 7$ 2 (2-8)
13. 3^4 81 (2-4)
14. 4^3 64 (2-4)
15. 12^4 20,736 (2-4)
16. How are the two graphs alike? How are they different? (1-2)
Same vertical scale.
Different horizontal scale.

NASA Payloads, 1950 – 1996

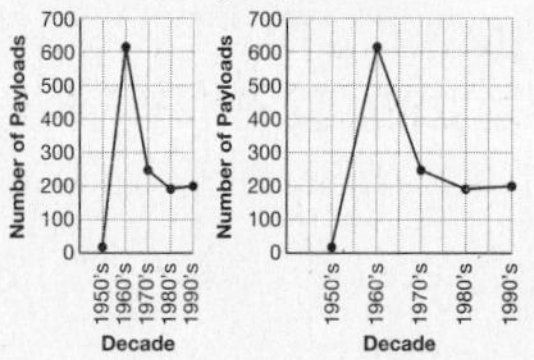

Name ______________________

Daily Review 2-13

Daily Cumulative Review

Is the equation true for the given value of the variable? *(Lesson 2-12)*

1. $x + 6 = 24, x = 30$ no
2. $13 - x = 7, x = 6$ yes
3. $6x = 42, x = 7$ yes
4. $y - 8 = 15, y = 7$ no
5. $y \div 8 = 3, y = 24$ yes
6. $24 + y = 36, y = 10$ no
7. $12 \times t = 144, t = 11$ no
8. $t \div 5 = 15, t = 75$ yes

Write an expression to answer each question. *(Lesson 2-11)*

9. What is the product of 24 and x? $24x$
10. What is the sum of x and 12? $x + 12$ (or $12 + x$)
11. What is the quotient of 32 and y? $32 \div y$ (or $\frac{32}{y}$)
12. What is the difference between y and 16? $y - 16$

Mixed Review

13. Evaluate $15 - x$ for x = 2, 3, and 4. 13, 12, 11 (2-10)
14. Insert parentheses to make this statement true. (2-8)
$(6 + 4) \div 2 = 5$
15. New Jersey has 1,792 miles of shoreline. Virginia has 3,315 miles of shoreline. (2-6)
Estimate the difference in miles of shoreline. 1500 miles

Compare. Use > or <.

16. 3251 < 3252 (2-3)
17. 234,625,129 < 234,626,874 (2-3)

Round to the given place value.

18. 3,957,243; hundred thousand (2-2)
4,000,000
19. 3,697,205; hundred (2-2)
3,697,200

Name ______________________

Daily Review 3-1

Daily Cumulative Review

Solve the following equations. *(Lesson 2-13)*

1. $x + 8 = 32$ 24
2. $m - 7 = 15$ 22
3. $\frac{x}{5} = 12$ 60
4. $9t = 63$ 7
5. $15 + x = 38$ 23
6. $m - 23 = 71$ 94

Write an equation for each situation. *(Lesson 2-12)*

7. Todd had 6 shirts. He bought x more. Then he had 13 shirts.
$6 + x = 13$
8. Terri had c pieces of candy. She gave Mike 7 pieces. She had 23 pieces left.
$c - 7 = 23$
9. A package of 42 cookies was equally divided among x children. Each child had 7 cookies.
$\frac{42}{x} = 7$
10. Each of the 32 school buses had t tires. If all the buses got new tires, there would be 192 new tires.
$32t = 192$

Mixed Review

11. Evaluate $3k$ when k = 4, 6, 10. 12; 18; 30 (2-10)

Estimate.

12. $61,305 \div 4,988$ 12 (2-7)
13. 102×72 7200 (2-7)
14. Compare, using <, >, or =. 1^{10} < 10^1 (2-4)
15. Order from least to greatest. 333; 3,333; 33; 3; 33,333 (2-3)
3; 33; 333; 3,333; 33,333

Name ______________________

Daily Review 3-2

Daily Cumulative Review

Write the following numbers as decimals. *(Lesson 3-1)*

1. five tenths 0.5
2. twenty-two thousandths 0.022
3. two and five hundredths 2.05

Solve the following equations. *(Lesson 2-13)*

4. $x - 15 = 27$ 42
5. $m + 8 = 37$ 29
6. $\frac{s}{7} = 12$ 84
7. $11y = 55$ 5
8. $b - 27 = 101$ 128
9. $7u = 84$ 12

Mixed Review

10. Use the data set to make a bar graph. (1-5)

Number of Televisions in House	
0	1
1	4
2	10
3 or more	3

Televisions in House

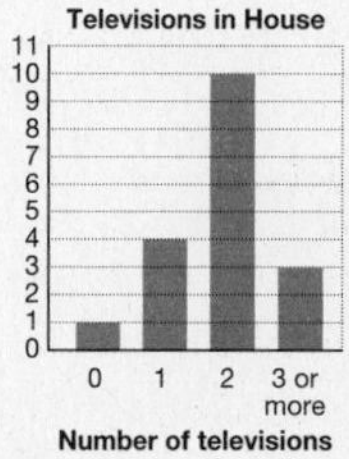

11. Find the mean, median, and mode(s) without the outlier. (1-9)
mean 32 median 32
mode(s) 22 and 20

Stem	Leaf
2	0 0 2 2 4
3	0 2 6 7
4	0 3 4 6
8	0

12. Mars is 128,400,000 miles from the sun. Write this distance in word form and in number-word form. (2-1)
one hundred twenty-eight million, four hundred thousand
128 million, 400 thousand

Name ____________________

Daily Review 3-3

Daily Cumulative Review

Round to the underlined place value. *(Lesson 3-2)*

1. 31.4 — 31
2. 8.8931 — 8.9
3. 85.07 — 85.1
4. 13.1063 — 13.106
5. 2.77 — 2.8
6. 35.16 — 35
7. 293.7 — 294
8. 6.092 — 6.09

Write the decimal in word form. *(Lesson 3-1)*

9. 0.57 — fifty seven hundredths
10. 6.5 — six and five tenths
11. 0.013 — thirteen thousandths
12. 0.06 — six hundredths

Mixed Review

13. *(2-13)* Find the values for the variable that will provide the given values for the expression.

x	$x + 14$
4	18
46	60
74	88

14. *(2-10)* Complete the table. One large pizza feeds 3 hungry boys.

Number of boys	Number of pizzas
3	1
9	3
15	5
b	$b \div 3$

15. *(2-4)* Write 9 cubed in standard form. 729

16. *(1-7)* Find the median, mode(s), and range of the following test scores:
98, 86, 98, 98, 87, 92, 92

median 92 mode(s) 98 range 12

Name ____________________

Daily Review 3-4

Daily Cumulative Review

Compare using >, <, or =. *(Lesson 3-3)*

1. 0.487 (>) 0.478
2. 5.2 (<) 5.21
3. 6.45 (>) 6.449
4. 7.15 (<) 7.51
5. 91.06 (<) 91.6
6. 18.97 (=) 18.970

Estimate each object's length to the nearest centimeter and tenth of a centimeter. *(Lesson 3-2)*

7. nearest cm: 5 cm nearest tenth: 4.6 cm

8. nearest cm: 5 cm nearest tenth: 5.1 cm

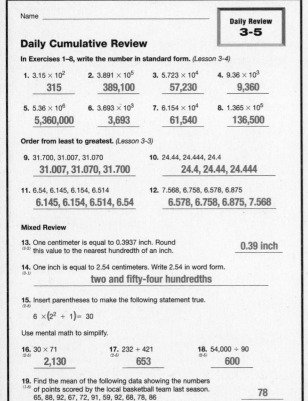

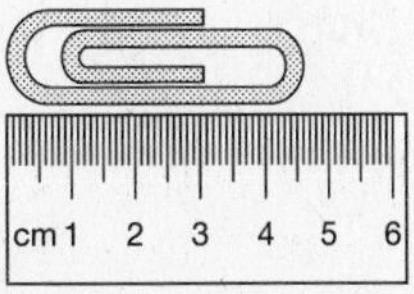

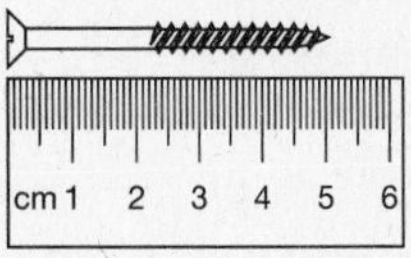

Mixed Review

9. *(2-12)* Is $64 \div n = 16$ true when $n = 8$? No
10. *(2-11)* Write "x less than 25" as an expression. $25 - x$
11. *(2-9)* Find the next three numbers in the pattern.
1, 3, 9, 27, 81, 243, 729, 2187
12. *(2-2)* Round 851,309,069,823 to the nearest million. 851,309,000,000
13. *(1-6)* For the given data, make a stem-and-leaf diagram.
17, 19, 20, 23, 22, 21, 16, 14, 17, 13, 16, 20, 23, 26, 23, 21

Stem	Leaf
1	3 4 6 6 7 7 9
2	0 0 1 1 2 3 3 3 6

14. *(1-7)* In the data for Exercise 13, what are the median and mode(s)?
median 20 mode(s) 23

Name ____________________

Daily Review 3-5

Daily Cumulative Review

In Exercises 1–8, write the number in standard form. *(Lesson 3-4)*

1. 3.15×10^2 — 315
2. 3.891×10^5 — 389,100
3. 5.723×10^4 — 57,230
4. 9.36×10^3 — 9,360
5. 5.36×10^6 — 5,360,000
6. 3.693×10^3 — 3,693
7. 6.154×10^4 — 61,540
8. 1.365×10^5 — 136,500

Order from least to greatest. *(Lesson 3-3)*

9. 31.700, 31.007, 31.070 — 31.007, 31.070, 31.700
10. 24.44, 24.444, 24.4 — 24.4, 24.44, 24.444
11. 6.54, 6.145, 6.154, 6.514 — 6.145, 6.154, 6.514, 6.54
12. 7.568, 6.758, 6.578, 6.875 — 6.578, 6.758, 6.875, 7.568

Mixed Review

13. *(3-2)* One centimeter is equal to 0.3937 inch. Round this value to the nearest hundredth of an inch. 0.39 inch
14. *(3-1)* One inch is equal to 2.54 centimeters. Write 2.54 in word form.
two and fifty-four hundredths
15. *(2-8)* Insert parentheses to make the following statement true.
$6 \times (2^2 + 1) = 30$

Use mental math to simplify.

16. *(2-5)* 30×71 — 2,130
17. *(2-5)* $232 + 421$ — 653
18. *(2-5)* $54{,}000 \div 90$ — 600
19. *(1-8)* Find the mean of the following data showing the numbers of points scored by the local basketball team last season.
65, 88, 92, 67, 72, 91, 59, 92, 68, 78, 86 — 78

Name ____________________

Daily Review 3-6

Daily Cumulative Review

Estimate each sum, difference, product, or quotient. *(Lesson 3-5)*

1. $4.68 + 2.75$ — 8
2. 28.89×6.8 — 210
3. $21.837 - 1.12$ — 21
4. $80.89 \div 8.9$ — 9
5. $14.675 + 4.91$ — 20
6. $27.264 - 7.35$ — 20
7. 41.16×4.91 — 200
8. $84.12 \div 6.22$ — 14

Write in scientific notation. *(Lesson 3-4)*

9. 26,500 — 2.65×10^4
10. 12 million — 1.2×10^7
11. 40,000 — 4×10^4
12. 23,590 — 2.359×10^4
13. 82 billion — 8.2×10^{10}
14. 6,813,000,000,000 — 6.813×10^{12}

Mixed Review

Use the bar graph to answer the following questions.

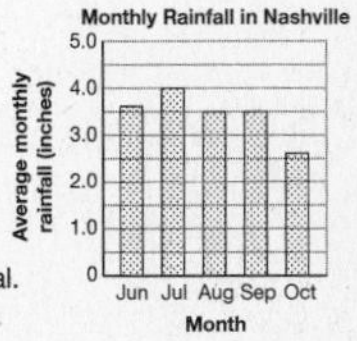

15. *(3-3)* Which month had the most rainfall? July
16. *(3-3)* Which months had the same amount of rainfall? August and September
17. *(3-1)* Write two hundred sixty-one thousandths as a decimal. 0.261

Round to the given place.

18. *(2-2)* 6,703; hundreds — 6,700
19. *(2-2)* 6,875,000; hundred-thousands — 6,900,000
20. *(1-4)* Draw a line plot of the hours spent doing homework each week.
10, 6, 7, 10, 7, 8, 9, 10, 7, 7, 6, 7, 8, 10, 8, 6, 9

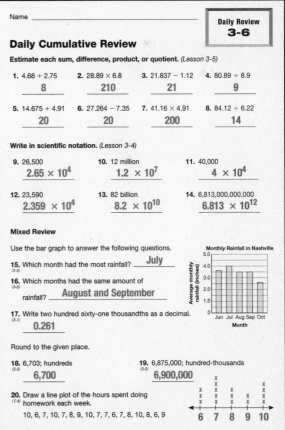

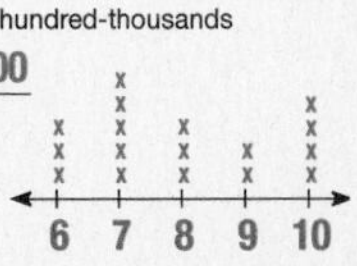

Name ______________________

Daily Review 3-7

Daily Cumulative Review

Simplify. *(Lesson 3-6)*

1. 2.72 + 2.8 **5.52**
2. 4.934 − 1.85 **3.084**
3. 8.976 + 1.328 **10.304**
4. 7.58 − 1.32 **6.26**
5. \$2.85 + \$13.91 **\$16.76**
6. 32.874 − 4.69 **28.184**
7. 6.2 + 7.31 **13.51**
8. 85.7 − 6.913 **78.787**

Estimate each sum, difference, product, or quotient. *(Lesson 3-5)*

9. 2.08 + 3.01 **5**
10. \$62.91 − \$15.25 **\$48**
11. 16.95 × 1.82 **34**
12. 56.23 ÷ 13.9 **4**
13. 56.13 + 9.2 **65**
14. 213.45 − 23.2 **190**
15. 4.6 × 5.12 **25**
16. 12.13 ÷ 3.57 **3**

Mixed Review

17. (3-4) Venus is 66,800,000,000 miles from the sun. Write the number in scientific notation. **6.68×10^{10}**

18. (3-3) In 1996, a German deutsche mark was worth \$0.66454, a Canadian dollar was worth \$0.73341, and a United Kingdom pound was worth \$0.64033. Order these currencies from the least value to the greatest.
\$0.64033, \$0.66454, \$0.73341

19. (1-6) Make a stem-and-leaf diagram of the data showing the number of books read by a sixth-grade class during the school year.
5, 8, 12, 18, 22, 6, 9, 8, 12, 13, 21, 20, 26, 9, 3, 15, 17, 19, 23, 21, 9, 4, 24, 16, 10

Stem	Leaf
0	3 4 5 6 8 8 9 9 9
1	0 2 2 3 5 6 7 8 9
2	0 1 1 2 3 4 6

Solve the following equations.

20. (2-13) $x - 5 = 23$ **28**
21. (2-13) $m + 15 = 47$ **32**

Name ______________________

Daily Review 3-8

Daily Cumulative Review

Solve each equation. *(Lesson 3-7)*

1. $h + 3.8 = 8.8$ $h =$ **5**
2. $b - 6 = 15.1$ $b =$ **21.1**
3. $8 + t = 14.6$ $t =$ **6.6**
4. $9 - a = 2.4$ $a =$ **6.6**
5. $m + 6.2 = 8.1$ $m =$ **1.9**
6. $d - 8.3 = 1.8$ $d =$ **10.1**
7. $6.38 + f = 12.5$ $f =$ **6.12**
8. $3.8 - c = 3.2$ $c =$ **0.6**

Simplify. *(Lesson 3-6)*

9. 6.97 + 3.421 **10.391**
10. 6.723 − 1.38 **5.343**
11. \$46.23 − \$26.52 **\$19.71**
12. 22 + 2.315 **24.315**
13. 3.275 + 6.941 + 9.2894 **19.5054**
14. 7.23 + 12.6 + 5.73 **25.56**

Mixed Review

Estimate.

15. (3-5) 5.12 + 1.87 **7**
16. (3-5) 68.73 × 9.8 **690**
17. (3-5) 25.967 − 11.98 **14**
18. (3-5) 62.9 ÷ 7.12 **9**

Round to the underlined place value.

19. (3-2) 5<u>3</u>.4 **53**
20. (3-2) 6.<u>6</u>961 **6.7**
21. (3-2) 12.10<u>9</u>2 **12.109**
22. (3-2) 69.3<u>0</u>5 **69.31**

23. (2-6) In 1996, London's Heathrow airport handled 56,037,813 arrivals and departures. In the same year, Tokyo International Airport handled 46,631,475. Estimate the combined arrivals and departures of these two busy airports.
103,000,000

Name ______________________

Daily Review 3-9

Daily Cumulative Review

Insert a decimal point in the answer to make the equation true. *(Lesson 3-8)*

1. 14 × 8.56 = 119.84
2. 3.27 × 6 = 19.62
3. 2.375 × 8 = 19.000
4. 6 × 3.891 = 23.346
5. 9.17 × 14 = 128.38
6. 3.27 × 22 = 71.94

Solve. *(Lesson 3-7)*

7. $x + 2.5 = 8.5$ $x =$ **6**
8. $a - 7 = 14.7$ $a =$ **21.7**
9. $11 - b = 6.2$ $b =$ **4.8**
10. $14.2 + f = 21.6$ $f =$ **7.4**

Mixed Review

11. (3-4) Pluto is 8.374×10^8 miles from the sun. Write this number in standard form. **837,400,000**

12. (3-1) Write 8.374 in word form. **eight and three hundred seventy-four thousandths**

13. (2-10) Evaluate $40 - x$ when $x = 3, 15, 22$. **37; 25; 18**

14. (2-4) Write 2^8 in standard form. **256**

15. (2-12) Is $\frac{x}{4} = 22$ true when $x = 84$? Explain.
No; When $x = 84$, $\frac{x}{4} = 21$. If $x = 88$, then $\frac{x}{4} = 22$.

16. (1-3) Determine if there is a trend on the scatterplot. If there is, describe the pattern of the data.
There is a trend. The pattern is as age increases, sleep decreases.

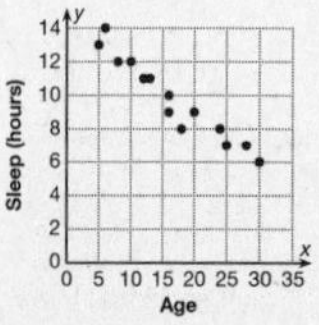

Name ______________________

Daily Review 3-10

Daily Cumulative Review

Insert a decimal point in the answer to make the equation true. *(Lesson 3-9)*

1. 4.7 × 21.6 = 101.52
2. 6.3 × 18.7 = 117.81
3. 3.8 × 12.56 = 47.728
4. 10.8 × 10.312 = 111.3696

Multiply. *(Lesson 3-8)*

5. 3.75 × 10 **37.5**
6. 3.75 × 100 **375**
7. 3.75 × 1000 **3,750**
8. 6.125 × 20 **122.5**

Mixed Review

9. (3-7) Solve. $x + 2.6 = 11$ $x =$ **8.4**
10. (3-6) Add. 8.45 + 6.38 + 6.42 + 31.62 **52.87**
11. (3-2) Measure the crayon to the nearest centimeter. **7 cm**

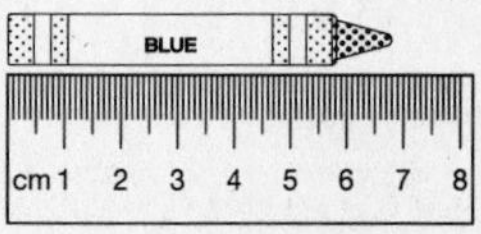

12. (2-9) Find the next three numbers in the pattern.
5, 8, 14, 26, 50, **98**, **194**, **386**

13. (2-8) Evaluate $(21 - 17)^2 + 5$. **21**

Use the bar graph for Exercises 14 and 15.

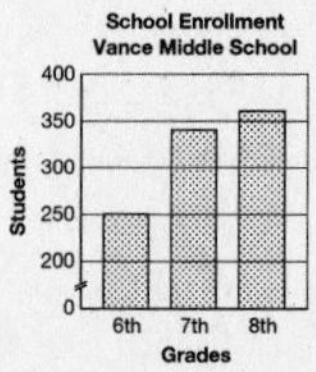

14. (1-2) What is the number of eighth-grade students at Vance Middle School? **360**

15. (1-2) Could the graph be misleading? If so, how would you correct the graph?
It looks as if there are twice as many 8th-grade students as 6th-grade students. Correct the graph by changing the vertical scale.

Name ______________________

Daily Review 3-11

Daily Cumulative Review

Insert a decimal point in the answer to make the equation true. *(Lesson 3-10)*

1. 44.764 ÷ 76 = 0.5 8 9 **2.** 98.784 ÷ 28 = 3.5 2 8 **3.** 35.34 ÷ 6 = 5.8 9

4. 5.6 ÷ 7 = 0.8 **5.** 14.505 ÷ 3 = 4.8 3 5 **6.** 7.896 ÷ 3 = 2.6 3 2

Multiply. *(Lesson 3-9)*

7. 8.032 × 0.5 **4.016** **8.** 0.02 × 8.3 **0.166** **9.** 51.8 × 0.8 **41.44** **10.** 0.03 × 0.6 **0.018**

Mixed Review

11. (3-8) Multiply. 4 × 16.83 **67.32**

12. (3-7) Solve. $c + 4.7 = 8.9$ c = **4.2**

Estimate.

13. (3-5) 1.08 + 5.03 **6** **14.** (3-5) 28.89 − 12.72 **16** **15.** (3-5) 95.87 ÷ 11.9 **8**

16. (2-5) Jason earns $75 per day on his job. If he worked 200 days last year, how much did he earn? **$15,000**

17. (1-9) The line plot shows the highest temperature recorded by several states during a drought year.

a. Find the mean, median, and mode(s) of the data.

mean **111.1°** median **111°**

mode(s) **112°**

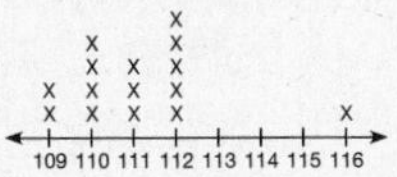

b. Did the outlier affect the mean? Explain.

No, both round to 111°

18. (1-5) What is the range of the data for the temperatures in Exercise 17? **7°**

33

Name ______________________

Daily Review 3-12

Daily Cumulative Review

Insert a decimal point in the answer to make the equation true. *(Lesson 3-11)*

1. 11.2602 ÷ 2.1 = 5.3 6 2 **2.** 15.2358 ÷ 3.79 = 4.0 2

3. 5.018 ÷ 2.6 = 1.9 3 0 **4.** 8.892 ÷ 1.3 = 6.8 4

Divide. *(Lesson 3-10)*

5. 37.848 ÷ 12 **3.154** **6.** 210.56 ÷ 28 **7.52** **7.** 174.4 ÷ 8 **21.8** **8.** 9.87 ÷ 42 **0.235**

Mixed Review

9. (3-9) Multiply. 53.7 × 0.06 **3.222** **10.** (3-8) Multiply. $11.73 × 9 **$105.57** **11.** (3-6) Simplify. 183.6 − 21.92 **161.68**

12. (3-4) Write 63 trillion in scientific notation. **6.3×10^{13}**

13. (3-3) Order from least to greatest. 7.34, 7.243, 7.234, 7.324

7.234, 7.243, 7.324, 7.34

14. (3-1) Write sixteen thousandths as a decimal. **0.016**

15. (2-13) Solve. $x - 8 = 32$ x = **40**

16. (2-11) Write an expression for the phrase "5 less than k" **$k - 5$**

17. (2-8) Evaluate $4 + (2 + 3)^3$ **129**

18. (2-4) Compare using <, >, or =. 4^3 (>) 4×3

19. (2-1) Write 32 million in standard form. **32,000,000**

20. (1-7) Find the median and mode(s).

3, 9, 10, 12, 14, 9, 4, 8, 10, 9, 22, 7, 30, 17, 15, 25, 18

median **10** mode(s) **9**

34

Name ______________________

Daily Review 4-1

Daily Cumulative Review

Solve. *(Lesson 3-12)*

1. $4x = 10.08$ x = **2.52** **2.** $\frac{a}{3.1} = 2.36$ a = **7.316** **3.** $0.8k = 5.04$ k = **6.3** **4.** $\frac{s}{0.62} = 3.2$ s = **1.984**

Divide. *(Lesson 3-11)*

5. 4.392 ÷ 0.6 **7.32** **6.** 0.325 ÷ 0.13 **2.5** **7.** 13.26 ÷ 4.25 **3.12** **8.** 0.1456 ÷ 2.6 **0.056**

Mixed Review

9. (3-10) Divide. 20.605 ÷ 5 **4.121**

10. (3-9) Multiply. 53.2 × 0.06 **3.192**

11. (3-8) Multiply. $2.63 × 5 **$13.15**

12. (3-7) Solve. $4.17 + x = 6.3$ x = **2.13**

13. (2-7) Estimate. 64,895 ÷ 131 **500**

14. (2-5) Simplify. 25 × 40 × 18 **18,000**

15. (1-8) Find the mean of the data in the stem-and-leaf plot. **37**

Stem	Leaf
2	4 7 8
3	0 1 3 3 7 9
4	1 1 4 6
5	0 1

16. (1-4) Make a line plot with the hours of sleep reported by college students:
6, 5, 7, 4, 8, 6, 6, 5, 7, 7, 5, 4, 8, 7, 6, 5

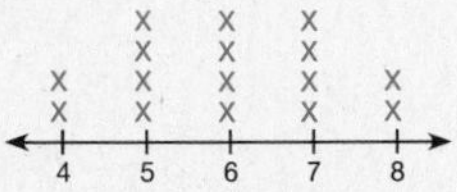

Use the scatterplot to answer the questions.

17. (1-3) Which point represents the tallest person? ***H***

18. (1-3) Name two points that represent people who are the same height. ***E* and *F***

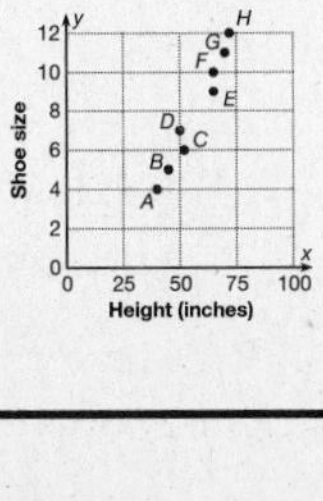

35

Name ______________________

Daily Review 4-2

Daily Cumulative Review

Find the perimeter. *(Lesson 4-1)*

1. **16 cm** **2.** **33 ft** **3.** **20 m**

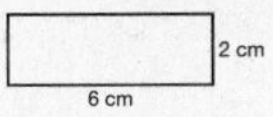

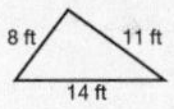

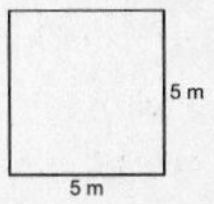

Solve. *(Lesson 3-12)*

4. $6n = 7.95$ n = **1.325** **5.** $\frac{d}{3.6} = 1.325$ d = **4.77** **6.** $0.1x = 2.3$ x = **23** **7.** $\frac{m}{2.309} = 5$ m = **11.545**

Mixed Review

8. (3-11) Divide. 1.836 ÷ 0.2 **9.18**

9. (3-6) Add. 5.2 + 7.38 **12.58**

10. (3-3) Compare with > or <

75.6 (>) 75.06

11. (2-13) Solve. $x + 23 = 35$ x = **12**

12. (2-8) Evaluate. 8 + 6 ÷ 2 **11**

13. (2-5) Simplify. 360 − 142 **218**

14. (2-1) Write 730,153 in words.

seven hundred thirty thousand, one hundred fifty-three

15. (1-6) Make a stem-and-leaf diagram of the data showing scores on a test:
83, 92, 71, 86, 74, 85, 96, 67, 73, 85, 90, 63, 82, 78, 79, 71, 82, 75, 89, 76

Stem	Leaf
6	3 7
7	1 1 3 4 5 6 8 9
8	2 2 3 5 5 6 9
9	0 2 6

16. (1-5) What is the range of the data for the test scores in Exercise 15? **33**

36

Name ______________________

Daily Review 4-3

Daily Cumulative Review

Name an appropriate metric unit of measure. *(Lesson 4-2)*

1. Weight of a pencil **gram**
2. Height of a basketball player **meter**
3. Amount of milk in a carton **liter**
4. Distance from Dallas to New York City **kilometer**

Find the length of each unknown side. *(Lesson 4-1)*

5. $a =$ **3 cm**, $b =$ **6 cm** 6. $c =$ **2 ft**, $d =$ **2 ft** 7. $x =$ **24 in.**, $y =$ **8 in.**

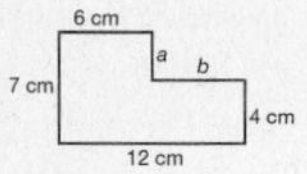

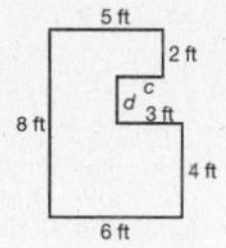

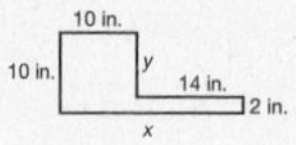

Mixed Review

8. Solve using inverse operations. (3-12)

a. $0.7p = 3.01$ $p =$ **4.3**

b. $\frac{m}{3.9} = 0.51$ $m =$ **1.989**

9. Divide. $0.7296 \div 0.16$ (3-10) **4.56**

10. Multiply. 9×4.183 (3-8) **37.647**

11. Simplify. $184.8 - 21.73$ (3-6) **163.07**

12. Write $\frac{27}{1000}$ as a decimal. (3-1) **0.027**

13. Find the next three numbers in the pattern. (2-9)

6, 13, 20, 27, 34, **41**, **48**, **55**

14. Write $3 \times 3 \times 3 \times 3 \times 3$ using exponents. (2-4) $\mathbf{3^5}$

15. Identify the outlier in the data set. 91, 88, 112, 96, 10, 106, 95, 86 (1-9) **10**

Name ______________________

Daily Review 4-4

Daily Cumulative Review

Convert. *(Lesson 4-3)*

1. 23 feet = **276** inches
2. 26 quarts = **6.5** gallons
3. 12 pounds = **192** ounces
4. 13,200 feet = **2.5** miles

Convert within the metric system. *(Lesson 4-2)*

5. 68 g = **0.068** kg 6. 3.2 L = **3,200** mL 7. 82 cm = **0.82** m

Mixed Review

8. Find the perimeter of the figure. (4-1) **52 km**

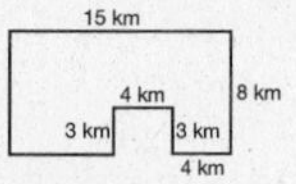

9. Multiply. 6.5×4.7 (3-9) **30.55**

10. Write 6.31×10^7 in standard form. (3-4) **63,100,000**

11. Write an expression for "the product of 31 and x." (2-11) **31*x***

12. Round 26,321 to the thousands place. (2-2) **26,000**

13. Write 12,000,000,000 in number-word form. (2-1) **12 billion**

Use the 1996 Election Results graph to answer the following.

14. Who had the most votes? (1-1) **Bill Clinton**

15. Estimate the total number of votes shown in the data. (1-1) **94 million**

16. About how many more votes did Bob Dole get than Ross Perot? (1-1) **30 million**

17. Estimate how many people didn't vote for Bob Dole. (1-1) **55 million**

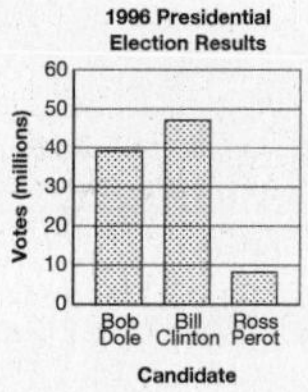

Name ______________________

Daily Review 4-5

Daily Cumulative Review

Find the missing measurement for each rectangle. *(Lesson 4-4)*

1. Area = $\mathbf{72\ ft^2}$ Base = 6 ft Height = 12 ft
2. Area = $56\ cm^2$ Base = **7 cm** Height = 8 cm
3. Area = $108\ in^2$ Base = 9 in. Height = **12 in.**

Convert. *(Lesson 4-3)*

4. 36 ft = **12** yd 5. 80 oz = **5** lb 6. 9 gal = **36** qt

Mixed Review

7. Convert. 24,800 m = **24.8** km (4-2)

8. Solve. $6.3x = 20.223$; $x =$ **3.21** (3-12)

9. Estimate. \$52.81 − \$14.21 (3-5) **\$39**

10. One kilometer is about 0.621 mile. Round this value to the nearest tenth of a mile. (3-2) **0.6**

11. Estimate. 28,124 + 91,052 + 67,213 + 52,620 (2-6) **240,000**

12. Order the following from least to greatest. 82,370; 83,207; 82,200; 83,170 (2-3)

82,200; 82,370; 83,170; 83,207

13. Find the median and mode(s) of the data in the stem-and-leaf diagram. (1-7)

median **57.5**

mode(s) **None**

Stem	Leaf
4	5 7 9
5	0 2 3 7 8
6	2 4 6 7
7	2 3

14. What is the range of the values in the stem-and-leaf diagram? (1-6) **28**

15. Find the perimeter of the figure at the right. (4-1) **42 ft**

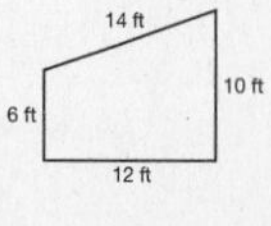

Name ______________________

Daily Review 4-6

Daily Cumulative Review

Find the area of each parallelogram. The dashed line is a height. *(Lesson 4-5)*

1.

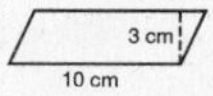

$\mathbf{30\ cm^2}$

2.

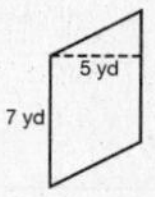

$\mathbf{35\ yd^2}$

3.

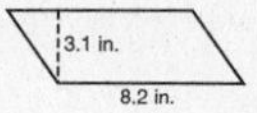

$\mathbf{25.42\ in^2}$

Find the area of each figure. *(Lesson 4-4)*

4. Square with sides of length 9 ft $\mathbf{81\ ft^2}$
5. Rectangle with sides 3.7 m and 7.2 m $\mathbf{26.64\ m^2}$
6. Rectangle with sides 12 in. and 7 in. $\mathbf{84\ in^2}$

Mixed Review

7. Convert. 64 qt = **16** gal (4-3)

8. Convert. 6.21 kg = **6,210** g (4-2)

9. Find the perimeter. (4-1) **6.22 mi**

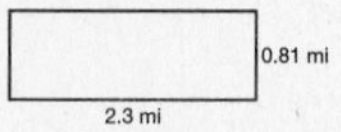

10. Estimate the length of the clothespin to the nearest tenth of a centimeter. (3-2) **4.8 cm**

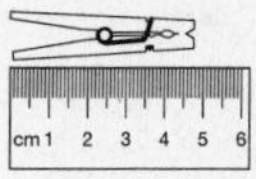

11. Write an equation. James had 85 trading cards. He bought x more. Then he had 92 cards. (2-12) $\mathbf{85 + x = 92}$

12. Compare using <, >, or =. (2-4)

a. 2^5 ⓞ < 5^3

b. $2 \times 2 \times 2$ ⓞ = 2^3

13. Make a line plot for the numbers of books read: (1-4)

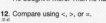

4, 2, 3, 1, 0, 1, 2, 1, 0, 3, 1, 0, 1, 2, 0, 1

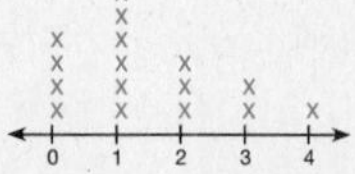

Name ______________________

Daily Review 4-7

Daily Cumulative Review

Find the area of each triangle. The dashed line is a height. *(Lesson 4-6)*

1. 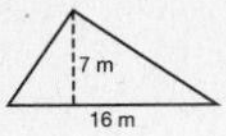

2. 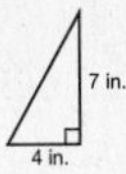

3. 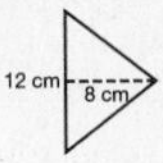

1. $56\ m^2$ 2. $14\ in^2$ 3. $48\ cm^2$

Find the area if *b* is the base and *h* is the height of a parallelogram *(Lesson 4-5)*

4. $b = 6$ cm, $h = 11$ cm — $66\ cm^2$
5. $b = 6.8$ m, $h = 11.1$ m — $75.48\ m^2$
6. $b = 24$ in., $h = 88$ in. — $2{,}112\ in^2$

Mixed Review

7. (4-4) Find the area of a square with sides of length 18 cm. — $324\ cm^2$

8. (4-2) Name an appropriate metric unit of measure for the amount of medicine in an eyedropper. — mL

9. (3-11) Divide. $8.449 \div 3.55$ — 2.38

10. (3-9) Multiply 6.01×3.9 — 23.439

11. (3-7) Solve. $8 - x = 2.3$ — $x =$ 5.7

12. (2-10) Complete the table. The children at Kennedy School eat 600 slices of bread each day.

Number of days	Number of bread slices
2	1200
4	2400
s	600*s*

13. (1-6) Make a stem-and-leaf diagram: 6, 11, 8, 1, 16, 23, 0, 2, 9, 19, 11, 2, 5, 3, 9, 14

Stem	Leaf
0	0 1 2 2 3 5 6 8 9 9
1	1 1 4 6 9
2	3

Name ______________________

Daily Review 4-8

Daily Cumulative Review

Find each circumference. Use 3.14 for π. *(Lesson 4-7)*

1. 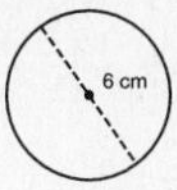

2. 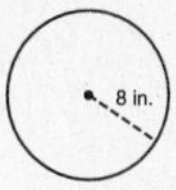

3. 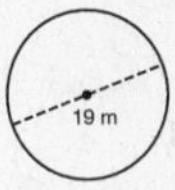

1. 18.84 cm 2. 50.24 in. 3. 59.66 m

Find the area if *b* is the base and *h* is the height of a triangle. *(Lesson 4-6)*

4. $b = 14$ ft, $h = 7$ ft — $49\ ft^2$
5. $h = 5$ cm, $b = 9$ cm — $22.5\ cm^2$
6. $b = 6.1$ mi, $h = 8$ mi. — $24.4\ mi^2$

Mixed Review

7. (4-7) Find the area of a parallelogram with base 7 in. and height 8.6 in. — $60.2\ in^2$

8. (4-1) Find the perimeter of a square with sides of length 12 cm. — 48 cm

Estimate each sum, difference, product or quotient.

9. (3-5) $13.72 + 5.06$ — 19
10. (3-5) $5.96 - 1.24$ — 5
11. (3-5) $\$8.12 \times 6.1$ — \$48
12. (3-5) $36.14 \div 8.91$ — 4

Simplify.

13. (2-5) 80×30 — 2400
14. (2-5) $272 + 27$ — 299
15. (2-5) $3{,}600 \div 40$ — 90

16. (1-2) Use the Longest Rivers graph.

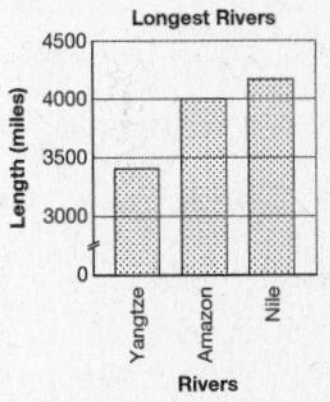

a About how many times longer does the Nile River appear to be than the Yangtze? — 2

b. If the graph is misleading, how would you correct it? — Change the vertical scale and adjust the bars.

Name ______________________

Daily Review 4-9

Daily Cumulative Review

Find the area of each circle. Use 3.14 for π. *(Lesson 4-8)*

1. 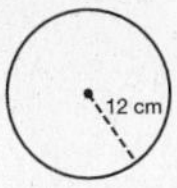

2. 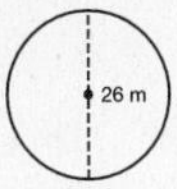

3. 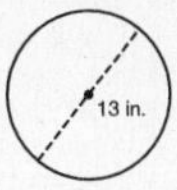

1. $452.16\ cm^2$ 2. $530.66\ m^2$ 3. $132.665\ in^2$

Find the missing measurements for each circle where *r* = radius, *d* = diameter, and *c* = circumference. Use 3.14 for π. *(Lesson 4-7)*

4. $r = 6$ cm, $d = 12$ cm, $c =$ 37.68 cm
5. $r =$ 16 in., $d = 32$ in., $c = 100.48$ in.
6. $r = 3.5$ mm, $d =$ 7 mm, $c =$ 21.98 mm

Mixed Review

7. (4-3) Convert. 12 mi = 63,360 ft

8. (3-12) Solve. $\frac{m}{12} = 0.13$ — $m =$ 1.56

9. (3-4) Write 6 million in scientific notation. — 6×10^6

10. (2-11) Write "15 more than *x*" as an expression — $x + 15$

Use the City Budget graph.

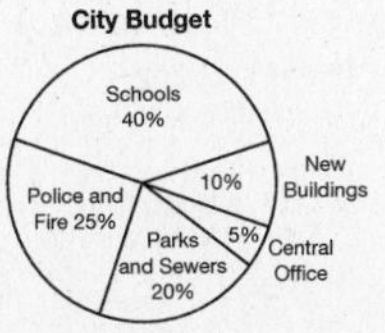

11. (1-1) How much more of the budget is spent on schools than on the central office? — 35%

12. (1-1) For every \$100 spent on the budget, how much is spent on police, fire, and new buildings? — \$35

Name ______________________

Daily Review 5-1

Daily Cumulative Review

Find the area of each irregular figure. *(Lesson 4-9)*

1. $155\ m^2$ 2. $180\ ft^2$ 3. $67\ cm^2$

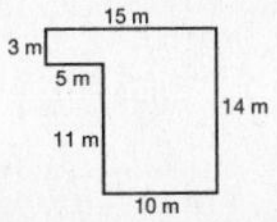

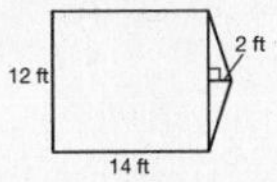

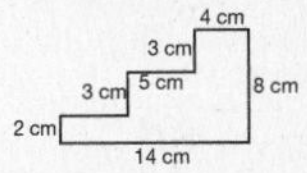

Find the area of each circle where *r* = radius and *d* = diameter. Use 3.14 for π. *(Lesson 4-8)*

4. $r = 9$ in. — $254.34\ in^2$
5. $d = 24$ cm — $452.16\ cm^2$
6. $r = 4$ mi — $50.24\ mi^2$
7. $d = 42$ m — $1384.74\ m^2$

Mixed Review

8. (4-7) Find the circumference of a circle whose radius is 3.5 mm. Use 3.14 for π. — 21.98 mm

9. (4-5) Find the area of a parallelogram whose base is 27 cm and whose height is 7.8 cm. — $210.6\ cm^2$

10. (3-11) Divide. $0.594 \div 1.8$ — 0.33

11. (3-8) Multiply. 7.25×20 — 145

12. (3-3) Compare using < or >. 12.53 (>) 12.503

13. (2-9) Find the next three numbers in the pattern. 140, 134, 128, 122, 116, 110, 104, 98

14. (2-2) Round 5,387,264,183 to the hundred-millions place. — 5,400,000,000

15. (1-7) Make a line plot for the following data. Then find the median and mode(s).

13, 22, 18, 14, 20, 13, 18, 16, 22, 18, 15, 14

median 17 mode(s) 18

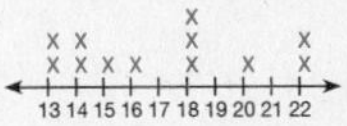

Name ______________________

Daily Review 5-2

Daily Cumulative Review

Tell whether the number is divisible by 2, 3, 5, 6, 7, 9, or 10. *(Lesson 5-1)*

1. 70 — 2, 5, 7, 10
2. 120 — 2, 3, 5, 6, 10
3. 63 — 3, 7, 9
4. 210 — 2, 3, 5, 7, 10

Find the area of each irregular figure. Use 3.14 for π. *(Lesson 4-9)*

5. 210 in^2
6. 66.28 yd^2
7. 21 cm^2

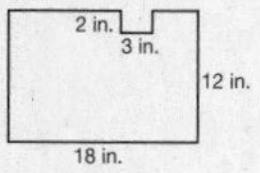

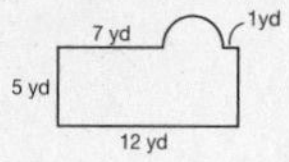

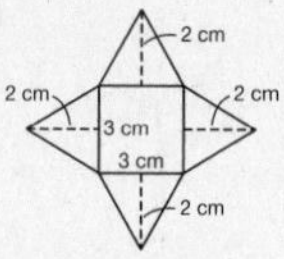

Mixed Review

8. If the circumference of a circle is 20.10 cm, what is the area rounded to the nearest tenth? *(4-8)* 32.2 cm^2
9. A large watermelon weighs 14.6 pounds. How many ounces it that? *(4-3)* 233.6 oz
10. Compare using <, >, or =. *(3-9)* 7.23 × 0.17 (<) 72.3 × 1.7
11. Round to the underlined place value. 821. 9̲6 *(3-2)* 822.0
12. Evaluate 6*x* for *x* = 2, 3, and 5. *(2-10)* 12; 18; 30
13. Write 5 cubed in standard form. *(2-4)* 125
14. Find the mean, median, and mode(s) for 5, 3, 8, 7, 4, 7, 6, 2, 8, 9, 4, 3, 9, 4, 5 *(1-8)*

mean 5.6 median 5 mode(s) 4

Name ______________________

Daily Review 5-3

Daily Cumulative Review

Find the prime factorization. *(Lesson 5-2)*

1. 38 — 2 × 19
2. 64 — 2 × 2 × 2 × 2 × 2 × 2
3. 70 — 2 × 5 × 7
4. 66 — 3 × 2 × 11

Tell whether the first number is divisible by the second. *(Lesson 5-1)*

5. 35, 2 No
6. 31, 3 No
7. 88, 11 Yes
8. 198, 11 Yes

Mixed Review

9. Find the area. Use 3.14 for π. *(4-9)* 54.625 m^2

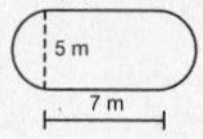

10. Find the circumference. *(4-7)* 94.2 m

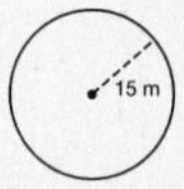

11. Solve. 2.58*x* = 16.254 *(3-12)* *x* = 6.3
12. Simplify 8.976 + 2.328 *(3-6)* 11.304
13. Write 6.013 in word form. *(3-1)* six and thirteen thousandths
14. Solve. *x* − 21 = 78 *(2-13)* *x* = 99
15. Evaluate. $(2 + 4^3) \div 11$ *(2-8)* 6
16. Write 3 million in standard form. *(2-1)* 3,000,000
17. Make a stem-and-leaf diagram of the data showing scores on a test. *(1-6)*
77, 85, 93, 78, 96, 86, 92, 99, 75, 83
75, 91, 86, 77, 95, 82, 94, 72, 81, 77

Stem	Leaf
7	2 5 5 7 7 7 8
8	1 2 3 5 6 6
9	1 2 3 4 5 6 9

Name ______________________

Daily Review 5-4

Daily Cumulative Review

Find the least common multiple of each pair. *(Lesson 5-3)*

1. 4, 23 92
2. 5, 35 35
3. 12, 5, 60
4. 11, 7 77

Tell whether the given number is prime or composite. *(Lesson 5-2)*

5. 29 Prime
6. 63 Composite
7. 52 Composite

Mixed Review

8. Is 95 divisible by 3? *(5-1)* No
9. Is 87 divisible by 3? *(5-1)* Yes
10. Find the area of a square with sides of length 6.4 ft. *(4-4)* 40.96 ft^2
11. Divide. 230.92 ÷ 46 *(3-10)* 5.02
12. Solve. 6.1 + *k* = 11.3 *(3-7)* *k* = 5.2
13. Solve. *x* ÷ 7 = 6 *(2-13)* *x* = 42
14. Estimate. 5138 + 4963 + 4874 + 5002 *(2-6)* 20,000
15. Estimate. 6199 + 3100 + 9798 + 3001 *(2-6)* 22,000
16. Find the mean, median, and mode(s) with and without the outliers. *(1-9)*

With outlier
mean 512,200
median 466,000
mode(s) None

Without outlier
mean 637,500
median 591,000
mode(s) None

National Preserves (thousands of acres)	
Anigkchak	466
Big Cypress	716
Gates of Arctic	949
Katmai	419
Tall Grass Prairie	11

17. What is the range of the data for Exercise 16? *(1-5)* 938,000

Name ______________________

Daily Review 5-5

Daily Cumulative Review

For each fraction, draw a model and name an equivalent fraction. *(Lesson 5-4)*

1. $\frac{2}{5}$ — $\frac{4}{10}$

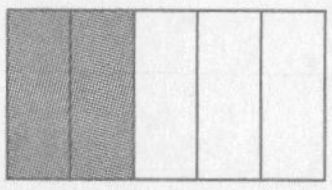

2. $\frac{6}{12}$ — $\frac{1}{2}$

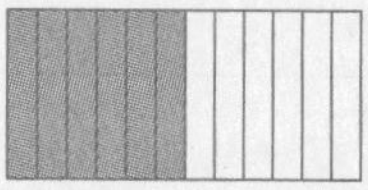

Find the LCM of each pair. *(Lesson 5-3)*

3. 7, 9 63
4. 12, 16 48
5. 14, 11 154

Mixed Review

6. Find the prime factorization of 120. *(5-2)* 2 × 2 × 2 × 3 × 5
7. Convert 0.12 km = 12,000 cm *(4-2)*
8. Estimate. $7.31 × 8.27 *(3-5)* $56
9. Simplify. 93,715 − 300 *(2-5)* 93,415
10. Order from least to greatest. 17 million; 3 million; 32 thousand; 302,000 *(2-3)*
32 thousand; 302,000; 3 million; 17 million
11. Make a bar graph from the data showing the height of several famous waterfalls. *(1-5)*

Waterfall	Height (ft)
Angel Falls, Venezuela	3,212
King George Falls, Guyana	1,600
Takakkaw, Canada	1,200
Silver Strand Falls, USA	1,170

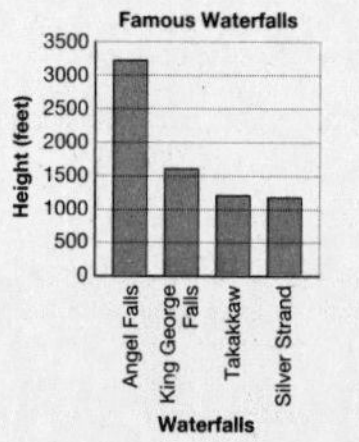

12. From the graph in Exercise 11, about how many times higher is the Angel Falls than the Silver Strand Falls? *(1-1)* 3

Name ____________________

Daily Review 5-6

Daily Cumulative Review

Write in lowest terms. *(Lesson 5-5)*

1. $\frac{8}{16}$ $\frac{1}{2}$
2. $\frac{5}{15}$ $\frac{1}{3}$
3. $\frac{8}{28}$ $\frac{2}{7}$
4. $\frac{4}{20}$ $\frac{1}{5}$

For each fraction, draw a model and name an equivalent fraction. *(Lesson 5-4)*

5. $\frac{3}{10}$ $\frac{6}{20}$
6. $\frac{9}{12}$ $\frac{3}{4}$
7. $\frac{2}{6}$ $\frac{1}{3}$

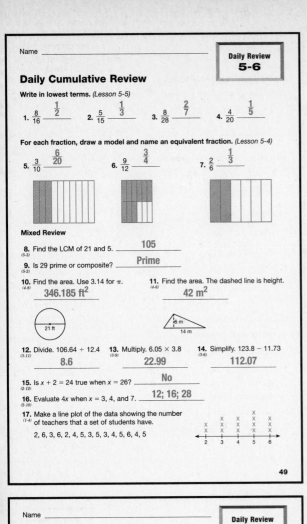

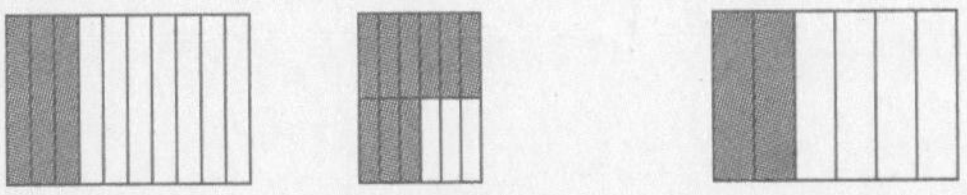

Mixed Review

8. Find the LCM of 21 and 5. (5-3) 105
9. Is 29 prime or composite? (5-2) Prime
10. Find the area. Use 3.14 for π. (4-8) $346.185\ ft^2$
11. Find the area. The dashed line is height. (4-6) $42\ m^2$

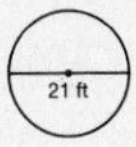

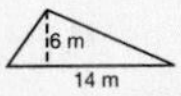

12. Divide. $106.64 \div 12.4$ (3-11) 8.6
13. Multiply. 6.05×3.8 (3-9) 22.99
14. Simplify. $123.8 - 11.73$ (3-6) 112.07
15. Is $x + 2 = 24$ true when $x = 26$? (2-12) No
16. Evaluate $4x$ when $x = 3, 4,$ and 7. (2-10) 12; 16; 28
17. Make a line plot of the data showing the number of teachers that a set of students have. (1-4)
    2, 6, 3, 6, 2, 4, 5, 3, 5, 3, 4, 5, 6, 4, 5

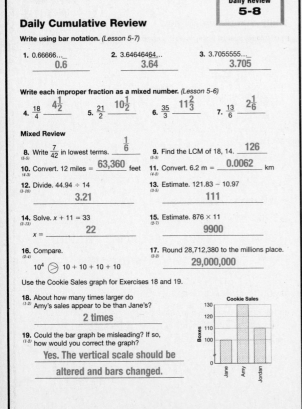

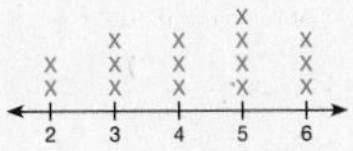

49

Name ____________________

Daily Review 5-7

Daily Cumulative Review

Write each mixed number as an improper fraction. *(Lesson 5-6)*

1. $3\frac{1}{6}$ $\frac{19}{6}$
2. $4\frac{1}{5}$ $\frac{21}{5}$
3. $1\frac{3}{8}$ $\frac{11}{8}$
4. $14\frac{1}{2}$ $\frac{29}{2}$

Find the greatest common factor of each pair. *(Lesson 5-5)*

5. 18, 10 2
6. 11, 16 1
7. 21, 6 3
8. 10, 6 2

Mixed Review

9. Find the prime factorization of 450. (5-2) $2 \times 3 \times 3 \times 5 \times 5$
10. Find the area. (4-5) $11.48\ cm^2$
11. Find the perimeter. (4-1) 38 cm

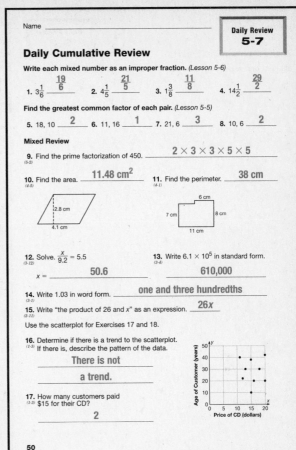

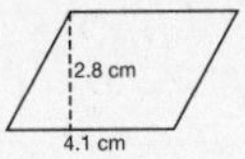

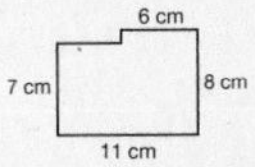

12. Solve. $\frac{x}{9.2} = 5.5$ (3-12) $x =$ 50.6
13. Write 6.1×10^5 in standard form. (3-4) 610,000
14. Write 1.03 in word form. (3-1) one and three hundredths
15. Write "the product of 26 and x" as an expression. (2-11) $26x$

Use the scatterplot for Exercises 17 and 18.

16. Determine if there is a trend to the scatterplot. If there is, describe the pattern of the data. (1-3) There is not a trend.
17. How many customers paid $15 for their CD? (1-3) 2

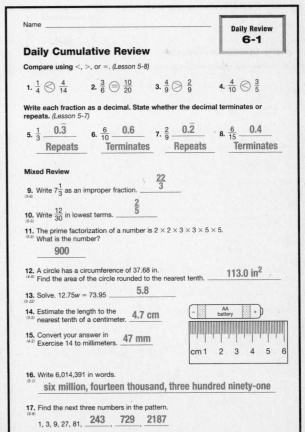

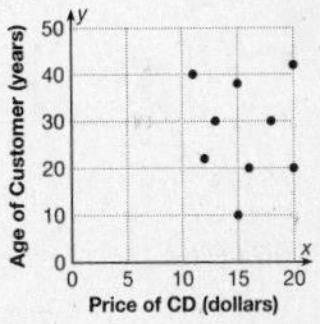

50

Name ____________________

Daily Review 5-8

Daily Cumulative Review

Write using bar notation. *(Lesson 5-7)*

1. 0.66666... $0.\overline{6}$
2. 3.64646464... $3.\overline{64}$
3. 3.7055555... $3.70\overline{5}$

Write each improper fraction as a mixed number. *(Lesson 5-6)*

4. $\frac{18}{4}$ $4\frac{1}{2}$
5. $\frac{21}{2}$ $10\frac{1}{2}$
6. $\frac{35}{3}$ $11\frac{2}{3}$
7. $\frac{13}{6}$ $2\frac{1}{6}$

Mixed Review

8. Write $\frac{7}{42}$ in lowest terms. (5-5) $\frac{1}{6}$
9. Find the LCM of 18, 14. (5-3) 126
10. Convert. 12 miles = 63,360 feet (4-3)
11. Convert. 6.2 m = 0.0062 km (4-2)
12. Divide. $44.94 \div 14$ (3-10) 3.21
13. Estimate. $121.83 - 10.97$ (3-5) 111
14. Solve. $x + 11 = 33$ (2-13) $x =$ 22
15. Estimate. 876×11 (2-7) 9900
16. Compare. (2-4) 10^4 (>) $10 + 10 + 10 + 10$
17. Round 28,712,380 to the millions place. (2-2) 29,000,000

Use the Cookie Sales graph for Exercises 18 and 19.

18. About how many times larger do Amy's sales appear to be than Jane's? (1-2) 2 times
19. Could the bar graph be misleading? If so, how would you correct the graph? (1-2) Yes. The vertical scale should be altered and bars changed.

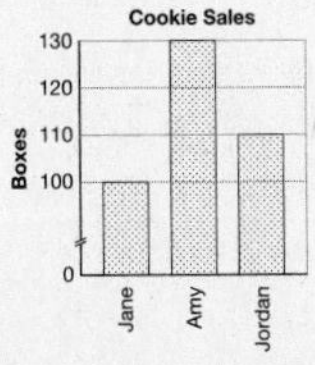

51

Name ____________________

Daily Review 6-1

Daily Cumulative Review

Compare using <, >, or =. *(Lesson 5-8)*

1. $\frac{1}{4}$ (<) $\frac{4}{14}$
2. $\frac{3}{6}$ (=) $\frac{10}{20}$
3. $\frac{4}{9}$ (>) $\frac{2}{9}$
4. $\frac{4}{10}$ (<) $\frac{3}{5}$

Write each fraction as a decimal. State whether the decimal terminates or repeats. *(Lesson 5-7)*

5. $\frac{1}{3}$ $0.\overline{3}$ Repeats
6. $\frac{6}{10}$ 0.6 Terminates
7. $\frac{2}{9}$ $0.\overline{2}$ Repeats
8. $\frac{6}{15}$ 0.4 Terminates

Mixed Review

9. Write $7\frac{1}{3}$ as an improper fraction. (5-6) $\frac{22}{3}$
10. Write $\frac{12}{30}$ in lowest terms. (5-5) $\frac{2}{5}$
11. The prime factorization of a number is $2 \times 2 \times 3 \times 3 \times 5 \times 5$. What is the number? (5-2) 900
12. A circle has a circumference of 37.68 in. Find the area of the circle rounded to the nearest tenth. (4-8) $113.0\ in^2$
13. Solve. $12.75w = 73.95$ (3-12) 5.8
14. Estimate the length to the nearest tenth of a centimeter. (3-2) 4.7 cm
15. Convert your answer in Exercise 14 to millimeters. (4-2) 47 mm

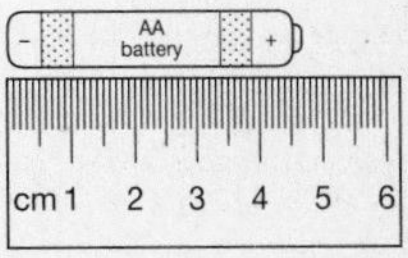

16. Write 6,014,391 in words. (2-1) six million, fourteen thousand, three hundred ninety-one
17. Find the next three numbers in the pattern. (2-9)
    1, 3, 9, 27, 81, 243, 729, 2187

52

Name ______________________

Daily Review 6-2

Daily Cumulative Review

Simplify. Write each answer in lowest terms. *(Lesson 6-1)*

1. $\frac{3}{10} - \frac{1}{10}$ $\frac{1}{5}$
2. $\frac{7}{15} + \frac{5}{15}$ $\frac{4}{5}$
3. $\frac{2}{3} + \frac{2}{3}$ $1\frac{1}{3}$
4. $\frac{7}{8} - \frac{5}{8}$ $\frac{1}{4}$

Order from smallest to largest. *(Lesson 5-8)*

5. $\frac{5}{8}, \frac{5}{9}, \frac{5}{10}$ $\frac{5}{10}, \frac{5}{9}, \frac{5}{8}$
6. $\frac{3}{5}, \frac{5}{3}, \frac{3}{3}$ $\frac{3}{5}, \frac{3}{3}, \frac{5}{3}$
7. $\frac{9}{10}, \frac{24}{25}, \frac{4}{5}$ $\frac{4}{5}, \frac{9}{10}, \frac{24}{25}$

Mixed Review

8. Draw a model for $\frac{9}{15}$. *(5-4)*

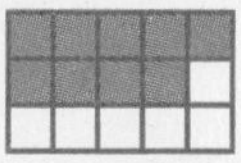

Name an equivalent fraction. $\frac{3}{5}$

9. Find the area. Use 3.14 for π. *(4-9)*

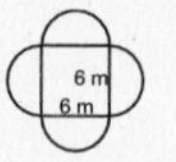

92.52 m^2

10. Convert. 136 ounces = 8.5 pounds. *(4-3)*

11. Divide. 45.7475 ÷ 7.25 *(3-11)* 6.31

12. Simplify. 3.275 + 5.841 + 7.3872 *(3-6)* 16.5032

13. Solve. $x - 12 = 79$ *(2-13)* $x =$ 91

14. Evaluate. 14 − (8 − 3) *(2-8)* 9

15. Simplify. 20 × 81 × 50 *(2-5)* 81,000

16. Find the median and mode(s). *(1-7)*

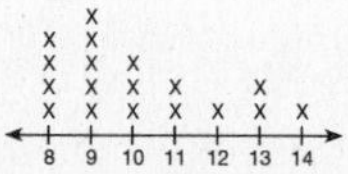

median 9.5 mode(s) 9

Name ______________________

Daily Review 6-3

Daily Cumulative Review

Simplify. Write each answer in lowest terms. *(Lesson 6-2)*

1. $\frac{3}{5} - \frac{1}{2}$ $\frac{1}{10}$
2. $\frac{3}{8} + \frac{7}{24}$ $\frac{2}{3}$
3. $\frac{7}{16} - \frac{1}{8}$ $\frac{5}{16}$
4. $\frac{4}{5} - \frac{5}{9}$ $\frac{11}{45}$

State whether the answer is greater than, less than, or equal to 1. *(Lesson 6-1)*

5. $\frac{7}{12} - \frac{5}{12}$ Less than 1
6. $\frac{7}{9} + \frac{2}{9}$ Equal to 1
7. $\frac{4}{5} + \frac{2}{5}$ Greater than 1

Mixed Review

8. Write $\frac{5}{9}$ as a decimal. *(5-7)* $0.\overline{5}$

9. Is 98 divisible by 6? *(5-1)* No

10. Find the area. *(4-6)* 99.2 yd^2

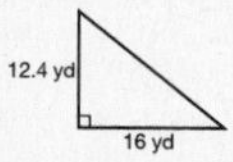

Use the scatterplot for Exercises 11 and 12.

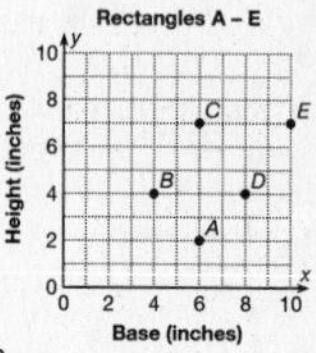

11. Find the area of Rectangle *A*. *(4-4)* 12 in^2

12. Which rectangle is a square? *(4-4)* B

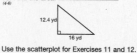

13. Compare using <, >, or =. *(3-9)* 3.7 × 8.16 (<) 3.7 × 81.6

14. Write 650,000,000,000 in scientific notation. *(3-4)* 6.5×10^{11}

15. Evaluate $x + 3$, $12 - x$, and $8x$ for $x = 5$. *(2-10)* 8; 7; 40

16. For the number 3^8, identify each of the following: *(2-4)*

base 3 power 8 exponent 8

Name ______________________

Daily Review 6-4

Daily Cumulative Review

Solve. Write each answer in lowest terms. *(Lesson 6-3)*

1. $\frac{5}{12} + a = \frac{8}{12}$ $\frac{1}{4}$
2. $x - \frac{1}{6} = \frac{3}{4}$ $\frac{11}{12}$
3. $\frac{7}{8} - y = \frac{11}{16}$ $\frac{3}{16}$
4. $g + \frac{1}{4} = \frac{9}{16}$ $\frac{5}{16}$

Simplify. Write each answer in lowest terms. *(Lesson 6-2)*

5. $\frac{1}{5} - \frac{1}{6}$ $\frac{1}{30}$
6. $\frac{1}{2} + \frac{3}{8}$ $\frac{7}{8}$
7. $\frac{4}{7} - \frac{1}{3}$ $\frac{5}{21}$
8. $\frac{1}{4} + \frac{15}{24}$ $\frac{7}{8}$

Mixed Review

9. The bar graph shows the animals in the pet shop. What fraction of the animals are cats and dogs? *(6-1)* $\frac{16}{27}$

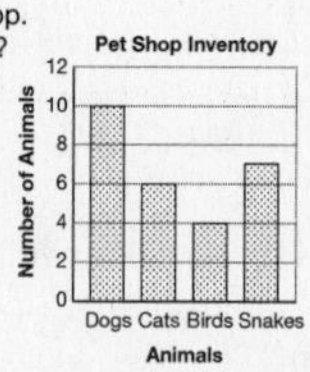

10. Write $\frac{18}{60}$ in lowest terms. *(5-5)* $\frac{3}{10}$

11. Write $\frac{102}{7}$ as a mixed number. *(5-6)* $14\frac{4}{7}$

12. Find the LCM of 15 and 9. *(5-3)* 45

13. Find the circumference of a circle whose radius is 7.5 mm. Use 3.14 for π. *(4-7)* 47.1 mm

14. A triangle has a perimeter of 79 m. If two of the sides have lengths 30 m and 25 m, what is the length of the third side? *(4-1)* 24 m

15. Solve. $2.89 + x = 6.2$ *(3-7)* $x =$ 3.31

16. Order from least to greatest. 57.77; 57.777; 57.7 *(3-3)* 57.7; 57.77; 57.777

17. Estimate. 57,613 − 12,302 *(2-6)* 46,000

Name ______________________

Daily Review 6-5

Daily Cumulative Review

Round to the nearest whole number. *(Lesson 6-4)*

1. $3\frac{4}{5}$ 4
2. $7\frac{21}{34}$ 8
3. $9\frac{7}{20}$ 9
4. $14\frac{6}{7}$ 15

Write a true equation using the fractions given. *(Lesson 6-3)*

5. $\frac{4}{7}, \frac{2}{5}, \frac{6}{35}$ $\frac{4}{7} - \frac{2}{5} = \frac{6}{35}$
6. $\frac{3}{7}, \frac{2}{7}, \frac{5}{7}$ $\frac{3}{7} + \frac{2}{7} = \frac{5}{7}$
7. $\frac{1}{9}, \frac{5}{6}, \frac{17}{18}$ $\frac{1}{9} + \frac{5}{6} = \frac{17}{18}$
8. $\frac{1}{3}, \frac{3}{8}, \frac{1}{24}$ $\frac{3}{8} - \frac{1}{3} = \frac{1}{24}$

Mixed Review

9. Simplify. $\frac{5}{8} - \frac{1}{2}$ *(6-2)* $\frac{1}{8}$

10. Is 65 prime or composite? *(5-2)* Composite

11. Write 0.625 as a fraction in lowest terms. *(5-7)* $\frac{5}{8}$

12. Find the area of a square with sides of length 6.8 in. *(4-4)* 46.24 in^2

13. Convert. 63 cm = 0.63 m *(4-2)*

14. Divide. 130.62 ÷ 21 *(3-10)* 6.22

15. Multiply. 52.3 × 1000 *(3-8)* 52,300

16. Estimate. 29 × 907 *(2-7)* 27,000

17. Is $x - 9 = 51$ true when $x = 42$? *(2-12)* No

18. Make a stem-and-leaf diagram of the data. *(1-6)*

67, 95, 70, 81, 90, 68, 73, 84, 79, 83,

68, 72, 79, 83, 92, 83, 71, 74, 87

Stem	Leaf
6	7 8 8
7	0 1 2 3 4 9 9
8	1 3 3 3 4 7
9	0 2 5

19. What is the range of the data in Exercise 18? *(1-5)* 28

Name ______________________

Daily Review 6-6

Daily Cumulative Review

Add. Write the answer as a whole number or mixed number in lowest terms. *(Lesson 6-5)*

1. $11\frac{1}{5} + 4\frac{3}{5}$ $15\frac{4}{5}$
2. $6\frac{3}{5} + 1\frac{2}{3}$ $8\frac{4}{15}$
3. $4 + 6\frac{3}{14}$ $10\frac{3}{14}$

Estimate. *(Lesson 6-4)*

4. $2\frac{1}{6} + 6\frac{7}{8}$ 9
5. $9\frac{1}{12} - 6\frac{7}{8}$ 2
6. $18\frac{4}{7} + 6\frac{1}{5}$ 25

Mixed Review

7. Solve. $\frac{5}{6} + x = \frac{23}{24}$ $x =$ $\frac{1}{8}$
(6-3)

8. What fraction does the shaded part represent?
(5-4)
$\frac{2}{6}$ or $\frac{1}{3}$

9. Find the prime factorization of 630. $2 \times 3 \times 3 \times 5 \times 7$
(5-2)

10. A quilt pattern is made of 12 triangles placed together. If each triangle has a base of 8 cm and a height of 12.5 cm, what is the area of the pattern?
(4-9)
600 cm^2

11. Estimate. 4.7×7.13 35
(3-5)

12. Write 0.08 in word form. eight hundredths
(3-1)

13. Order from least to greatest. 63 thousand; 63 million; 630,000
(2-3)
63 thousand; 630,000; 63 million

14. Make a line plot with the following data.
(1-4)
2, 2, 5, 5, 7, 7, 9, 9, 8, 2, 2, 3, 4, 5, 5, 6

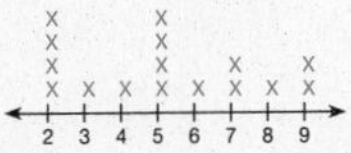

Name ______________________

Daily Review 7-1

Daily Cumulative Review

Subtract. Write the answer as a whole number or mixed number in lowest terms. *(Lesson 6-6)*

1. $6\frac{2}{5} - 5\frac{2}{3}$ $\frac{11}{15}$
2. $12\frac{7}{10} - 8\frac{1}{5}$ $4\frac{1}{2}$
3. $7\frac{5}{6} - 5\frac{5}{24}$ $2\frac{5}{8}$
4. $4\frac{5}{6} - 4\frac{7}{12}$ $\frac{1}{4}$

Add. Write the answer as a whole number or mixed number in lowest terms. *(Lesson 6-5)*

5. $5 + 7\frac{1}{2}$ $12\frac{1}{2}$
6. $12\frac{1}{8} + 10\frac{3}{5}$ $22\frac{29}{40}$
7. $5\frac{1}{7} + 18\frac{2}{5}$ $23\frac{19}{35}$
8. $15\frac{5}{12} + 1\frac{1}{3}$ $16\frac{3}{4}$

Mixed Review

9. Estimate. $2\frac{1}{8} + 7\frac{15}{16}$ 10
(6-4)

10. Write 0.82 as a fraction in lowest terms. $\frac{41}{50}$
(5-7)

11. Find the LCM of 12 and 28. 84
(5-3)

12. Find the circumference of a circle with diameter of length 18 inches. 56.52 in.
(4-7)

13. Divide. $9.106 \div 2.9$ 3.14
(3-11)

14. Multiply. 16.5×9 148.5
(3-8)

15. Compare using <, >, or =. 36.58 < 36.581
(3-3)

16. Solve. $x + 14 = 61$ $x =$ 47
(2-13)

17. Evaluate. $5 + (3^2 - 2)$ 12
(2-8)

18. Write 5^4 in expanded form. $5 \times 5 \times 5 \times 5$
(2-4)

19. Make a line plot for the data and find the median and mode(s).
(1-7)
25, 26, 24, 21, 25, 21, 23, 20, 25, 22, 21

median 23 mode(s) 21 and 25

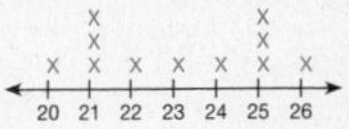

Name ______________________

Daily Review 7-2

Daily Cumulative Review

Estimate. *(Lesson 7-1)*

1. $5\frac{1}{3} \times 9\frac{1}{8}$ 45
2. $8\frac{1}{9} \div 3\frac{7}{8}$ 2
3. $6\frac{2}{3} \times 2\frac{5}{6}$ 21
4. $12\frac{2}{9} \div 4\frac{1}{8}$ 3

Subtract. Write each answer in lowest terms. *(Lesson 6-6)*

5. $5\frac{1}{7} - 3\frac{2}{3}$ $1\frac{10}{21}$
6. $18\frac{9}{10} - 12\frac{3}{5}$ $6\frac{3}{10}$
7. $8\frac{1}{4} - 6\frac{1}{12}$ $2\frac{1}{6}$
8. $16\frac{11}{14} - 14\frac{2}{7}$ $2\frac{1}{2}$

Mixed Review

9. Solve. Write answer in lowest terms. $\frac{7}{9} - x = \frac{5}{27}$ $x =$ $\frac{16}{27}$
(6-3)

10. Write $5\frac{3}{4}$ as an improper fraction. $\frac{23}{4}$
(5-6)

11. Find the prime factorization of 819. $3 \times 3 \times 7 \times 13$
(5-2)

12. Find the area of circle whose radius is 7 ft. 153.86 ft^2
(4-8)

13. Solve. $0.9x = 8.262$ $x =$ 9.18
(3-12)

14. Simplify. \$5.87 + \$12.32 \$18.19
(3-6)

15. Write six hundredths as a decimal. 0.06
(3-1)

16. Simplify. 200×380 76,000
(2-5)

17. Find the mean, median, and mode of the data set.
(1-8)

Mean 58

Median 59.5

Mode(s) 46, 59, 60, 61, and 64

Stem	Leaf
4	6 6 7
5	0 1 3 8 9 9
6	0 0 1 1 4 4 6 9
7	0

Name ______________________

Daily Review 7-3

Daily Cumulative Review

Simplify. *(Lesson 7-2)*

1. $6\frac{1}{2} \times 4$ 26
2. $3 \times 5\frac{2}{3}$ 17
3. $10 \times 4\frac{5}{6}$ $48\frac{1}{3}$
4. $14 \times 4\frac{1}{3}$ $60\frac{2}{3}$

Estimate. *(Lesson 7-1)*

5. $7\frac{1}{6} \times 8\frac{1}{9}$ 56
6. $13\frac{7}{8} \div 2\frac{1}{12}$ 7
7. $7\frac{1}{5} \times 7\frac{1}{3}$ 49
8. $14\frac{2}{3} \div 2\frac{7}{8}$ 5

Mixed Review

9. Add. $8\frac{7}{15} + 4\frac{7}{9}$ $13\frac{11}{45}$
(6-5)

10. Order $\frac{1}{6}, \frac{1}{7}, \frac{5}{42}$ from smallest to largest. $\frac{5}{42}, \frac{1}{7}, \frac{1}{6}$
(5-8)

11. Find the area. 44 in^2
(4-9)

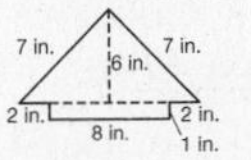

12. Find the perimeter. 29 ft
(4-1)

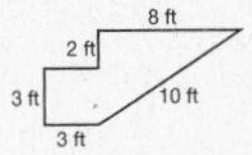

Estimate.

13. $2.78 + 1.91$ 5
(3-5)

14. 28.72×6.9 210
(3-5)

15. $15.816 - 5.12$ 11
(3-5)

16. $56.125 \div 8.1$ 7
(3-5)

17. Vance baked 7 loaves of bread, each weighing w ounces. The total weight was 84 oz. Write an equation for this situation. $7w = 84$
(2-12)

18. Find the next three numbers in the pattern.
(2-9)
132, 140, 138, 146, 144, 152, 150, 158

Name ______

Daily Review 7-4

Daily Cumulative Review

Find each product. *(Lesson 7-3)*

1. $6\frac{1}{2} \times \frac{1}{2}$ $3\frac{1}{4}$
2. $\frac{3}{4} \times \frac{5}{6}$ $\frac{5}{8}$
3. $\frac{8}{9} \times \frac{1}{3}$ $\frac{8}{27}$
4. $\frac{2}{3} \times 5\frac{1}{4}$ $3\frac{1}{2}$

Simplify. *(Lesson 7-2)*

5. $5 \times 3\frac{2}{3}$ $18\frac{1}{3}$
6. $5 \times 5\frac{1}{7}$ $25\frac{5}{7}$
7. $8\frac{1}{2} \times 2$ 17
8. $12\frac{1}{5} \times 4$ $48\frac{4}{5}$

Mixed Review

9. (6-6) Subtract. $12\frac{7}{18} - 5\frac{1}{3}$ $7\frac{1}{18}$

10. (6-3) Solve. $\frac{1}{6} + w = \frac{19}{24}$ $w = \frac{5}{8}$

The bar graph shows the number of jeans, t-shirts, shorts, and sweats in Tim's closet. Use the graph for Exercises **11** and **12**.

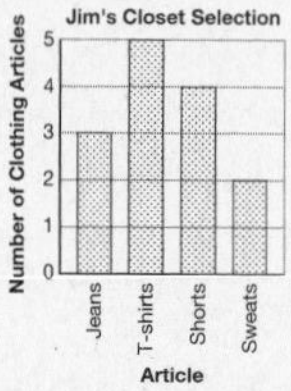

11. (6-1) What fraction of the clothes are jeans and shorts? $\frac{1}{2}$

12. (6-1) What fraction of the clothes are t-shirts and sweats? $\frac{1}{2}$

13. (4-5) Find the area. The dashed line is the height. $13.02\ cm^2$

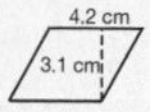

14. (2-11) Write "one-third of x" as an expression. $\frac{1}{3}x$

15. (2-1) Write $17,000,000,000 in word-number form. $17 billion

61

Name ______

Daily Review 7-5

Daily Cumulative Review

Simplify. *(Lesson 7-4)*

1. $12 \div \frac{1}{6}$ 72
2. $6 \div \frac{2}{3}$ 9
3. $4 \div 1\frac{5}{8}$ $2\frac{6}{13}$
4. $9 \div 2\frac{1}{3}$ $3\frac{6}{7}$

Find each product. *(Lesson 7-3)*

5. $\frac{2}{3} \times \frac{3}{8}$ $\frac{1}{4}$
6. $\frac{5}{6} \times \frac{2}{7}$ $\frac{5}{21}$
7. $\frac{3}{8} \times \frac{4}{5}$ $\frac{3}{10}$
8. $\frac{1}{12} \times \frac{3}{7}$ $\frac{1}{28}$

Mixed Review

9. (7-2) Multiply. $10 \times 7\frac{1}{5}$ 72

10. (6-6) Subtract. $8\frac{4}{5} - 6\frac{3}{20}$ $2\frac{13}{20}$

11. (6-2) Simplify. $\frac{13}{15} - \frac{7}{10}$ $\frac{1}{6}$

12. (5-7) Write $\frac{3}{11}$ as a decimal. $0.\overline{27}$

13. (5-1) Is 117 divisible by 9? Yes

14. (4-3) Convert. 372 inches = 31 feet

15. (3-11) Divide. 3.5584 ÷ 1.112 3.2

16. (3-9) Compare using <, >, or =. $7.32 \times 23.0 = 73.2 \times 2.3$

17. (2-10) Evaluate $80 \div x$ for $x = 2, 5, 8$. $x =$ 40; 16; 10

Use the Enrollment graph to answer the questions.

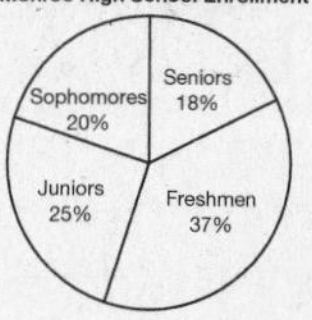

18. (1-1) What class has the largest enrollment? Freshmen

19. (1-1) If Monroe High has 1,000 students, how many are juniors? 250

62

Name ______

Daily Review 7-6

Daily Cumulative Review

Simplify. *(Lesson 7-5)*

1. $2\frac{3}{5} \div \frac{1}{3}$ $7\frac{4}{5}$
2. $2\frac{2}{3} \div \frac{1}{8}$ $21\frac{1}{3}$
3. $\frac{1}{2} \div \frac{2}{3}$ $\frac{3}{4}$
4. $\frac{5}{6} \div 1\frac{1}{3}$ $\frac{5}{8}$

Simplify. *(Lesson 7-4)*

5. $14 \div \frac{1}{3}$ 42
6. $8 \div \frac{1}{4}$ 32
7. $11 \div \frac{5}{6}$ $13\frac{1}{5}$
8. $7 \div 1\frac{8}{9}$ $3\frac{12}{17}$

Mixed Review

9. (7-3) Simplify. $\frac{3}{5} \times \frac{3}{7}$ $\frac{9}{35}$

10. (6-5) Add. $8\frac{1}{2} + 12\frac{1}{7}$ $20\frac{9}{14}$

11. (5-8) Compare using <, >, or =. $\frac{10}{12} > \frac{3}{4}$

12. (5-4) A class had 12 boys and 8 girls. What fraction of the class was boys? $\frac{12}{20}$ or $\frac{3}{5}$

13. (4-4) Find the area of a rectangle with sides 4.2 cm and 7.3 cm. $30.66\ cm^2$

14. (3-10) Divide. 7.3 ÷ 73 0.1

15. (3-4) Write 68 billion in scientific notation. 6.8×10^{10}

16. (2-6) Estimate. 163,624 + 4,210 168,000

17. (1-3) Determine if there is a trend to the scatterplot. If there is, describe the pattern of the data.
There is a trend. The more one pays, the more the sales tax.

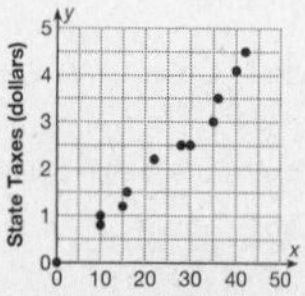

63

Name ______

Daily Review 8-1

Daily Cumulative Review

Solve. *(Lesson 7-6)*

1. $x \div 2\frac{1}{3} = \frac{1}{4}$ $x = \frac{7}{12}$
2. $3\frac{2}{5}m = \frac{1}{2}$ $m = \frac{5}{34}$
3. $f \div 4\frac{1}{3} = \frac{1}{6}$ $f = -\frac{13}{18}$
4. $\frac{1}{2}n = 6\frac{3}{4}$ $n = 13\frac{1}{2}$

Simplify. *(Lesson 7-5)*

5. $\frac{1}{2} \div \frac{3}{5}$ $\frac{5}{6}$
6. $1\frac{3}{4} \div 1\frac{1}{8}$ $1\frac{5}{9}$
7. $\frac{1}{4} \div \frac{5}{9}$ $\frac{9}{20}$

Mixed Review

8. (7-3) Find the product. $\frac{13}{15} \times \frac{1}{10}$ $\frac{13}{150}$

9. (7-1) Estimate. $8\frac{2}{7} \div 4\frac{1}{8}$ 2

10. (6-5) Add. $3\frac{19}{22} + 2\frac{1}{2}$ $6\frac{4}{11}$

11. (5-8) Order from smallest to largest. $\frac{9}{10}, \frac{24}{25}, \frac{4}{5}$ $\frac{4}{5}, \frac{9}{10}, \frac{24}{25}$

12. (5-2) Is 23 prime or composite? prime

13. (4-7) Find the diameter of a circle whose circumference is 17.27 in. 5.5 in.

14. (4-2) Convert. 32 cm = 320 mm

15. (3-9) Multiply. 0.7×0.013 0.0091

16. (3-2) Estimate the length of the worm to the nearest centimeter. 4 cm

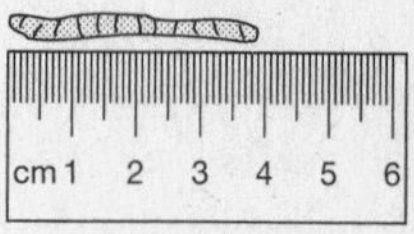

17. (2-8) Evaluate. $3 + 4 \times 6$ 27

18. (2-4) Compare using <, >, or =. $6^4 < 4^6$

19. (1-8) Find the mean. 15.7

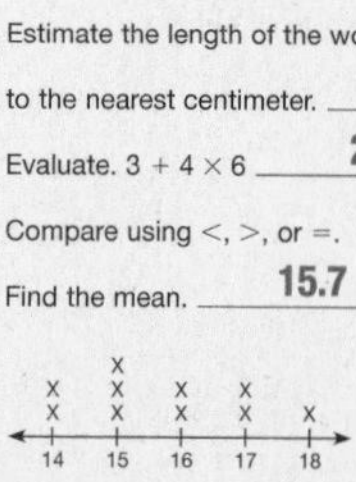

64

Name ______________________

Daily Review 8-2

Daily Cumulative Review

Draw an example of each. *(Lesson 8-1)*

1. $\overleftrightarrow{AB}$ 2. $\overrightarrow{AB}$ 3. $\overline{AB}$

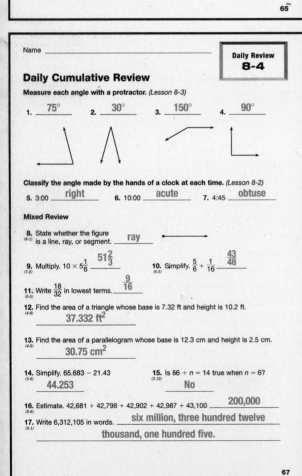

Solve. *(Lesson 7-6)*

4. $2x = 2\frac{1}{6}$ $x =$ $1\frac{1}{12}$
5. $t \div 1\frac{1}{5} = 4$ $t =$ $4\frac{4}{5}$
6. $3\frac{1}{4}p = \frac{1}{8}$ $p =$ $\frac{1}{26}$
7. $k \div \frac{9}{10} = \frac{1}{5}$ $k =$ $\frac{9}{50}$

Mixed Review

8. (7-5) Simplify. $\frac{2}{5} \div 3\frac{1}{5}$ $\frac{1}{8}$
9. (6-3) Solve. $\frac{2}{5} + p = \frac{4}{5}$; $p =$ $\frac{2}{5}$
10. (5-7) Write 0.125 as a fraction in lowest terms. $\frac{1}{8}$
11. (5-1) Is 192 divisible by 8? yes
12. (4-3) Convert. 112 quarts = 28 gallons
13. (3-12) Solve. $\frac{k}{3.72} = 10.6$ $k =$ 39.432
14. (3-7) Solve. $5.61 - x = 3.102$ $x =$ 2.508
15. (3-4) Write 6.23×10^8 in standard form. 623,000,000
16. (2-10) Complete the table.

One pizza will serve 5 children.

Number of Pizzas	Number of Servings
2	10
3	15
4	20
p	$5p$

17. (1-7) Find the median and mode(s).

median 40 mode(s) 42

Stem	Leaf
2	3 5 5 7
3	1 2 5 6
4	0 1 2 2 2 8
5	1 2 5

Name ______________________

Daily Review 8-3

Daily Cumulative Review

Classify each angle as acute, right, obtuse, or straight. *(Lesson 8-2)*

1. obtuse 2. right 3. acute 4. straight

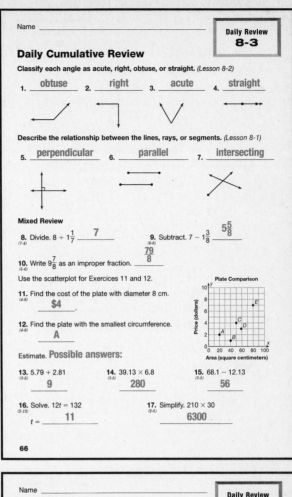

Describe the relationship between the lines, rays, or segments. *(Lesson 8-1)*

5. perpendicular 6. parallel 7. intersecting

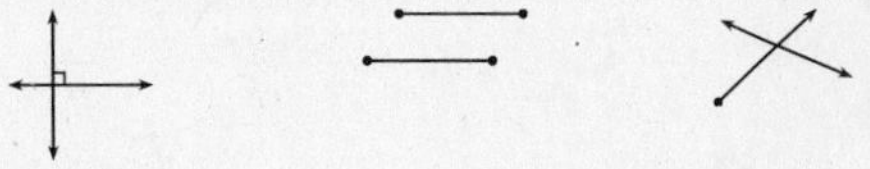

Mixed Review

8. (7-4) Divide. $8 \div 1\frac{1}{7}$ 7
9. (6-6) Subtract. $7 - 1\frac{3}{8}$ $5\frac{5}{8}$
10. (5-6) Write $9\frac{7}{8}$ as an improper fraction. $\frac{79}{8}$

Use the scatterplot for Exercises 11 and 12.

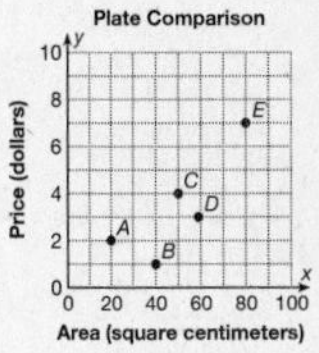

11. (4-8) Find the cost of the plate with diameter 8 cm. $4
12. (4-8) Find the plate with the smallest circumference. A

Estimate. Possible answers:

13. (3-5) $5.79 + 2.81$ 9
14. (3-5) 39.13×6.8 280
15. (3-5) $68.1 - 12.13$ 56
16. (2-13) Solve. $12t = 132$ $t =$ 11
17. (2-5) Simplify. 210×30 6300

Name ______________________

Daily Review 8-4

Daily Cumulative Review

Measure each angle with a protractor. *(Lesson 8-3)*

1. 75° 2. 30° 3. 150° 4. 90°

Classify the angle made by the hands of a clock at each time. *(Lesson 8-2)*

5. 3:00 right 6. 10:00 acute 7. 4:45 obtuse

Mixed Review

8. (8-1) State whether the figure is a line, ray, or segment. ray

9. (7-2) Multiply. $10 \times 5\frac{1}{6}$ $51\frac{2}{3}$
10. (6-2) Simplify. $\frac{5}{6} + \frac{1}{16}$ $\frac{43}{48}$
11. (5-5) Write $\frac{18}{32}$ in lowest terms. $\frac{9}{16}$
12. (4-6) Find the area of a triangle whose base is 7.32 ft and height is 10.2 ft. 37.332 ft^2
13. (4-5) Find the area of a parallelogram whose base is 12.3 cm and height is 2.5 cm. 30.75 cm^2
14. (3-6) Simplify. $65.683 - 21.43$ 44.253
15. (2-12) Is $56 \div n = 14$ true when $n = 6$? No
16. (2-6) Estimate. $42,681 + 42,798 + 42,902 + 42,987 + 43,100$ 200,000
17. (2-1) Write 6,312,105 in words. six million, three hundred twelve thousand, one hundred five.

Name ______________________

Daily Review 8-5

Daily Cumulative Review

Classify each triangle as acute, right, or obtuse. *(Lesson 8-4)*

1. right 2. obtuse 3. acute 4. obtuse

Measure each angle. Find its complement and supplement *(Lesson 8-3)*

5. measure: 80° complement: 10° supplement: 100°
6. measure: 90° complement: 0° supplement: 90°
7. measure: 20° complement: 70° supplement: 160°

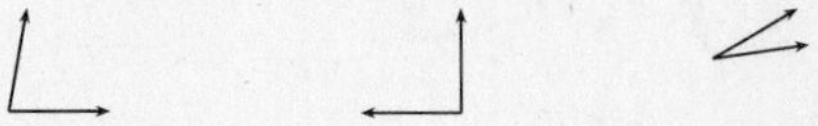

Mixed Review

8. (8-1) Describe the relationship between the lines shown. perpendicular

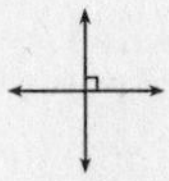

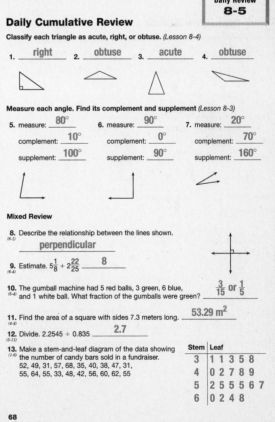

9. (6-4) Estimate. $5\frac{1}{8} + 2\frac{22}{25}$ 8
10. (5-4) The gumball machine had 5 red balls, 3 green, 6 blue, and 1 white ball. What fraction of the gumballs were green? $\frac{3}{15}$ or $\frac{1}{5}$
11. (4-4) Find the area of a square with sides 7.3 meters long. 53.29 m^2
12. (3-11) Divide. $2.2545 \div 0.835$ 2.7
13. (1-6) Make a stem-and-leaf diagram of the data showing the number of candy bars sold in a fundraiser.
52, 49, 31, 57, 68, 35, 40, 38, 47, 31,
55, 64, 55, 33, 48, 42, 56, 60, 62, 55

Stem	Leaf
3	1 1 3 5 8
4	0 2 7 8 9
5	2 5 5 5 6 7
6	0 2 4 8

Name

Daily Review 8-6

Daily Cumulative Review

Classify each triangle as scalene, equilateral, or isosceles. *(Lesson 8-5)*

1. isosceles 2. scalene 3. equilateral 4. scalene

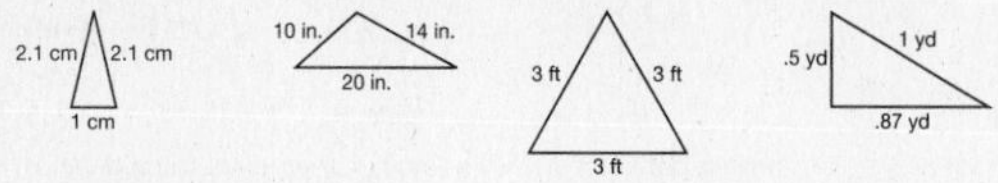

Classify each triangle as acute, right, or obtuse. *(Lesson 8-4)*

5. $m\angle T = 43°$, $m\angle U = 85°$, $m\angle V = 52°$ — acute
6. $m\angle A = 60°$, $m\angle R = 15°$, $m\angle F = 105°$ — obtuse

Mixed Review

7. Solve. $k \div \frac{1}{5} = 2\frac{1}{3}$ — $\frac{7}{15}$ (7-6)
8. Simplify. $\frac{9}{13} + \frac{1}{6}$ — $\frac{67}{78}$ (6-2)
9. Find the area. Use 3.14 for π. (4-9) — 149.13 ft^2

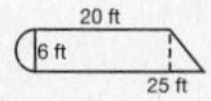

10. Find the lengths of the unknown sides. (4-1) $a =$ 26 ft $b =$ 7 ft

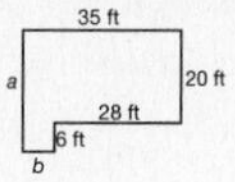

11. Divide. 193.44 ÷ 62 — 3.12 (3-10)
12. Make a frequency chart for the data in the line plot showing scores on a 10 point quiz. (1-4)

Frequency Chart

score	frequency
6	2
7	5
8	4
9	2
10	2

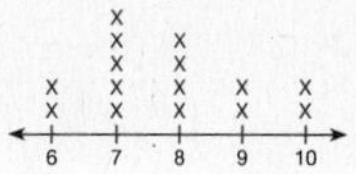

Name

Daily Review 8-7

Daily Cumulative Review

Name each polygon and tell if it is regular or irregular. *(Lesson 8-6)*

1. quadrilateral or parallelogram; irregular

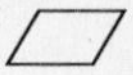

2. hexagon; regular

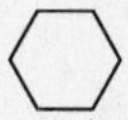

3. quadrilateral or rhombus; regular

4. quadrilateral or square; regular

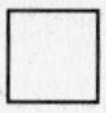

State whether the given lengths can form a triangle. *(Lesson 8-5)*

5. 8 in., 4 in., and 11 in. — Yes
6. 30 cm, 20 cm, 10 cm — No
7. 8 m, 8m, 18 m — No

Mixed Review

8. Find the measure of the missing angle in triangle *ABC*. (8-4)
$m\angle A = 92°$, $m\angle B = 49°$, $m\angle C =$ 39°
9. What is the supplement of an angle with measure 118°? (8-3) 62°
10. Simplify. $\frac{8}{9} \div \frac{1}{3}$ (7-5) — $1\frac{2}{3}$
11. Multiply. $\frac{3}{4} \times \frac{2}{7}$ (7-3) — $\frac{3}{14}$
12. Simplify. $\frac{14}{18} + \frac{7}{18}$ (6-1) — $1\frac{1}{6}$
13. Write $\frac{11}{9}$ as a decimal. (5-7) $1.\overline{2}$
14. Find the area of a parallelogram with base 7 cm and height 8.9 cm. (4-5) 62.3 cm^2
15. Write 7.036 in word form. (3-1) seven and 36 thousandths
16. Find the next three numbers in the pattern. (2-9)
6, 13, 20, 27, 34, 41, 48, 55

Name

Daily Review 8-8

Daily Cumulative Review

Classify each figure in as many ways as possible. *(Lesson 8-7)*

1. quadrilateral, parallelogram, rhombus

2. quadrilateral trapezoid

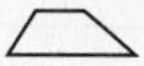

What kind of polygon is each quilt piece? *(Lesson 8-6)*

3. quadrilateral 4. triangle 5. pentagon 6. hexagon

Mixed Review

7. Draw an example of $\overrightarrow{XY}$. (8-1)

8. The circle graph shows the number of hours Peter plays sports. How many more hours did Peter spend jogging than playing tennis? (6-6) $1\frac{3}{4}$ hr

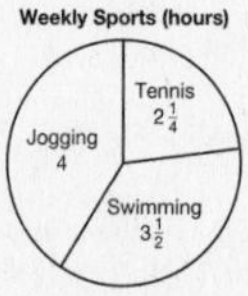

9. Multiply. 15 × 18.13 (3-8) — 271.95
10. Write a phrase for "*x* increased by 15." (2-11) — $x + 15$
11. Round 62,293,635,811 to the hundred-millions place. (2-2) — 62,300,000,000
12. Identify the outlier. (1-9) — 22
72, 85, 91, 77, 76, 22, 88, 92, 95

Name

Daily Review 8-9

Daily Cumulative Review

Tell if the picture has line symmetry. If it does, tell how many lines of symmetry it has. *(Lesson 8-8)*

1. yes, 1 2. yes, 1 3. yes, 2 4. no

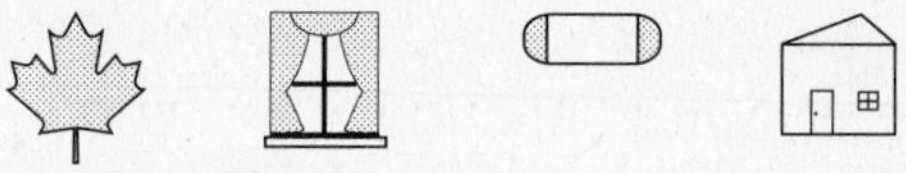

Draw an example of each figure. *(Lesson 8-7)*

5. A quadrilateral that is not a parallelogram
6. A rhombus
7. A parallelogram that is not a rectangle

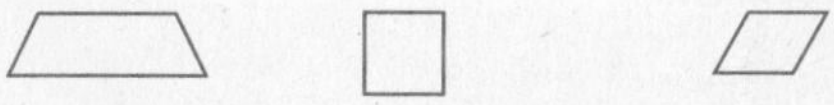

Mixed Review

8. Name the angle three ways. (8-2) $\angle ABC$, $\angle CBA$, $\angle B$

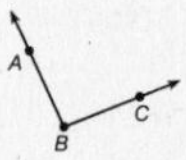

9. Complete the table for calories in a certain ice cream. (7-2)

Servings	$\frac{2}{3}$	1	$1\frac{1}{3}$	$2\frac{1}{2}$
Ounces	$5\frac{1}{3}$	8	$10\frac{2}{3}$	20
Calories	$206\frac{2}{3}$	310	$413\frac{1}{3}$	775

10. The graph shows the normal monthly rainfall for Denver, CO. On average, how much rain does Denver receive during the first six months of the year? (1-1) 8.3 in.

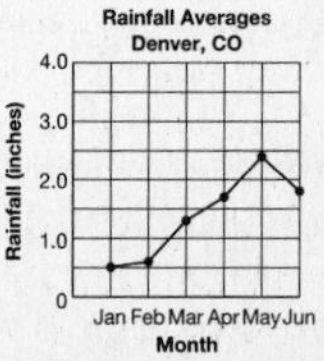

11. Colorado is about 378 miles long and about 283 miles wide. About how many square miles does this rectangular shaped state have? (2-7) 120,000 mi^2

Name ______________________

Daily Review 8-10

Daily Cumulative Review

What is the least rotation that will land the figure on top of itself? *(Lesson 8-9)*

1. 72° 2. 360° 3. 180° 4. 180°

Tell if each pair of figures are congruent. *(Lesson 8-8)*

5. no 6. yes 7. yes

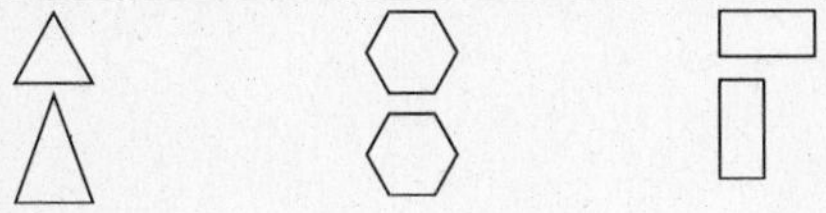

Mixed Review

8. Classify a triangle with sides of length 6 cm, 8 cm, 6 cm. isosceles
(8-5)

9. Solve. $\frac{1}{4}x = 18$
(7-6)
$x =$ 72

10. Write a true equation using $\frac{1}{6}, \frac{3}{4}, \frac{11}{12}$.
(6-3)
$\frac{1}{6} + \frac{3}{4} = \frac{11}{12}$

11. Find the prime factorization of 162. $2 \times 3 \times 3 \times 3 \times 3$
(5-2)

12. Solve. $4.61 + p = 4.98$
(3-7)
$p =$ 0.37

13. Evaluate. $(3^2 - 1) + 12$
(2-8)
20

Use the Popcorn Sales graph for Exercises 14 and 15.

14. Give the total sales of the three troops.
(1-2)
$1,850

15. If the bar graph is misleading, how would you correct it?
(1-2)
Adjust the vertical scale and bars

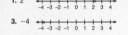

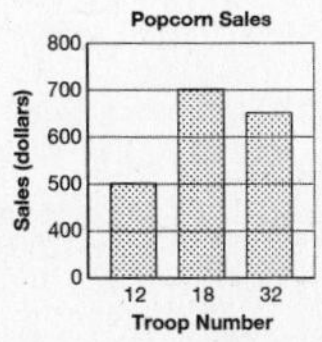

Name ______________________

Daily Review 9-1

Daily Cumulative Review

Name the polygon that is tessellated in each design. *(Lesson 8-10)*

1. Square

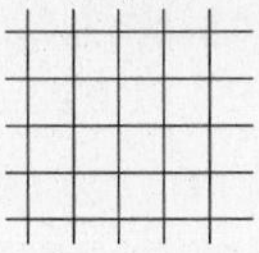

2. Hexagon

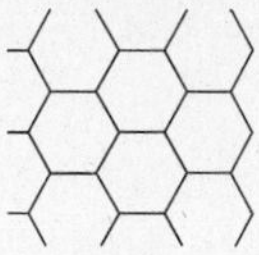

Draw a 45° clockwise rotation of the figure. *(Lesson 8-9)*

3.

4.

Mixed Review

5. Simplify.
(7-5)
$5\frac{4}{7} \div 2\frac{1}{3}$ $2\frac{19}{49}$

6. Subtract.
(6-6)
$7\frac{2}{3} - 2\frac{9}{10}$ $4\frac{23}{30}$

7. If a rhombus has a perimeter of 48 inches, what is the length of each side?
(8-7)
12 inches

8. State the angle measure that is complementary to an angle of 48°.
(8-3)
42°

9. If the circumference of a circle is 18.2 yards, what is the circle's radius and area rounded to the nearest tenth?
(4-8)
$r =$ 2.9 yd $A =$ 26.4 yd²

10. Estimate the length to the nearest tenth of a centimeter. 4.6 cm
(3-2)

11. The Roberts family traveled 2,389 miles on a summer vacation. The trip took 11 days. Estimate how far they traveled on the average each day. 200 miles
(2-7)

Name ______________________

Daily Review 9-2

Daily Cumulative Review

Locate each integer on the number line. *(Lesson 9-1)*

1. 2

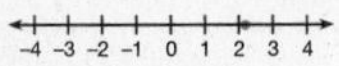

2. −2

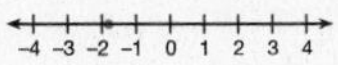

3. −4

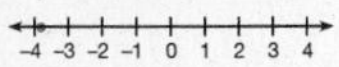

4. 3

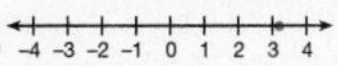

State if each figure will tessellate. Make a drawing to show your answer. *(Lesson 8-10)*

5. Does not tessellate.

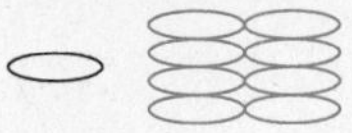

6. Tessellates

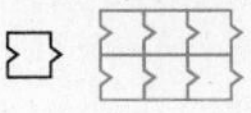

Mixed Review

7. Solve.
(7-6)
$x \div 2\frac{1}{3} = 8$
$x =$ $18\frac{2}{3}$

8. Solve.
(6-3)
$m + \frac{1}{4} = \frac{9}{16}$
$m =$ $\frac{5}{16}$

9. Write $\frac{5}{6}$ as a decimal. $0.8\overline{3}$.
(5-7)
Does $\frac{5}{6}$ repeat or terminate? Repeats

10. Solve.
(3-7)
$x - 10.6 = 1.8$
$x =$ 12.4

11. Evaluate.
(2-8)
$6^2 - 3^3$
9

12. Write 13 squared in standard form.
(2-4)
169

13. Make a line plot for the data. Then find the median and mode(s).
(1-7)
26, 32, 28, 27, 30, 32, 28, 29, 31, 28, 27, 30, 31

median 29 mode(s) 28

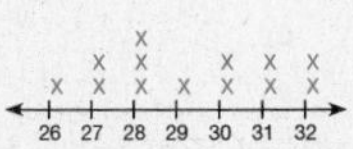

14. Find the area.
(4-9)
40.5 in²

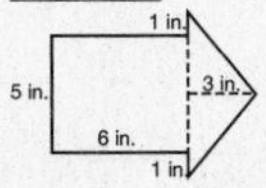

15. If gasoline costs $1.059 per gallon, how much would you pay for 14.73 gallons? (Round your answer to the nearest cent.) $15.60
(3-9)

Name ______________________

Daily Review 9-3

Daily Cumulative Review

Add. *(Lesson 9-2)*

1. $-8 + 13$ 5
2. $43 + (-2)$ 41
3. $-5 + (-6)$ −11
4. $0 + (-5)$ −5
5. $-8 + 3$ −5
6. $7 + 2$ 9

Compare using > or <. *(Lesson 9-1)*

7. −6 (<) 6 8. −3 (>) −4 9. 0 (>) −5 10. 18 (>) −19

Mixed Review

11. Find the product.
(7-3)
$\frac{1}{3} \times \frac{6}{13}$ $\frac{2}{13}$

12. Round to the nearest whole number.
(6-4)
$6\frac{17}{20}$ 7

13. Write in lowest terms.
(5-5)
$\frac{40}{56}$ $\frac{5}{7}$

14. Convert.
(4-3)
27 mi = 142,560 ft

15. Divide.
(3-10)
246.79 ÷ 29 8.51

16. Round 531,692 to the ten-thousands place.
(2-2)
530,000

17. Is the line a line of symmetry?
(8-8)
No

18. Measure each angle of the triangle.
(8-4)
$m\angle A$ 30°
$m\angle B$ 120°
$m\angle C$ 30°

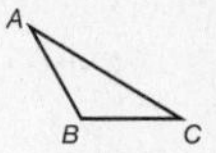

19. Make a bar graph showing the following top four movies in 1996.
(1-5)

Movie	Gross (millions)
The Rock	$134
Twister	$242
Independence Day	$306
Mission: Impossible	$181

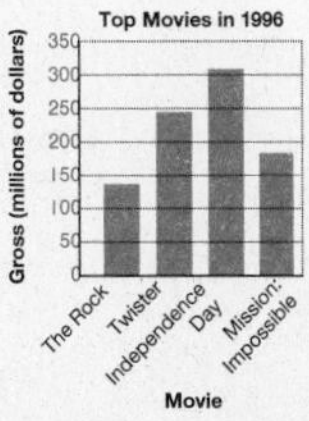

Name ______________________

Daily Review 9-4

Daily Cumulative Review

Subtract. *(Lesson 9-3)*

1. $-1-(-5)$ **4**
2. $12-(-5)$ **17**
3. $18-5$ **13**
4. $0-(-8)$ **8**
5. $-3-22$ **−25**
6. $-27-0$ **−27**

Add. *(Lesson 9-2)*

7. $9+(-12)$ **−3**
8. $-63+27$ **−36**
9. $26+8$ **34**
10. $-2+(-6)$ **−8**
11. $15+(-15)$ **0**
12. $-26+8$ **−18**

Mixed Review

Simplify.

13. (7-4) $8 \div 2\frac{1}{6}$ **$3\frac{9}{13}$**
14. (6-5) $12\frac{7}{15} + 14\frac{2}{3}$ **$27\frac{2}{15}$**
15. (2-5) $250{,}000 \div 5{,}000$ **50**
16. (4-2) Convert. 376 mL = **0.376** L
17. (3-8) Multiply. $9 \times \$11.74$ **\$105.66**
18. (5-2) Is 83 prime or composite? **Prime**
19. (9-1) Order from greatest to least. 16, −14, −18, 19 **19, 16, −14, −18**
20. (8-6) Draw a regular pentagon.

21. (8-2) Give one name for the angle. **Sample: ∠GMX**

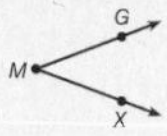

22. (1-7) Find the median of 16, 44, 71, 77, 22, 30. **37**
23. (1-3) Use the scatterplot to answer the following.
    a. What is the area of rectangle A? **12 cm²**
    b. Which rectangle has the greatest height? **B**
    c. Which rectangle has the greatest area? **D**

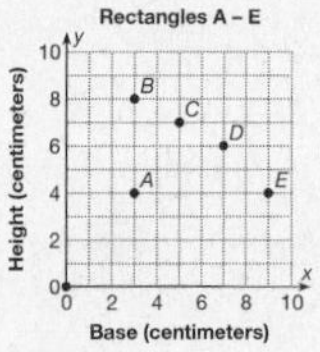

Name ______________________

Daily Review 9-5

Daily Cumulative Review

Multiply or divide. *(Lesson 9-4)*

1. -3×4 **−12**
2. $44 \div (-4)$ **−11**
3. $-1 \times (-11)$ **11**
4. $2 \times (-8)$ **−16**
5. $-56 \div (-7)$ **8**
6. $-35 \div 5$ **−7**

Subtract. *(Lesson 9-3)*

7. $-3-(-7)$ **4**
8. $18-(-3)$ **21**
9. $15-7$ **8**
10. $0-(-9)$ **9**
11. $-7-21$ **−28**
12. $-18-0$ **−18**

Mixed Review

13. (9-2) Add. $-32+5$ **−27**
14. (7-2) Simplify. $12\frac{3}{7} \times 5$ **$62\frac{1}{7}$**
15. (3-12) Solve. $5.6x = 16.24$ $x =$ **2.9**
16. (6-3) Find the LCM of 6 and 20. **60**
17. (4-2) Convert. 27 mm = **2.7** cm
18. (4-3) Convert. 24 qt = **6** gal

Estimate.

19. (3-5) $4.71 + 1.86$ **7**
20. (3-5) $11.838 - 2.15$ **10**
21. (3-5) 36.17×7.837 **320**
22. (8-5) Classify a triangle with sides of length 8 ft, 14 ft, and 8 ft. **Isosceles**
23. (8-2) Classify the angle made the hands of a clock at 4:00. **Obtuse**
24. (6-1) In Mrs. Ortiz's class, $\frac{5}{12}$ of the students are male. What fraction of the class is female? **$\frac{7}{12}$**
25. (2-12) Marsha had a package of 48 cookies to give to *k* friends. Each friend received 4 cookies. Write an equation for this situation. **$48 \div k = 4$**

Name ______________________

Daily Review 9-6

Daily Cumulative Review

Give the coordinate of each point. *(Lesson 9-5)*

1. *A* **(0, 3)**
2. *B* **(−2, 4)**
3. *C* **(3, 1)**
4. *D* **(−2, 0)**
5. *E* **(1, −3)**
6. *F* **(−3, −2)**
7. *G* **(4, 4)**
8. *H* **(0, −2)**

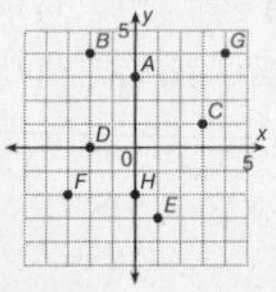

Multiply or divide. *(Lesson 9-4)*

9. $-25 \div 5$ **−5**
10. $3 \times (-7)$ **−21**
11. $-5 \times (-11)$ **55**
12. $27 \div (-3)$ **−9**
13. 7×15 **105**
14. $-18 \div (-2)$ **9**

Mixed Review

Add or subtract.

15. (9-3) $-56 - 10$ **−66**
16. (6-2) $\frac{4}{5} - \frac{1}{25}$ **$\frac{19}{25}$**
17. (3-6) $\$49.23 - \$26.74$ **\$22.49**
18. (5-6) Write $\frac{43}{9}$ as a mixed number. **$4\frac{7}{9}$**
19. (6-4) Round $5\frac{4}{7}$ to the nearest whole number. **6**
20. (6-3) Solve. $\frac{3}{4} + n = \frac{5}{6}$ **$\frac{1}{12}$**
21. (8-1) True or false. Perpendicular lines intersect at right angles. **True**
22. (7-1) A CD box measures $5\frac{5}{8}$ inches across. A music store manager wants to display 9 CDs side-by-side on a 49-inch shelf. Is there enough room for the display? **No**
23. (1-9) a. Identify the outlier in the data at the right. **14**
    b. Find the mean without the outlier. **42.72**

Stem	Leaf
1	4
3	5 7 8
4	0 2 2 3 5 7 9
5	2

Name ______________________

Daily Review 9-7

Daily Cumulative Review

Consider △*ABC* with vertices at *A*(−2, 3), *B*(3, 1), and *C*(0, −2). *(Lesson 9-6)*

1. Draw the graph of △*ABC*.
2. Create △*A′B′C′* by translating △*ABC* 2 units right and 1 unit down.
3. Give the coordinates of the vertices of △*A′B′C′*.
   A′ **(0, 2)** *B′* **(5, 0)** *C′* **(2, −3)**

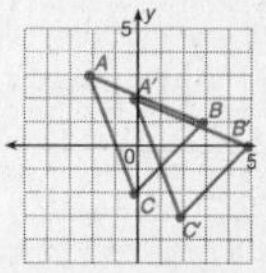

State which quadrant each point is in. *(Lesson 9-5)*

4. (4, −10) **IV**
5. (−15, −30) **III**
6. (−12, 20) **II**

Mixed Review

Simplify.

7. (9-4) $-48 \div -6$ **8**
8. (9-4) $(-2)^4$ **16**
9. (9-3) $-18 - 13$ **−31**
10. (7-6) Solve. $1\frac{3}{10}m = 1\frac{19}{20}$ $m =$ **$1\frac{1}{2}$**
11. (6-3) Solve. $x + \frac{5}{13} = \frac{25}{26}$ $x =$ **$\frac{15}{26}$**
12. (5-7) Write 0.125 as a fraction in lowest terms. **$\frac{1}{8}$**
13. (8-9) If the star shown is rotated 360°, how many times will it land on its original position? **4**

14. (4-1) Find the perimeter. **16 in.**

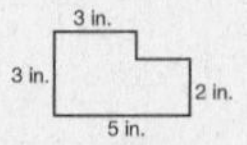

15. (3-4) Write 34,900,000 in scientific notation. **3.49×10^7**
16. (3-5) Note pads are priced at \$0.49. Estimate how many you could buy for \$5.00. **10**

Name ______________________

Daily Review 10-1

Daily Cumulative Review

Make a T-table with five (x, y) pairs. Graph the equation. *(Lesson 9-7)*

Sample pairs shown.

1. $y = x + 3$

x	y
0	3
1	4
2	5
–1	2
–2	1

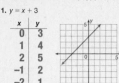

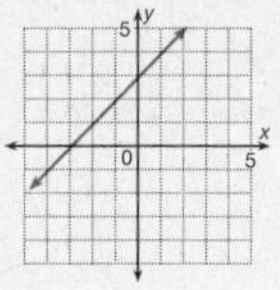

2. $y = -2x$

x	y
–2	4
–1	2
0	0
1	–2
2	–4

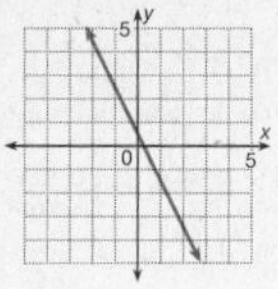

Plot the image of quadrilateral *GHIJ*. *(Lesson 9-6)*

3. Translate *GHIJ* 3 units right and 2 units down.

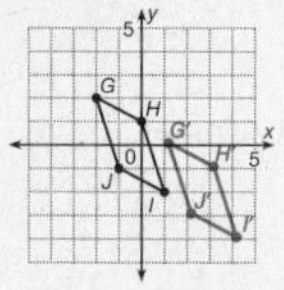

4. Slide *GHIJ* 2 units right and 2 units up.

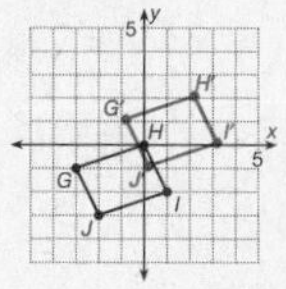

Mixed Review

Simplify.

5. $-9 \div (-3)$ **3** (9-4)
6. $8 - 12$ **–4** (9-3)
7. $-9 + (-8)$ **–17** (9-2)
8. $6\frac{1}{7} \div 2\frac{1}{3}$ **$2\frac{31}{49}$** (7-5)
9. $3 \times 12\frac{5}{8}$ **$37\frac{7}{8}$** (7-2)
10. $\frac{5}{6} + \frac{1}{24}$ **$\frac{7}{8}$** (6-2)
11. Find the GCF of 60 and 42. **6** (5-5)
12. Find the area of a circle with diameter 11 cm, rounded to the nearest tenth of a centimeter. **95.0 cm²** (4-8)
13. Compare using >, <, or =. 8.34 × 17.0 (>) 83.4 × 0.17 (3-9)
14. Karen earns $75 per day at her job. If she works 20 days in a month, how much will she earn? **$1,500** (2-5)

Name ______________________

Daily Review 10-2

Daily Cumulative Review

A box contains 10 green chips, 6 blue chips, and 5 white chips. Give each ratio in three ways. *(Lesson 10-1)*

1. Green chips to blue chips. **$\frac{5}{3}$; 5 to 3; 5:3**
2. Blue chips to white chips. **$\frac{6}{5}$; 6 to 5; 6:5**
3. White chips to green chips. **$\frac{1}{2}$; 1 to 2; 1:2**
4. Green chips to white chips. **$\frac{2}{1}$; 2 to 1; 2:1**

Graph each equation. *(Lesson 9-7)*

5. $y = 3x$

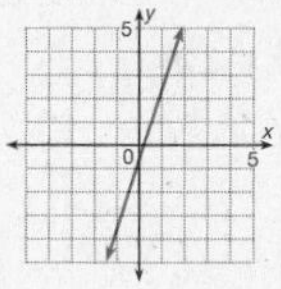

6. $y = x+1$

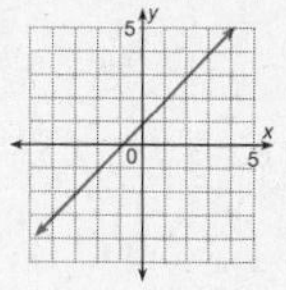

7. $y = 2$

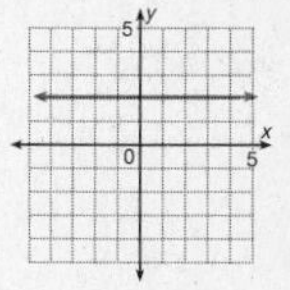

Mixed Review

Simplify.

8. $-48 \div 12$ **–4** (9-4)
9. $-12 + 12$ **0** (9-2)
10. $8 \div \frac{2}{9}$ **36** (7-4)
11. $6\frac{1}{8} - 1\frac{3}{4}$ **$4\frac{3}{8}$** (6-6)
12. Find the prime factorization of 225. **3 × 3 × 5 × 5** (5-2)
13. If the point *X*(3, 1) is reflected about the *x*-axis, what would be the coordinate of *X*′? **(3, –1)** (9-6)
14. The base of a parallelogram is 1.8m and its height is 0.6m. What is the area of the parallelogram? **1.08m²** (4-5)
15. The circumference of a circle is 50.24 cm. What is its area rounded to the nearest tenth? Use 3.14 for π. **201.0cm²** (4-8)

Name ______________________

Daily Review 10-3

Daily Cumulative Review

State if the ratios are equal. *(Lesson 10-2)*

1. 6:10; 3:5 **Equal**
2. $\frac{4}{8}, \frac{5}{6}$ **Not equal**
3. 3:15, $\frac{1}{5}$ **Equal**

Use the shapes to find the ratio. *(Lesson 10-1)*

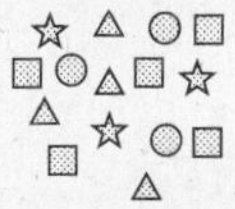

4. What is the ratio of stars to squares? **$\frac{3}{5}$**
5. What is the ratio of circles to stars? **1:1**
6. What is the ratio of circles to the whole group? **$\frac{1}{5}$**

Mixed Review

7. Graph the line $y = -4x$. (9-7)

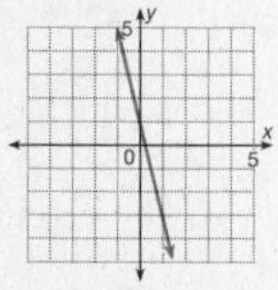

8. Classify the figure in as many ways as possible. (8-7)

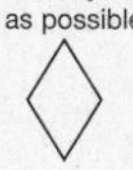

Quadrilateral
Parallelogram
Rhombus

9. Measure the angle at the right with a protractor. (8-3) **110°**

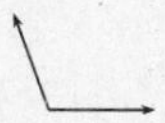

10. Convert. (4-3) 73 yards = **219** feet
11. Divide. (3-11) 72.576 ÷ 11.52 **6.3**
12. Write 6.25×10^5 in standard form. (3-4) **625,000**
13. Evaluate. (2-8) $(48 \div 6)^2 - 5$ **59**
14. Compare. (2-4) 3^5 (>) 5 × 3
15. Write 79 trillion in standard form. (2-1) **79,000,000,000,000**

Name ______________________

Daily Review 10-4

Daily Cumulative Review

State if the ratio is a unit rate. *(Lesson 10-3)*

1. $\frac{4 \text{ cats}}{5 \text{ dogs}}$ **No**
2. $\frac{20 \text{ miles}}{1 \text{ minute}}$ **Yes**
3. $\frac{5 \text{ pounds}}{1 \text{ dollar}}$ **Yes**
4. $\frac{12 \text{ yards}}{1 \text{ yard}}$ **No**

Complete each table of equal ratios. *(Lesson 10-2)*

5. 8 girls for every 10 boys

Girls	8	16	24	32
Boys	10	20	30	40

6. 5 trucks for every 3 cars

Cars	3	6	9	12
Trucks	5	10	15	20

Mixed Review

7. Plot and label each point. (9-5) *W*(–2, 3), *X*(1, –2), *Y*(3, 0), *Z*(–2, –3)

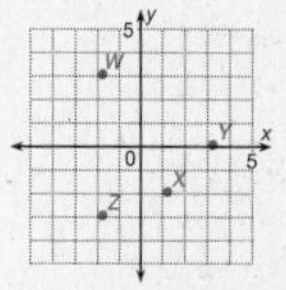

8. Compare using > or <. (9-1) –6 (<) 8
9. Simplify. $12\frac{8}{9} + 7$ (6-5) **$19\frac{8}{9}$**
10. Write 0.48 as a fraction in lowest terms. (5-7) **$\frac{12}{25}$**
11. Find the area of a triangle with a base of 9 cm and a height of 6.2 cm. (4-6) **27.9 cm²**

Solve.

12. $6.55x = 7.86$ (3-12) $x =$ **1.2**
13. $21.5 - m = 9.72$ (3-7) $m =$ **11.78**
14. $\frac{a}{7} = 15$ (2-13) $a =$ **105**
15. Classify a triangle with sides of length 7 cm, 7 cm, and 7 cm. (8-5) **Equilateral**
16. A recipe calls for $4\frac{1}{2}$ cups of flour. How much flour would you need to make $\frac{2}{3}$ of the original recipe? (7-3) **3 cups**
17. On Tuesday, the low temperature was –4°F and the high temperature was 11°F. What is the difference between these temperatures? (9-3) **15°F**

Name ______________________

Daily Review 10-5

Daily Cumulative Review

State whether or not each pair of ratios forms a proportion. *(Lesson 10-4)*

1. $\frac{5}{12} \stackrel{?}{=} \frac{10}{14}$ **No**
2. $\frac{7}{20} \stackrel{?}{=} \frac{6}{10}$ **No**
3. $\frac{12}{20} \stackrel{?}{=} \frac{18}{30}$ **Yes**

For each situation give two equal rates. *(Lesson 10-3)*

4. Joan drove 30 miles in 40 minutes. $\frac{3 \text{ miles}}{4 \text{ min}}, \frac{60 \text{ miles}}{80 \text{ min}}$
5. Mike earned $21 for working 3 hours. $\frac{\$7}{1 \text{ hr}}, \frac{\$14}{2 \text{ hr}}$

Mixed Review

Simplify.

6. (9-4) -9×11 **−99**
7. (9-3) $-8 - (-8)$ **0**
8. (9-2) $-12 + 22$ **10**

9. (8-10) State if the figure tessellates. Make a drawing to show your answer. **Tessellates**

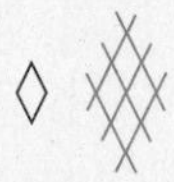

10. (4-9) Find the area. Use 3.14 for π. **36.0325 cm^2**

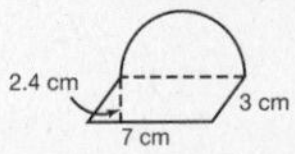

11. (4-1) Find the perimeter of the figure in Exercise 10. **23.99 cm**
12. (3-2) Round to the underlined place value. 816.92 **816.9**

13. (2-13) Write an equation for this situation and solve it. A section of the auditorium has 12 rows of x chairs. There are 108 chairs all together. How many chairs are in each row? **$12x = 108$; $x = 9$**

14. (1-8) Find the mean, median, and mode(s) of the data showing the number of home runs hit by leading ball players.
25, 32, 40, 28, 42, 30, 45, 28, 41, 34, 27

mean **$33.\overline{81}$** median **32** mode(s) **28**

Name ______________________

Daily Review 10-6

Daily Cumulative Review

Solve each proportion. *(Lesson 10-5)*

1. $\frac{8}{a} = \frac{2}{15}$ $a =$ **60**
2. $\frac{3}{9} = \frac{t}{27}$ $t =$ **9**
3. $\frac{b}{2} = \frac{15}{5}$ $b =$ **6**
4. $\frac{4}{3.5} = \frac{1.6}{d}$ $d =$ **1.4**

Determine if the proportion is written correctly. *(Lesson 10-4)*

5. $\frac{8 \text{ pies}}{3 \text{ cakes}} = \frac{6 \text{ cakes}}{16 \text{ pies}}$ **No**
6. $\frac{15 \text{ gal}}{5 \text{min}} = \frac{6 \text{ gal}}{2 \text{ min}}$ **Yes**
7. $\frac{19 \text{ chairs}}{2 \text{ rows}} = \frac{6 \text{ rows}}{57 \text{ chairs}}$ **No**

Mixed Review

For Exercises 8–12, estimate.

8. (7-1) $8\frac{3}{4} \times 10\frac{1}{6}$ **90**
9. (6-4) $11\frac{1}{9} + 4\frac{5}{9} + 3\frac{1}{7}$ **19**
10. (3-5) $52.91 − $12.12 **$41**
11. (2-7) 450,123 ÷ 897 **500**
12. (2-6) 62,163 + 59,920 + 60,125 + 58,685 **240,000**

13. (10-3) Is $\frac{5 \text{ bananas}}{\$1}$ a unit rate? **Yes**

14. (8-4) A triangle has two angles with measures of 68° and 46°. What is the measure of the third angle? **66°**

15. (1-6) Make a stem-and-leaf diagram of the data showing the number of stuffed animals owned by some students.
6, 15, 22, 18, 8, 23, 12, 8, 11, 22, 19, 28, 9, 29, 21, 4, 28

Stem	Leaf
0	4 6 8 8 9
1	1 2 5 8 9
2	1 2 2 3 8 8 9

16. (1-5) What is the range of the data in Exercise 15? **25**

17. Rosie's gas tank was $\frac{3}{4}$ full when she left home. After driving all morning, the tank was $\frac{1}{3}$ full. What fraction of a tank of gas did she use? **$\frac{5}{12}$**

Name ______________________

Daily Review 10-7

Daily Cumulative Review

Find the unit rate for each. *(Lesson 10-6)*

1. $\frac{15 \text{ books}}{3 \text{ shelves}}$ **$\frac{5 \text{ books}}{\text{shelf}}$**
2. $\frac{180 \text{ mi}}{4 \text{ hr}}$ **$\frac{45 \text{ mi}}{\text{hr}}$**
3. $\frac{21 \text{ boys}}{21 \text{ girls}}$ **$\frac{1 \text{ boy}}{1 \text{ girl}}$**

Solve each proportion. *(Lesson 10-5)*

4. $\frac{a}{6} = \frac{5}{15}$ $a =$ **2**
5. $\frac{40}{y} = \frac{16}{6}$ $y =$ **15**
6. $\frac{8}{36} = \frac{m}{90}$ $m =$ **20**
7. $\frac{18}{24} = \frac{3}{K}$ $K =$ **4**

Mixed Review

8. (9-7) Graph $y = x - 2$.

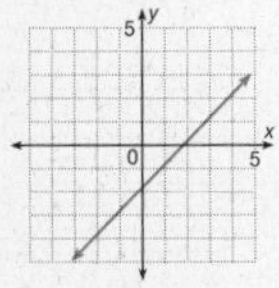

9. (8-9) Draw a 45° clockwise rotation of the figure.

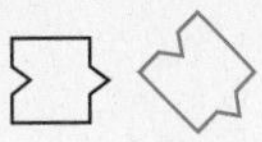

10. (8-1) Draw an example of $\overline{JK}$.

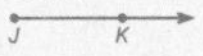

11. (7-6) Solve. $x \div 3\frac{1}{4} = 6$ $x =$ **$19\frac{1}{2}$**
12. (6-3) Solve. $g + \frac{1}{3} = \frac{4}{9}$ $g =$ **$\frac{1}{9}$**
13. (5-6) Write $2\frac{3}{5}$ as an improper fraction. **$\frac{13}{5}$**

14. (4-5) Find the area of a parallelogram with base 3.5 in. and height 2.7 in. **9.45 in^2**
15. (3-8) Multiply. 1000 × 3.802 **3,802**

16. (2-1) Write $45,000,000 in word form and in number-word form. **Forty-five million dollars; 45 million dollars**

17. (2-1) Write in standard form. Six million, seven hundred twenty-eight thousand, sixty **6,738,060**

Name ______________________

Daily Review 10-8

Daily Cumulative Review

In each pair of similar figures, find the missing side lengths. *(Lesson 10-7)*

1. $A =$ **8 in.** $B =$ **12 in.** $C =$ **8 in.**

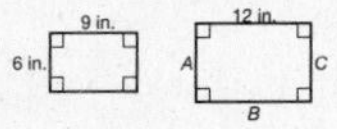

2. $A =$ **18 cm** $B =$ **13.5 cm**

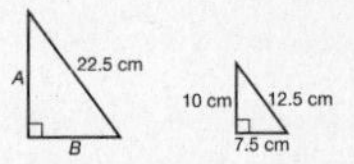

Find the unit rate for each. *(Lesson 10-6)*

3. $\frac{12 \text{ tsp}}{3 \text{ gal}}$ **$\frac{4 \text{ tsp}}{\text{gal}}$**
4. $\frac{24 \text{ CDs}}{6 \text{ tapes}}$ **$\frac{4 \text{ CDs}}{\text{tape}}$**
5. $\frac{625 \text{ ft}^2}{25 \text{ people}}$ **$\frac{25 \text{ ft}^2}{\text{person}}$**

Mixed Review

6. (10-5) Solve. $\frac{50}{5} = \frac{a}{2}$ $a =$ **20**

7. (9-5) Give the coordinate of each point.
A **(3, 2)**
B **(−2, 3)**
C **(−2, −3)**
D **(3, −2)**

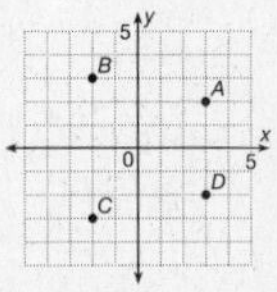

8. (8-2) Classify the following angle. **Acute**

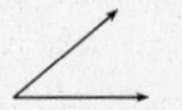

9. (5-8) Order from least to greatest. $\frac{1}{2}, \frac{3}{8}, \frac{1}{3}$ **$\frac{1}{3}, \frac{3}{8}, \frac{1}{2}$**

10. (5-1) Is 585 divisible by 9? **Yes**
11. (4-2) Convert. 23.5 kg = **23,500** g
12. (3-10) Divide. 17.71 ÷ 7 **2.53**
13. (3-6) Add. 7.23 + 11.7 + 6.74 **25.67**
14. (3-4) Write 17 million in scientific notation. **1.7×10^7**
15. (2-13) Solve the equation. $14m = 98$ **7**

Name ______________________

Daily Review 10-9

Daily Cumulative Review

Give the percent of each figure that is shaded. *(Lesson 10-8)*

1. 50% 2. 23% 3. 70%

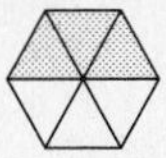
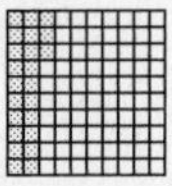
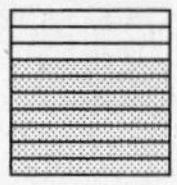

Find the missing side lengths of the similar figures. *(Lesson 10-7)*

4. $A =$ 10.8 ft $B =$ 16.2 ft

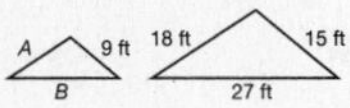

5. $A =$ $9.\overline{3}$ cm $B =$ $2.\overline{6}$ cm $C =$ 8 cm

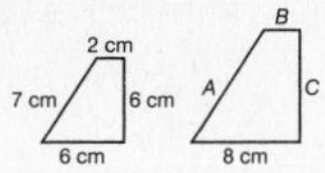

Mixed Review

6. (10-2) Complete the table of equal ratios. 32 children for every 2 teachers.

Children	16	32	48	64
Teachers	1	2	3	4

7. (8-8) How many lines of symmetry does this figure have? 8

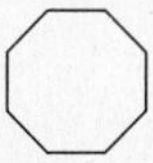

8. (5-3) Find the LCM of 8 and 32 32

9. (3-3) Compare using <, >, or =.
54.37 (<) 54.371

10. (2-8) Evaluate. $(18 - 6)^2 \div 9$ 16

11. (2-3) Order from least to greatest. 12 million; 1 billion; 12 thousand
12 thousand; 12 million; 1 billion

12. (1-9) Identify the outlier in this data. 95
7, 12, 23, 15, 8, 95, 23, 16, 9, 14, 24, 29, 6

Name ______________________

Daily Review 10-10

Daily Cumulative Review

Estimate what percent of each figure is shaded. *(Lesson 10-9)*

1. 75% 2. 40% 3. 33%

The circle graph shows the makeup of a local high school band. Use the graph for Exercises 4–6. *(Lesson 10-8)*

4. What percent of the band is
brass? 40%
percussion? 25%

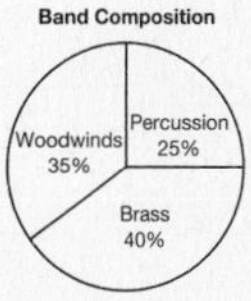

5. What category has the highest percent of band members. Brass

6. What two categories combine to make up 75% of the band?
Brass and woodwinds

Mixed Review

7. (9-3) Temperatures in Portland, Maine, have reached a high of 103° F and an all time low of −39° F. Find the difference between these temperatures. 142° F

8. (2-9) Find the next three numbers in the pattern.
123, 175, 227, 279, 331, 383, 435, 487

9. (1-3) For the scatterplot, determine if there is a trend. If there is, describe the pattern of the data.
It appears that the more high school courses a person takes, the better the person's ACT score.

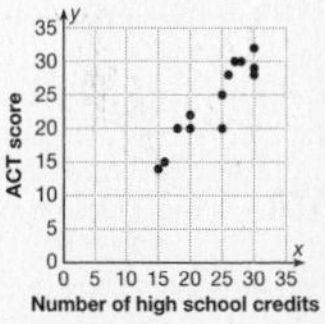

Name ______________________

Daily Review 10-11

Daily Cumulative Review

Convert to a fraction in lowest terms. *(Lesson 10-10)*

1. 90% $\frac{9}{10}$ 2. 28% $\frac{7}{25}$ 3. 75% $\frac{3}{4}$ 4. 115% $\frac{23}{20}$ or $1\frac{3}{20}$

5. 15% $\frac{3}{20}$ 6. 98% $\frac{49}{50}$ 7. 4% $\frac{1}{25}$ 8. 125% $\frac{5}{4}$ or $1\frac{1}{4}$

Estimate the percent. *(Lesson 10-9)*

9. 12 out of 65 20% 10. 22 out of 108 20% 11. $\frac{58}{73}$ 75%

Mixed Review

12. (10-5) Solve. $\frac{x}{2} = \frac{45}{10}$ $x =$ 9

13. (10-1) Write 12 out of 38 as a ratio in lowest terms. $\frac{6}{19}$

14. (9-4) Divide. $48 \div (-6)$ −8

15. (8-5) Can the lengths of 9 in., 4 in., and 3 in. form a triangle? No

16. (7-1) Estimate. $3\frac{3}{4} \times 4\frac{1}{10}$ 16

17. (6-2) Simplify. $\frac{7}{25} - \frac{1}{8}$ $\frac{31}{200}$

18. (5-7) Write $\frac{5}{11}$ as a decimal. $0.\overline{45}$

19. (5-3) Find the LCM of 24 and 36. 72

20. (5-2) Find the prime factorization of 44. $2 \times 2 \times 11$

21. (4-2) Name an appropriate metric unit for the weight of a thumb tack. Gram

22. (3-8) In a typical day, Mike works for 8 hours at the rate of $8.41 per hour. He also buys lunch for $6.50. How much does he have at the end of the day? $60.78

23. (3-4) Uranus is about 1,698,800,000,000 miles from the sun. Write this number in scientific notation. 1.6988×10^{12}

24. (2-4) Write 12^3 in standard form. 1728

25. (2-1) Write 3 million in standard form. 3,000,000

Name ______________________

Daily Review 11-1

Daily Cumulative Review

Simplify. Round your answer to the nearest hundredth. *(Lesson 10-11)*

1. 28% of 14 3.92 2. 33% of 48 15.84 3. 95% of 59 56.05

4. 2% of 85 1.70 5. 15% of $8.96 $1.34 6. 30% of 98 29.40

Convert to a percent. *(Lesson 10-10)*

7. $\frac{8}{10}$ 80% 8. $\frac{29}{50}$ 58% 9. 0.43 43% 10. 0.05 5%

Mixed Review

Give the percent of each figure that is shaded.

11. (10-8) 20% 12. (10-8) 30% 13. (10-8) 17%

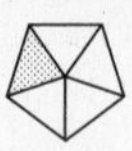
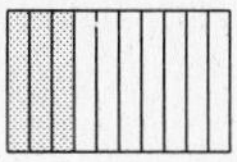
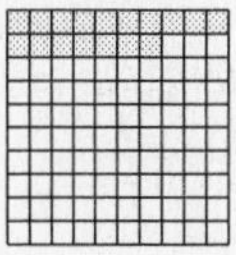

Order from greatest to least.

14. (9-1) 6, 0, −9, 4, −6
6, 4, 0, −6, −9

15. (9-1) −1, 5, 3, −6, 1
5, 3, 1, −1, −6

16. (8-4) If a triangle has two angles with measures 51° and 68°, what is the measure of the third angle? 61°

Solve.

17. (7-6) $x \div 2\frac{1}{2} = 6\frac{1}{4}$ $x =$ $15\frac{5}{8}$

18. (6-3) $\frac{6}{7} - K = \frac{13}{21}$ $K =$ $\frac{5}{21}$

19. (3-12) $5.7b = 20.406$ $b =$ 3.58

Insert parentheses to make the following true.

20. (2-8) $36 \div (12 \times 3) = 1$

21. (2-8) $4 \times (5 + 3 \times 2) = 44$

Name ______________________

Daily Review 11-2

Daily Cumulative Review

Classify each solid. If it is a polyhedron, tell how many vertices, edges, and faces it has. *(Lesson 11-1)*

1. Rectangular prism
   V: 8 E: 12 F: 6

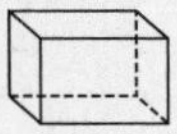

2. Rectangular pyramid
   V: 5 E: 8 F: 5

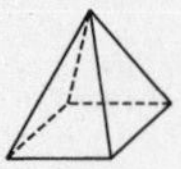

Simplify. Round your answers to the nearest hundredth. *(Lesson 10-11)*

3. 36% of 11.4 4.10
4. 8% of $64.75 $5.18
5. 91% of 98 89.18

Mixed Review

Solve each problem.

6. (10-5) $\frac{14}{36} = \frac{f}{54}$ $f =$ 21
7. (10-5) $\frac{1}{8} = \frac{t}{10}$ $t =$ 1.25
8. (10-5) $\frac{a}{64} = \frac{8}{32}$ $a =$ 16
9. (10-5) $\frac{36}{x} = \frac{18}{4}$ $x =$ 8

Give two ratios equal to the given ratio. **Possible answers:**

10. (10-2) $\frac{21}{35}$ $\frac{3}{5}, \frac{42}{70}$
11. (10-2) 12:30 2:5, 24:60

Simplify.

12. (9-4) -7×6 −42
13. (9-3) $-12 - (-5)$ −7
14. (9-2) $-8 + (-21)$ −29

15. (8-8) How many lines of symmetry does the figure have? 2

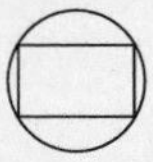

16. (4-9) Find the area. 132 ft²

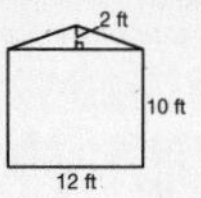

17. (3-4) Write 6,953,000,000,000 in scientific notation. 6.953×10^{12}

Name ______________________

Daily Review 11-3

Daily Cumulative Review

Find the area of each net. Classify the solid. *(Lesson 11-2)*

1. SA: 36 in²
   Triangular Prism

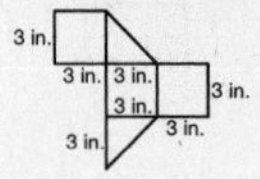

2. SA: 48 cm²
   Rectangular Prism

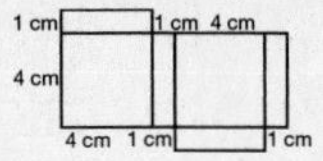

Draw an example of each. *(Lesson 11-1)*

3. Rectangular pyramid

4. Sphere

5. Cone

Mixed Review

6. (10-7) Find the missing side lengths in the similar triangles
   $A =$ 9.2 in. $B =$ 6.9 in.

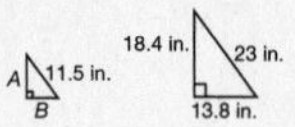

7. (9-5) Plot and label each point.
   $M(-2, 2)$
   $A(3, 2)$
   $T(2, -1)$
   $H(-1, -1)$

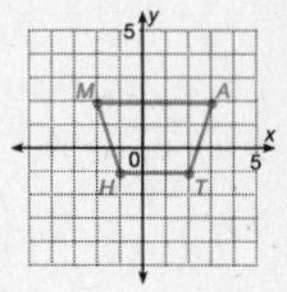

8. (8-7) Connect the points in Exercise 7. Classify the figure in as many ways as possible.
   Quadrilateral, Trapezoid

Simplify.

9. (7-5) $\frac{3}{4} \div \frac{5}{2}$ $\frac{3}{10}$
10. (7-3) $3\frac{1}{10} \times 6$ $18\frac{3}{5}$
11. (6-6) $5\frac{5}{6} - 3\frac{5}{7}$ $2\frac{5}{42}$
12. (6-2) $\frac{2}{5} + \frac{3}{10}$ $\frac{7}{10}$

13. (7-6) Bob said, "I'm thinking of a number. If I divide it by $1\frac{3}{4}$, I get $\frac{4}{7}$." What number is Bob thinking of? 1

Name ______________________

Daily Review 11-4

Daily Cumulative Review

Find the surface area. *(Lesson 11-3)*

1. 112 in²

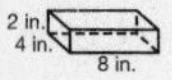

2. 465 cm²

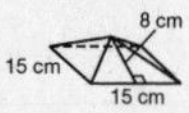

3. 238.14 ft²

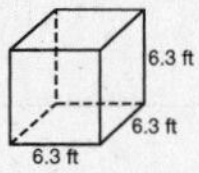

4. $28\frac{3}{4}$ yd²

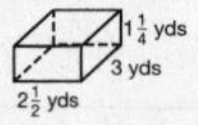

State the number of faces. Then classify each face and find the total surface area. *(Lesson 11-2)*

5. 6 faces; all rectangles
   SA: 412 in²

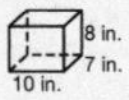

6. 5 faces; 3 rectangles and 2 triangles
   SA: 4,004 mm²

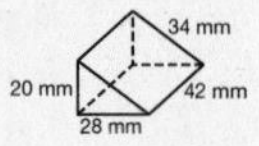

Mixed Review

Find the unit rate.

7. (10-6) $\frac{\$304}{38 \text{ hours}}$ $\frac{\$8}{\text{hr}}$
8. (10-6) $\frac{6 \text{ pt}}{2 \text{ min}}$ $\frac{3 \text{ pt}}{\text{min}}$
9. (10-6) $\frac{400 \text{ mi}}{8 \text{ hr}}$ $\frac{50 \text{ mi}}{\text{hr}}$

Simplify.

10. (7-4) $9 \div \frac{3}{7}$ 21
11. (6-5) $3\frac{19}{22} + 5\frac{1}{2}$ $9\frac{4}{11}$
12. (7-2) $5 \times 3\frac{1}{8}$ $15\frac{5}{8}$

Find the prime factorization.

13. (5-2) 540 2×2×5×3×3×3
14. (5-2) 280 2×2×2×5×7
15. (5-2) 148 2×2×37

16. (3-11) Divide. 871.2 ÷ 16.5 52.8
17. (3-6) Simplify. 3.275 + 7.541 + 8.3984 19.2144

Name ______________________

Daily Review 11-5

Daily Cumulative Review

Find the surface area of each cylinder. Use 3.14 for π. *(Lesson 11-4)*

1. 533.8 cm²

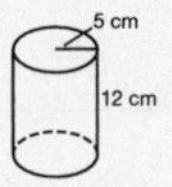

2. 846.23 ft²

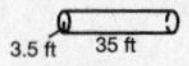

3. 942 mm²

4. 178.5875 in²

Find the surface area. *(Lesson 11-3)*

5. 24.3 mm²

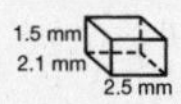

6. 232 in²

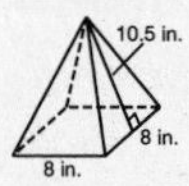

7. $158\frac{1}{12}$ ft²

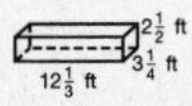

8. 1,350 in²

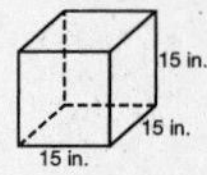

Mixed Review

9. (10-1) In a recent survey, 12 out of 18 students liked Brand A over Brand B. Write this ratio in lowest terms. $\frac{2}{3}$

10. (8-5) Classify a triangle with sides of length 12 yd, 14 yd, and 12 yd.
    Isosceles triangle

Estimate.

11. (7-1) $11\frac{5}{6} \times 10\frac{2}{9}$ 120
12. (6-4) $34\frac{3}{5} - 27\frac{19}{20}$ 7
13. (3-5) $95.86 − $51.02 45
14. (2-6) 7265 − 2105 5000

15. (2-3) Order from least to greatest.
    38,280; 38,276; 38,308; 38,380 38,276; 38,280; 38,308; 38,380

16. (1-4) The data set shows the scores on a 25 point quiz. Make a line plot for the data.

    20, 18, 23, 24, 19, 18, 24, 25, 18, 17, 22, 24, 18, 21, 17, 25, 23, 18

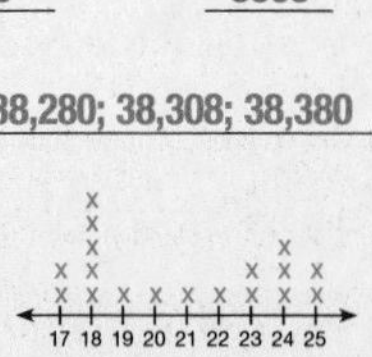

Name ______

Daily Review 11-6

Daily Cumulative Review

Use the three-dimensional figure. *(Lesson 11-5)*

1. Each cube in the solid is 3 cm by 3 cm by 3 cm. There are no hidden cubes.

a. How many cubes are in the solid? 12

b. How tall is the solid at its highest point? 9 cm

c. How wide is the solid at its widest point? 9 cm

Given the radius and height of each cylinder, find the surface area. Use 3.14 for π. *(Lesson 11-4)*

2. $r = 4.6$, $h = 12$ SA ≈ 479.5

3. $r = 11$, $h = 6$ SA ≈ 1174.4

4. $r = 9.1$, $h = 30$ SA ≈ 2234.5

Mixed Review

5. (11-1) How many vertices, edges, and faces does the solid have?

V: 6 E: 9 F: 5

For Exercises 6-8, Use the bar graph.

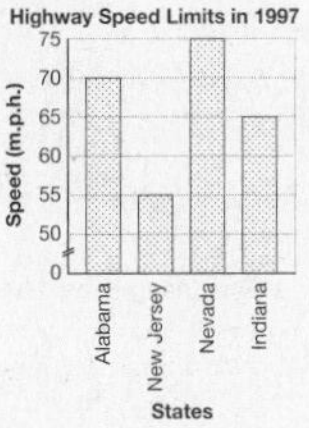

6. (10-3) Give a rate that uses the number 75.

State: Nevada Rate: $\frac{75 \text{ mi}}{\text{hr}}$

7. (10-3) Give three different rates that describe the speed limit in Alabama.

$\frac{70 \text{ mi}}{\text{hr}}, \frac{140 \text{ mi}}{2 \text{ hr}}, \frac{210 \text{ mi}}{3 \text{ hr}}$

8. (10-3) Use the speed limit in Nevada to give a rate that compares a distance to $\frac{1}{3}$ hour. $\frac{25 \text{ mi}}{\frac{1}{3} \text{ hr}}$

9. (5-6) Write $9\frac{1}{8}$ as an improper fraction. $\frac{73}{8}$

10. (4-3) Convert.

833.6 oz = 52.1 lb.

Name ______

Daily Review 11-7

Daily Cumulative Review

Find the volume of each solid. *(Lesson 11-6)*

1. 405 units^3 **2.** 40 units^3 **3.** 27 units^3

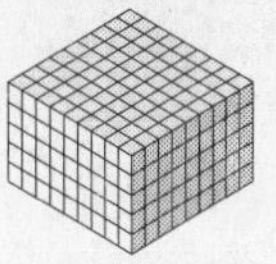

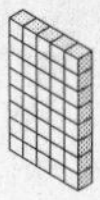

Draw the front, side, and top view of this solid. *(Lesson 11-5)*

4.

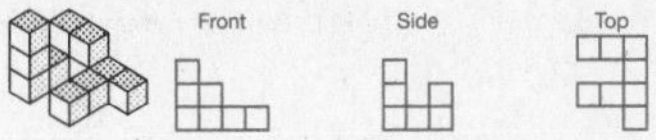

Mixed Review

Compare using >, <, or =.

5. (5-8) $\frac{7}{11} < \frac{11}{12}$

6. (3-3) 6.823 > 6.283

7. (2-4) $4^4 > 3^5$

Simplify.

8. (3-10) 17.64 ÷ 63 = 0.28

9. (3-9) 0.4 × 38.6 = 15.44

10. (2-5) 25 × 39 × 40 = 39,000

11. (1-9) Identify the outlier. 10

Stem	Leaf
1	0
4	5 7 8
5	0 2 2 3 5 8 9
6	0 1

12. (1-8) Find the mean of the data in Exercise 11. 50

13. (9-6) Plot the image of the quadrilateral *GHIJ* translated 3 units right and 2 units down.

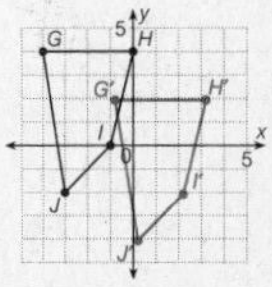

Name ______

Daily Review 12-1

Daily Cumulative Review

Find the volume of each solid. *(Lesson 11-7)*

1. 120 ft^3 **2.** 225 cm^3 **3.** 125 in^3 **4.** 147.825 m^3

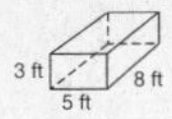

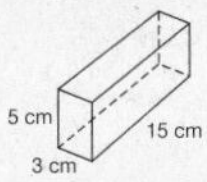

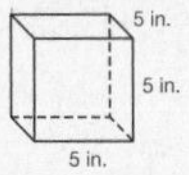

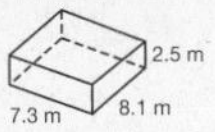

Find the volume of each solid. *(Lesson 11-6)*

5. 64 units^3 **6.** 42 units^3 **7.** 84 units^3

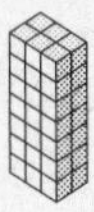

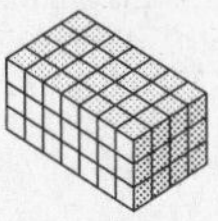

Mixed Review

8. (11-4) Find the surface area of the cylinder shown below. Use 3.14 for π.

659.4 yd^2

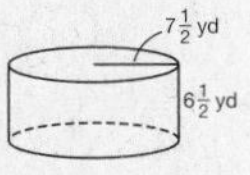

9. (10-10) Give the shaded part of the figure as a percent, fraction, and decimal.

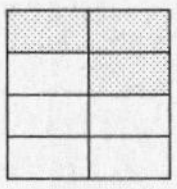

Percent: 37.5 %

Fraction: $\frac{3}{8}$

Decimal: 0.375

Simplify.

10. (9-4) −12 ÷ (−3) = 4

11. (9-3) 8 − 15 = −7

12. (9-2) −12 + (−12) = −24

13. (7-5) $\frac{4}{5} \div 2\frac{1}{5}$ = $\frac{4}{11}$

14. (6-5) $10\frac{1}{8} + 7\frac{7}{8}$ = 18

15. (6-2) $\frac{13}{15} - \frac{3}{10}$ = $\frac{17}{30}$

16. (3-6) 6.53 + 20.194 = 26.724

17. (2-5) 70 × 800 = 56,000

Name ______

Daily Review 12-2

Daily Cumulative Review

A set of 15 cards is labeled 1 through 15. Suppose you choose one card at random. Find the probability of each event. *(Lesson 12-1)*

1. P(3) $\frac{1}{15}$

2. P(even number) $\frac{7}{15}$

3. P(multiple of 4) $\frac{1}{5}$

4. P(less than 10) $\frac{3}{5}$

5. P(15) $\frac{1}{15}$

6. P(multiple of 5) $\frac{1}{5}$

Find the volume of each solid. *(Lesson 11-7)*

7. 729 in^3 **8.** 432 m^3 **9.** 389.844 cm^3 **10.** $76\frac{1}{2} \text{ yd}^3$

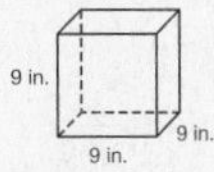

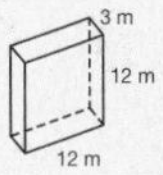

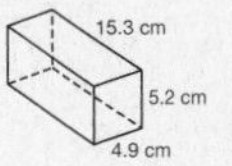

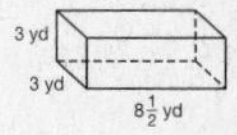

Mixed Review

11. (11-3) Find the surface area of the prism in Exercise 8.

432 m^2

12. (10-5) Solve the proportion $\frac{30}{x} = \frac{20}{22}$

x = 33

13. (9-7) Graph $y = 3 - x$

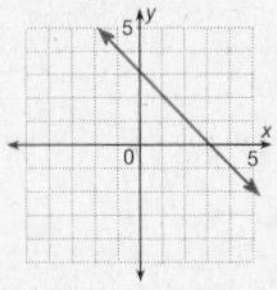

14. (8-9) Estimate the number of degrees and state the direction in which the figure has been rotated.

clockwise 135°

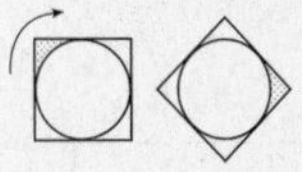

Solve.

15. (7-6) $2\frac{1}{3}x = 8\frac{1}{6}$ $3\frac{1}{2}$

16. (6-3) $k - \frac{5}{6} = \frac{1}{12}$ $\frac{11}{12}$

17. (3-12) $\frac{m}{2.901} = 6$ 17.406

18. (3-7) p + \$18.03 = \$21 \$2.97

Name ____________________

Daily Review 12-3

Daily Cumulative Review

Use the data recorded in the chart for Exercises 1–3. *(Lesson 12-2)*

Trial	1	2	3	4	5	6	7	8
Outcome	blue	red	yellow	red	red	blue	yellow	green

1. How many different outcomes were there? 4
2. How many times was the outcome blue? 2
3. What is the probability of the outcome being red? $\frac{3}{8}$

There are 10 cards that spell out S U M M E R T I M E. Suppose you choose one card. Find the probability of the event. *(Lesson 12-1)*

4. P(M) $\frac{3}{10}$ 5. P(consonant) $\frac{3}{5}$ 6. P(vowel) $\frac{2}{5}$

Mixed Review

7. Classify the solid. *(11-1)* Cone

8. Find the total amount. *(10-11)*
55% of 86 is 47.3

Compare using <, >, or =.

9. −12 < −10 *(9-1)* 10. $\frac{2}{5}$ > $\frac{2}{9}$ *(5-8)* 11. 4^3 < 3^4 *(4-3)* 12. 6.03 = 6.030 *(3-3)*

13. Each class period is 50 minutes. On Friday each period is shortened *x* minutes so they are 40 minutes. Write an equation for this situation. *(2-12)*
$50 - x = 40$

14. Find the next three numbers in this pattern. *(2-9)*
1, 3, 9, 27, 81, 243, 729, 2187

Name ____________________

Daily Review 12-4

Daily Cumulative Review

Suppose you drop a token on each shape in Exercises 1–4. Find the probability of the token landing on the shaded area. *(Lesson 12-3)*

1. $\frac{1}{4}$ 2. $\frac{5}{6}$ 3. $\frac{1}{2}$ 4. $\frac{2}{5}$

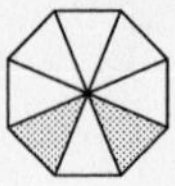
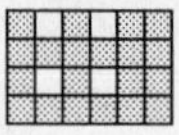

Make predictions using the chart for Exercises 5–7 *(Lesson 12-2)*

Trial	1	2	3	4	5	6	7	8
Outcome	square	circle	circle	triangle	square	triangle	circle	triangle

5. How many different outcomes were there? 3
6. What is the probability of the outcome being a square? $\frac{1}{4}$
7. What is the probability of the outcome being a pentagon? 0

Mixed Review

8. Find the volume of a rectangular prism which has a length of 21 in., a width of 11 in., and a depth of 8 in. *(11-7)* 1848 in^3
9. Give three equal ratios. A pet store has 4 cats for every 3 dogs. *(10-2)* $\frac{8}{6}, \frac{12}{9}, \frac{16}{12}$
10. Classify the triangle that has sides of length 8 ft, 7 ft, 6 ft. *(8-5)* scalene
11. Write $\frac{16}{24}$ as a fraction in lowest terms. *(5-5)* $\frac{2}{3}$
12. Find the area of a circle rounded to the nearest tenth whose circumference is 24.1 yd. *(4-8)* 46.2 yd^2
13. Find the mean of the data set. *(1-8)*
6, 4, 8, 7, 5, 6, 8, 3, 9, 9, 4, 3, 9, 4, 5 Mean 6

Name ____________________

Daily Review 12-5

Daily Cumulative Review

Draw a tree diagram for the situation. *(Lesson 12-4)*

1. A combo meal at a local restaurant has the following choices: pick one meat from beef, pork, chicken; and pick one side-dish from coleslaw, french fries, or beans.

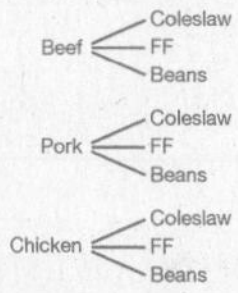

Suppose you drop a token on each shape. To the nearest percent, find the probability of the token landing on the shaded area. *(Lesson 12-3)*

2. 40% 3. 54% 4. 43% 5. 50%

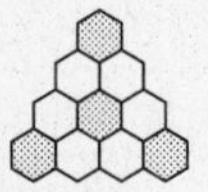
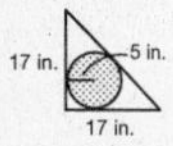

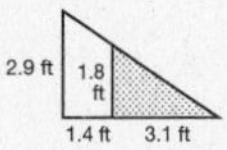

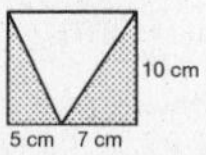

Mixed Review

6. Find the missing side lengths in the similar triangles. *(10-7)*
$A =$ 10.5 cm $B =$ 25.2 cm

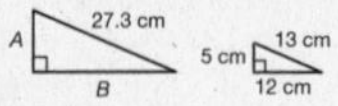

7. Name the polygon that is tessellated in Exercise 2. *(8-10)* hexagon

Simplify.

8. $9 \div 1\frac{5}{9}$ *(7-4)* $5\frac{11}{14}$ 9. $6\frac{3}{5} \times 10$ *(7-2)* 66 10. $120.48 \div 48$ *(3-10)* 2.51 11. 9×4.713 *(3-8)* 42.417

12. Write 6,305,120 in words. *(2-1)*
six million, three hundred five thousand, one hundred twenty

Name ____________________

Daily Review 12-6

Daily Cumulative Review

Six cards numbered 1, 2, 3, 4, 5, and 6 are in a paper bag. Each time a card is drawn it is replaced. Find the probability of each event. *(Lesson 12-5)*

1. P(even, then even) $\frac{1}{4}$ 2. P(even, then odd) $\frac{1}{4}$ 3. P(odd, even, odd) $\frac{1}{8}$

Draw a tree diagram for the following situation. *(Lesson 12-4)*

4. Jane has 2 skirts, 2 vests, and 3 blouses to make an outfit. (Use Skirt A, Skirt B, Vest A, Vest B, Blouse A, Blouse B, Blouse C)

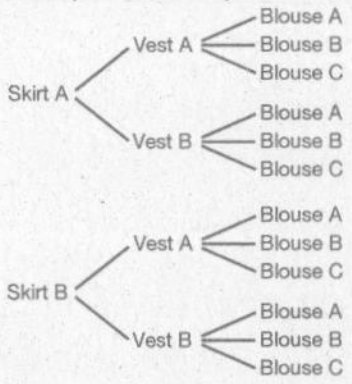

5. How many different outfits are possible? 12

Mixed Review

6. Is 78 divisible by 4? *(5-1)* no
7. Draw an example of $\overline{AB}$. *(8-1)*

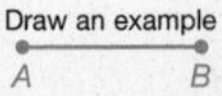

8. The bar graph shows Jim's clothing selections. What fraction of the clothes are T-shirts or sweatshirts? *(6-1)* $\frac{1}{2}$

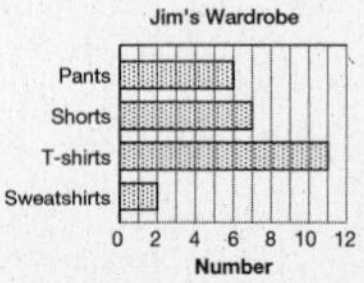

9. Use a protractor to measure the angle. Then classify the angle. *(8-3)*

Classification: acute
Measure: 70°

10. Measure the nail to the nearest centimeter. *(3-2)* 3 cm

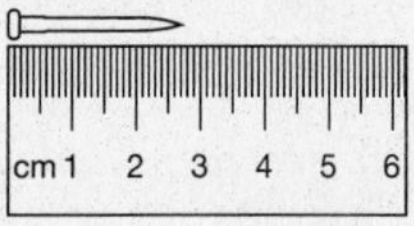